Psychiatric Rehabilitation in Practice

Psychiatric Rehabilitation in Practice

Robert W. Flexer

KENT STATE UNIVERSITY

Phyllis L. Solomon

HAHNEMANN UNIVERSITY

With 30 Contributing Authors

Andover Medical Publishers

Boston   London   Oxford   Singapore   Sydney   Toronto   Wellington

Andover Medical Publishers is an imprint of
Butterworth–Heinemann.

Library of Congress Cataloging-in-Publication Data

Psychiatric rehabilitation in practice / [edited by]
   Robert W. Flexer, Phyllis L. Solomon
        p.   cm.
   Includes bibliographical references and index.
   ISBN 1-56372-025-6 (ppc   :   case)
   1. Mentally ill—Rehabilitation.   I. Flexer,
Robert W.   II. Solomon, Phyllis L.
   [DNLM:1. Community Mental Health Services.
2. Mental Disorders—rehabilitation.
WM 29.1 P9738]
   RC439.5.P77   1993
   362.2—dc20
   DNLM/DLC
   for Library of Congress   92-49873
                                                     CIP

British Library Cataloguing-in-Publication Data

A catalogue record for this book is available from the
British Library.

Butterworth-Heinemann
80 Montvale Avenue
Stoneham, MA 02180

10   9   8   7   6   5   4   3   2

Printed in the United States of America

Contents

Contributors

A. ANTHONY ARCE, M.D.
Chairman of Psychiatry
North Philadelphia Health System
Professor and Vice Chairman
Department of Psychiatry
Medical College of Pennsylvania
Philadelphia, PA

ROBERT BAER, LISW
Doctoral Candidate in Special Education
Adult, Counseling, Health and Vocational
Education Department
Kent State University
Kent, OH

ROGER A. BOOTHROYD, PH.D.
Research Scientist
Bureau of Evaluation and Services Research
NY State Office of Mental Health
Albany, NY

KAAREN STRAUCH BROWN, M.S.W.
Professor, Department of Social Work
Eastern Michigan University
Ypsilanti, MI

PAUL J. CARLING, PH.D.
Executive Director
Center for Community Change Through
Housing and Support
Trinity College of Vermont
Burlington, VT

JUDITH A. COOK, PH.D.
Director, Thresholds National Research
and Training Center on Rehabilitation and
Mental Illness
Chicago, IL

MARK A. DAVIS, M.A.
Founding President of Pennsylvania
Mental Health Consumers Association
Philadelphia, PA

JEFFREY DRAINE, M.S.W.
Research Associate. Section of Mental
Health Services and Systems Research
Department of Psychiatry and Mental
Health Sciences
Hahnemann University
Philadelphia, PA

MARY E. EVANS, PH.D.
Assistant Director
Bureau of Evaluation and Services Research
NY State Office of Mental Health
Albany, NY

ROBERT W. FLEXER, PH.D.
Professor of Rehabilitation and Special
Education
Adult, Counseling, Health and Vocational
Education Department
Kent State University
Kent, OH

SANDRA L. FORQUER, PH.D.
Deputy Commissioner
Quality Assurance Division
NY State Office of Mental Health
Albany, NY

GENE GOEBEL, M.ED.
Doctoral Candidate in Special Education
Adult, Counseling, Health and Vocational
Education Department
Kent State University

MARTHA HODGE, M.S.
Consultant
Community Support Consultants
St. George Island, FL

SARA J. HOFFSCHMIDT
(Formerly) Research Associate,
Thresholds National Research and
Training Center on Rehabilitation and

Mental Illness
Chicago, IL

CILLE KENNEDY, PH.D.
Research Psychologist, Division of
Epidemiology and Services Research
National Institute of Mental Health
Rockville, MD

MILES C. LADENHEIM, M.D.
Attending Psychiatrist
North Philadelphia Health System
Medical Director, Acute Treatment Unit
Department of Psychiatry, Girard Medical
Center
Philadelphia, PA

BERYL LAWN, M.D.
Assistant Professor
Department of Psychiatry and Mental
Health Sciences,
Hahnemann University
Philadelphia, PA

HARRIET P. LEFLEY, PH.D.
Professor, Department of Psychiatry
University of Miami, School of Medicine
Miami, FL

JEANNIE MCVEIGH
Administrative Assistant/Backup
Coordinator
Northeast Consumer Center
Project SHARE, Mental Health
Association of Southeastern Pennsylvania
Philadelphia, PA

ARTHUR T. MEYERSON, M.D.
Professor and Chairman
Department of Psychiatry and Mental
Health Sciences
Hahnemann University
Philadelphia, PA

CAROL T. MOWBRAY, PH.D.
Associate Professor
School of Social Work
Wayne State University
Detroit, MI

DAVID P. MOXLEY, PH.D.
Associate Professor, School of Social Work
Wayne State University
Detroit, MI

ROBERT I. PAULSON, DSW
Professor, School of Social Work
University of Cincinnati
Visiting Research Professor

Portland State University
Cincinnati, OH and Portland, OR

JOHN H. PERRY
Assistant Director of Technical Assistance
National Association of State Mental
Health Program Directors
Alexandria, VA

CHARLES A. RAPP, PH.D.
Professor and Associate Dean
School of Social Welfare
University of Kansas
Lawrence, KS

FRANK SEPETAUC, LPC, M.ED., CRC
Vocational Day Treatment Unit Manager
Community Support Services of Summit
County, Inc.
Akron, OH

VIRGINIA SELLECK, PH.D., CRC
Consultant, Thresholds National Research
and Training Center on Rehabilitation and
Mental Illness
Chicago, IL

DAVID L. SHERN, PH.D.
Director
Bureau of Evaluation and Services Research
NY State Office of Mental Health
Albany, NY

THOMAS J. SIMMONS, PH.D.
Assistant Professor
Adult, Counseling, Health and Vocational
Rehabilitation
Kent State University
Kent, OH

PHYLLIS L. SOLOMON, PH.D.
Professor
Director, Section of Mental Health
Services and Systems Research
Department of Psychiatry and Mental
Health Sciences
Hahnemann University
Philadelphia, PA

ROBERT B. STEELE, M.ED.
Assistant Professor
Department of Teaching Specialties
University of North Carolina at Charlotte
Charlotte, NC

BETH A. STROUL, M.ED.
Vice President, Management & Training
Innovations
McLean, VA

Preface

The intention of this book is to provide an overview of the foundations and context in which psychiatric rehabilitation interventions are delivered, as well as an understanding of these specific interventions. This book is based on an integrated interdisciplinary approach to the provision of services for and with persons with psychiatric disabilities. Therefore, the intended audience for this book is the full range of professionals who serve this population, as well as service recipients, family members, and advocates. Our major hope is that when the readers have finished this book, they will view persons with psychiatric disabilities and their families with respect and a belief in each person's individual potential as a contributing member of society.

It is also our hope that our readers find this book to be a useful resource and text for those who now work in or who want, in the future, to work in the mental health and rehabilitation fields. We set out to design an up-to-date, relevant, and helpful guide of the best possible synthesis/integration of the rehabilitation and mental health fields. It will serve the purpose of raising pertinent, pointed questions for the field.

This book is about philosophy and the underlying values and beliefs about people with psychiatric disabilities—who they are and where they belong. This book is also about applying our best problem-solving skills and creativity in a committed manner to enhance the lives of individuals and to the improvement in how they are treated by society. Our specific motivation was to communicate a positive philosophy and a sense of hope for all those whose lives have intersected with individuals who have a severe mental disorder.

Acknowledgments

The editors would like to extend thanks and appreciation to several individuals. First, we would like to thank Laura Van Tosh for her very helpful comments and organizational efforts in developing the outline for Chapter 1. Second, we would like to thank the numerous members of Project SHARE, who spent valuable time and provided insightful input into the conceptualization of Chapter 1. We would especially like to thank Joe Yaskin for his collaboration with Laura.

Several individuals gave of their time to comment on the proposal for this book. The editors would like to thank William R. Shadish, Martha B. Kniseley, Ming Lai, Mark R. Munetz, Judy Flavell, Greg LaForm, Les Abel, and Joyce Campione. Carol Flexer is especially recognized for the support and confidence she provided during the rough times in completion of this book.

Introduction

In recent years, mental health professionals have increasingly recognized the need for rehabilitation interventions to complement existing mental health treatment, in order to more comprehensively meet the needs and desires of persons with disabilities that result from severe mental disorders (Dion & Anthony, 1987). Psychiatric rehabilitation focuses on individuals who are disabled in major life activities by a severe mental disorder (e.g., schizophrenia or major psychotic disorders). The individuals may have a limited capacity to engage across a variety of functions (e.g., an ability to converse with others and/or to perform certain social role functions, such as that of a worker). For persons who are severely mentally disabled, rehabilitation and mental health services consist of intensive supports, which may endure over long periods of time or require intermittent interventions responsive to the functional disabilities resulting from the episodic nature of some mental disorders. Rehabilitative interventions are not directed at persons who have less severe emotional problems, such as social adjustment problems, environmental problems, or mild depression without psychotic features such as hallucinations or delusions. Typically, mild emotional problems do not result in extensive disability, as do the major mental illnesses.

The current acceptance of psychiatric rehabilitation is based on the growing evidence of the efficacy of these interventions (Dion & Anthony, 1987) and on the realization that mental health treatment is most effective at alleviating symptoms but does little to address the functional deficits resulting from the disorder. Consequently, it is becoming more apparent that an integration of rehabilitation and mental health treatment has the greatest potential for providing the most positive outcomes for persons with severe mental disabilities.

That we speak of positive outcomes in relation to this population is very much a current perspective. Although the rehabilitation approach has been around since the 1940s with the establishment of Fountain House (Dincin, 1975), many in the mental health field believed that persons with these severe psychiatric disorders were on a progressively deteriorating course, with little hope for improved function or enhanced quality of life. However, recent research, such as that by Harding and her colleagues (Harding, Zubin, & Strauss, 1987), has suggested a more hopeful prognosis for this population. These findings, coupled with the potential for rehabilitation, have resulted in a more optimistic view of this disabled population.

The basic philosophy of psychiatric rehabilitation, which evolved from physical rehabilitation (i.e., interdisciplinary interventions aimed at restoring function and role performance), is one of hope and positive expectations. Along with this, there is a belief that all individuals, regardless of their disabilities, have strengths that enable them to learn, grow, and change (Anthony, Cohen, & Farkas, 1990; Peterson, Patrick, & Rissmeyer, 1990). *Rehabilitation* differs from *mental health* treatment by emphasizing personal assets and independence or interdependence, as opposed to focusing on a person's deficits or the alleviation of symptoms or pathology.

Psychiatric rehabilitation refers to various interventions that focus on changing the skills and/or environmental supports of individuals with severe mental disabilities. The expectation is that through these changes, a person's social and behavioral functioning will improve, as will the person's quality of life (Anthony & Liberman, 1986; Anthony et al., 1990; Dion & Anthony, 1987). The goal of rehabilitation is to have persons with severe mental disabilities function at their maximum potential, in their environments of choice, with the least professional support necessary.

Some professionals refer to *psychiatric rehabilitation* as *psychosocial rehabilitation*. This term emerged from the psychosocial movement that developed in the 1950s. These few agencies (e.g., Fountain House), had the expressed purpose of working with persons with severe mental disabilities (Rutman, 1987). For the National Institute of Mental Health, the International Association of Psychosocial Rehabilitation Services (IAPSRS), which was formed by these agencies, defined *psychosocial rehabilitation* as a service that helps individuals with psychiatric disabilities to "evaluate their strengths and weaknesses and set their own goals for optimal functioning in the community" (Peterson et al., 1990, p. 468). The philosophy of psychosocial rehabilitation "emphasizes common sense and practical needs and usually includes vocational, social/recreational, residential and educational services aimed at teaching the essential skills of community living" (Peterson et al., 1990, p. 468). The psychosocial setting is intentionally informal, in order to reduce psychological distance between staff and program clients. Clients are encouraged to assume productive social roles in both the program and the larger community, as the community setting is considered an integral part of the program (IAPSRS, 1985). Most important is the atmosphere of hope and the expectation that all individuals have the emotional strength and coping skills to attain a level of functioning that will bring them a sense of satisfaction and accomplishment (Peterson et al., 1990).

The original psychosocial model excluded medical management. Currently, it seems clear that medical management must be an integral part of the range of services for this population, along with the client being an active informed coequal participant. Increasingly, the terms *psychiatric rehabilitation*, based on a medical model, and *psychosocial rehabilitation*, based on a more social model, are used interchangeably, as the philosophical differences have been minimized in implementation.

As is evidenced by these various definitions, psychiatric or psychosocial rehabilitation is a philosophy, a set of beliefs, and a process. Furthermore, to implement the multiple aspects of rehabilitation requires an interdisciplinary approach to implementation, as a diversity of functions are necessary. Given the need for integration with mental health treatment (e.g., medication management) and with other human services (e.g., obtaining benefits for necessities of daily living), there is a need for psychiatrists, nurses, social workers, psychologists, and vocational rehabilitation counselors, as well as psychiatric rehabilitation specialists, to be involved in the delivery of services to the target population.

The field of psychiatric rehabilitation is continuing to evolve with a good deal of controversy. Much of this evolution and controversy is apparent over the use of differing terminology. For example, those individuals who compose the target population for rehabilitation have been referred to as "chronically mentally ill," "persons with chronic mental illness," "severely mentally disabled persons," or "persons with serious and persistent mental illness"; or in a different context, as "consumers," "ex-patients," "survivors," "participants," and "service recipients." Although the label that is given to someone may seem inconsequential, it does communicate a definite message. Some terms are more stigmatizing than others.

To understand rehabilitation and what it does and does not focus on, it is important to be aware of some related terms, which include *impairment*, *disability*, and *handicap*. *Impairment* refers to a sign or symptom of mental illness—for example, hallucinations or delusional thinking. *Disability* refers to functional loss resulting from the impairment—for example, inability to relate appropriately to others and, therefore, difficulty in obtaining and maintaining a job. *Handicap* refers to the societal response to a disability—for example, societal discrimination accentuates the impact of a given disability, further limiting the autonomy and function of a disabled person" (in Chapter 3 of this volume). This impairment is addressed through mental health treatment, whereas disability is addressed through rehabilitation. In addition, there are those who also believe that societal rehabilitation interventions directed at changing the system in which disabled persons function helps to overcome the handicapping aspects of severe mental disorders (Anthony & Liberman, 1986).

Of these three terms, *disability* has the least consensus with regard to a generally accepted definition. *Disability in America* (Pope & Tarlov, 1990) notes that *disability* is a social issue because persons are not always disabled by their disorder, but by the way they are "treated by others and restricted from normal social roles" because of their disorder (Pope & Tarlov, 1990, p. vi). Thus, this report defined disability as "limitations in physical or mental function, caused by one or more health conditions, in carrying out socially defined tasks and roles that individuals generally are expected to be able to do" (Pope & Tarlov, 1990, p. 35). In the present context, *disability* refers to a limitation in function, caused by a severe mental disorder, which hinders the individual's ability to carry out socially expected tasks and roles, which rehabilitation interventions are directed at restoring. Rehabilitation employs interventions to help individuals to increase their social competence by increasing the skills and abilities they possess, as well as increasing the appropriate use of these skills and abilities to interact on a daily basis within the community (Kennedy, 1987).

An important aspect of the rehabilitation process is the assistance in the development of environmental supports and resources. In addition to using the services of mental health and other human service delivery systems is the development of informal and formal social supports. This includes helping an individual to develop social supports, which is a network of individuals, friends, acquaintances, family members (informal), and service providers (formal) who provide emotional support (i.e., offer a sense of caring), functional support (i.e., provision of resources or help in completing tasks of daily living), and informational support (i.e., giving advice, facts, or directions) (Caplan, 1974; Weiss, 1982). Social networks or social support systems only refer to the individuals and the linkages among these individuals who interact with a given person (Mitchell & Trickett, 1980). Through the provision of emotional, functional, and informational supports, this network becomes supportive. However, not all persons in an individual's network are supportive. The degree to which network members adequately provide these functions determines whether they have positive or negative influences (Froland, 1978).

This overview is an attempt to provide the reader with the basic definitions and assumptions on which this book is based. The editors of this book believe in the integration of mental health treatment and rehabilitation for persons with severe mental disabilities. This integration requires an interdisciplinary, community-based approach to service delivery. The focus of Section I ("Foundations of Psychiatric Rehabilitation") is concerned with laying the foundation of this integrated approach and with the major political–social and professional issues and concerns in rehabilitation. Chapter 1 presents the experiences of persons who come into contact with the formal system of mental health and rehabilitation services, from the view of participants. Chapter 2 lays out the perspectives of families of persons with severe mental disabilities, related to rehabilitation and the roles and expertise they have to offer to the rehabilitation process. The third chapter concerns the etiology of the disorders, the mental health treatment aspects of these disorders, and the role of the psychiatrists in treating persons who are disabled due to a mental disorder. Chapter 4, "Rehabilitation in Community Support Systems," lays out the principles, philosophy, and service components of a supportive system of care. This is followed by Chapter 5, which defines and operationalizes how individual supports, persons, and interdisciplinary groups of professionals respond to and participate in the planning process to obtain necessary resources to address the major needs of the population and to define individually determined goals and expectations for reintegration into community life.

The second section ("Supports and Rehabilitation for Community Life") provides a comprehensive review of support and intervention strategies employed by a variety of professionals involved in the rehabilitation process. The initial chapter in this section (Chapter 6) provides an overview of an integrated psychosocial rehabilitation approach within a psychosocial agency. This is followed by Chapters 7, 8, and 9, which discuss specific areas of interventions—housing, vocational, and education. A discussion of case management (Chapter 10) concludes this section because of its organizational and process function, aimed at coordinating multiple services and benefits.

The final section of the book ("Rehabilitation and Mental Health Service Delivery") defines the context in which interdisciplinary groups of professionals deliver services to persons with severe mental disabilities. Chapter 11 provides information on how to define, support, and provide feedback on the efforts delivered by professionals on behalf of this population. This is followed by Chapter 12 on strategies through which a variety of agencies work together at the community level to achieve common goals. Chapter 13 discusses the integration of quality standards and evaluation efforts to monitor and improve rehabilitation and mental health services. Chapter 14 provides an overview of the legal

issues, including confidentiality and right-to-treatment issues that influence and set some of the guidelines for the delivery of services. The final chapter of this section summarizes past accomplishments and future challenges for providers of mental health and rehabilitation services.

References

Anthony, W., Cohen, M., & Farkas, M. (1990). *Psychiatric rehabilitation*. Boston: Center for Psychiatric Rehabilitation.

Anthony, W., & Liberman, R. (1986). The practice of psychiatric rehabilitation: Historical, conceptual, and research base. *Schizophrenia Bulletin, 12*, 524–559.

Caplan, G. (1974). *Support systems and community mental health*. New York: Behavioral Publications.

Dion, G., & Anthony, W. (1987). Research in psychiatric rehabilitation: A review of experimental and quasi-experimental studies. *Rehabilitation Counseling Bulletin, 30*, 177–203.

Dincin, J. (1975). Psychiatric rehabilitation. *Schizophrenia Bulletin, 13*, 131–147.

Froland, C. (1978). Talking about networks that help. In C. Froland & D. L. Pancoast (Eds.), *Proceedings of the conference on networks* (pp. 10–31). Portland, OR: Portland State University.

Harding, C., Zubin, J., & Strauss, J. (1987). Chronicity in schizophrenia: Fact, partial fact, or artifact? *Hospital and Community Psychiatry, 38*, 477–86.

IAPSRS. (1985). *Psychosocial Rehabilitation: Definitions Principles and Descriptions*. McLean, VA: Author.

Kennedy, M. L. (1987). *Community integration and well-being: A study of the effects of social competence and social support on young chronically mentally ill adults*. Unpublished doctoral dissertation, New York University, New York.

Mitchell, R. G., & Trickett, F. J. (1980). Social networks as mediators of social support: An analysis of the effects and determinants of social networks. *Community Mental Health Journal, 16*(10), 27–45.

Peterson, C., Patrick S., & Rissmeyer, D. (1990). Social work's contribution to psychosocial rehabilitation. *Social Work, 35*, 468–472.

Pope, A., & Tarlov, A. (Eds.). (1990). *Disability in America*. Washington, DC: National Academy Press.

Rutman, I. (1987). The psychosocial rehabilitation

movement in the United States. In A. Meyerson & T. Fine (Eds.), *Psychiatric disability: Clinical, legal, and administrative dimensions.* Washington, DC: American Psychiatric Press.

Weiss, R. S. (1982). Relationship of social support and psychological well-being. In H. C. Schulberg & M. Killilea (Eds.), *The modern practices of community mental health* (pp. 149–162). Washington, DC: Jossey-Bass.

SECTION I

FOUNDATIONS OF PSYCHIATRIC REHABILITATION

Chapter 1

Consumer Perspectives on Rehabilitation

JOHN H. PERRY
MARK A. DAVIS
JEANNIE MCVEIGH

It began with people talking.

Like other contemporary grass-roots efforts, the mental health consumer movement first started when people came together to share their experiences and express their frustrations. Alcoholics Anonymous was born over a kitchen table. The Civil Rights movement of the 1950s and 1960s was sparked at church meetings and informal gatherings. The women's movement grew from "consciousness-raising" groups. So it was for the consumer movement.

In the early 1970s, individuals who were former mental health patients and consumers began to meet on an informal basis, independent of the mental health system, for the first time. These gatherings grew out of discontent, anger, and a shared sense of injustice. As consumers and patients in the system, people felt powerless and disenfranchised. Coming together fostered a new sense of consumer empowerment (Chamberlin, 1978). Advocate Rae Unzicker describes her discovery of the ex-patient movement in this way: "It was like coming home—home to myself, my values, and most importantly, home to hope. It was there that I began to discover how angry I really was, and how powerful I could be. . . . I found there were others who were as angry as I was about the 'help' they received from the mental health system" (Unzicker, 1989, p. 74).

Ex-patients discovered that they were not alone and that other people had similar experiences, hopes, and ambitions. Group members wanted to work for change and demanded a share in determining the shape of their treatment and their lives. They also began to recognize that their informal discussions served a valuable therapeutic purpose; self-help became a group focus, along with efforts to change the mental health system and public attitudes (Chamberlin, Rogers, & Sneed, 1989). The ex-patient movement of the early 1970s developed into today's consumer support/self-help movement.

The philosophy of self-help is simple: By reaching out to someone else, we help to strengthen ourselves. For ex-patients, this is a particularly potent formula. The traditional mental health system often encourages individuals to view themselves as weak, needy, and dependent. Being a helper is empowering.

The early self-help groups had little or no funding and were relatively small, but they produced impressive results in helping members to improve their lives (Zinman, Harp, & Budd, 1987). During the 1980s and early 1990s, the consumer self-help movement has experienced tremendous growth. The number of consumer/ex-patient/survivor self-help projects has grown from a handful in the early 1970s to more than 2000 across the United States, Canada, England, and elsewhere. Many are developing innovative drop-in centers, housing and employment programs, and antistigma campaigns.

Although consumer-managed programs have become increasingly diverse, several self-help models have become common throughout the country, such as the following:

- *Drop-in centers.* These services provide a secure, central place for clients to visit when they choose. Drop-in centers often offer peer counseling, self-help groups, and recreation and socializing. They are usually controlled and staffed entirely by consumers and frequently offer advocacy, information, and referral.
- *Advocacy, self-help, and education projects.* These organizations usually offer advocacy and direct services, as well as education and information for the general public. Technical assistance in developing self-help programs is now commonly provided.

Numerous statewide and national organizations have also developed over this relatively short period (Mental Health Association of Southeastern Pennsylvania, no date.) On the national level, groups include the National Association of Psychiatric Survivors (NAPS), the National Mental Health Consumers' Association (NMHCA), the National Alliance for the Mentally Ill (NAMI) Consumer Council, and the National Depressive/Manic Depressive Association (NDMDA).

Through its Community Support Program, the National Institute of Mental Health (NIMH) also played an important role in supporting the growth of the consumer movement. NIMH began to include consumers in the development and planning of mental health policies and services; it also provided funding necessary for the initiation and expansion of consumer-run, self-help programs. NIMH funds have fueled organizations and activities such as the National Ex-Patient Teleconference, the National Mental Health Consumer Self-Help Clearinghouse, and the annual Alternatives Conference, which brings consumers together from across the country and abroad.

In recent years, the movement has expanded and diversified, reflecting the variety of its individual members. Groups and individuals now identify themselves as *clients*, *consumers*, *ex-patients*, or *survivors*, depending on their preference. The notion of the consumer has been refined to include *primary consumers*, those who are current or former recipients of mental health services, and *secondary consumers*, family members and other significant persons in the life of a primary consumer. The movement has grown to encompass a spectrum of ideologies and philosophies. Consumer advocate Mark Davis jokes, "We have everything from the 'anti-psychiatry, no-such-thing-as-mental-illness' folks to what I call the medical-model cheerleaders."

Judi Chamberlin, one of the earliest and most long-standing activists, acknowledges the divisions within the movement but also points to common concerns and aims. She writes, "Although the lack of a solidifying terminology continues to be troubling, such variety does not necessarily indicate wide variations in viewpoints and activities. Whether group members call themselves clients, consumers, ex-patients, users, or psychiatric survivors, groups throughout the world are united by the goals of self-determination and full citizenship rights for their members" (Chamberlin, 1990, pp. 335–336).

The following histories describe the perspectives of three consumers, on eight topics related to rehabilitation. A panel of consumers selected these topics as essential subject areas for any individual training in the field. Without the efforts of the past two decades, the voices of consumers would not be heard in this context. It is a testament to the consumer/ex-patient movement that this chapter is included.

Consumer Perspectives on Rehabilitation

Consumer Biographies

Jeannie McVeigh graduated from business school and completed some college. She worked for many years as a secretary and currently serves as an administrative assistant/back-up coordinator at the Northeast Consumer Center in Philadelphia. Jeannie identifies herself as a person with bipolar schizophrenia. Since 1971, she has experienced 14 hospitalizations.

Mark Davis has used mental health services since 1978. He has attempted suicide and experienced shock treatments, homelessness, misdiagnosis, experimental drug treatment, amnesia, and six psychiatric hospitalizations. Mark earned a master's degree in College Student Personnel at Bowling Green State University in 1981. In graduate school, Mark participated in extensive extracurricular activities, ranging from varsity cheerleading to serving as student government president. He then worked as a residential supervisor, overseeing 80 residents with mental retardation and a staff of 10, at Elwyn Institutes. He was later hired by Project Self-Help Advocacy Resource Exchange (SHARE) in 1985 and was founding director from 1987 to 1990 of I CAN (Involved Consumer Action Network) in Pennsylvania, a statewide mental health consumer self-help group development project. He served as coordinator of the Consumer Satisfaction Team, a consumer- and family-run evaluation project, and now works as community liaison for the Campaign for a New Start, an antistigma project in Philadelphia.

John Perry, a native of Washington, DC, has a history of manic depression and has been hospitalized twice. He is currently on extended leave from graduate school and works as an assistant director of technical assistance at the National Association of State Mental Health Program Directors (NASMHPD) in Alexandria, Virginia. He has worked as a newspaper reporter and continues to write on a free-lance basis. John spent several years working in agencies of the Massachusetts state government, including the Department of Mental Health. John Perry's opinions are his own and do not necessarily reflect the opinions of NASMHPD or its members.

Topics

The Philosophy of Hope

Consumers and caring professionals must share a fundamental belief that every person is capable of personal growth and that no person should be considered incapable of achieving a more productive life.

JEANNIE MCVEIGH (JM): I've always felt that there was hope. I had to fight for it: an independent living and holding a job, as opposed to a boarding home where someone was handing me my medication and telling me what time to take it. I always had a sense about myself, in spite of the fact that so many doctors put me down. What I see in the drop-in center is that there seems to be a lack of sense of self with many of the consumers. So many of them go along with what the world dictates. They don't think from within. They accept what their therapist says. Professionals never encourage a belief in yourself.

MARK DAVIS (MD): It is essential for caring professionals, family members, and consumers/ex-patients to understand that every person with mental illness is capable of personal growth. A cornerstone of the mental health consumer/ex-patient movement is the belief that all people with mental illness can achieve a more independent, productive life—and often in ways that go beyond the most optimistic hopes of peers, family members, professionals, and the public.

JOHN PERRY (JP): Hope is critical for recovery. Without genuine hope, we are simply going through the motions. In my case, the difficulty is that the nature of my illness itself robs me of hope at times. Major depression, in my experience, includes a profound sense of hopelessness. At the lowest points in my life, it has been essential that others believe and hope for me when I have been unable to do so for myself.

Often, it is easier for us to hope for others than it is to hope for ourselves—and that's where self-help plays such an important role. If we can reach out to others and allow others to reach out to us, then we weave our faith and hope together.

Professionals should strive at all times to maintain a sense of hope for the consumers with whom they work. Burn-out and professional disappointment can kill this crucial element of rehabilitation work. Without a sincere belief that a consumer can attain greater independence and wellness, a mental health professional is no better than an attendant or a guard.

The Obstacles

Forces that can hinder the rehabilitation process, both in the system and in society at large, are surprisingly diverse, but most of these forces can be overcome when consumers and professionals approach problems with a little courage and imagination.

JM: It does take courage and imagination to approach each individual's problem with a fresh perspective. As the system is now, too much emphasis is placed on medication and not near enough time and energy is put into the interaction between doctor and patient and between doctor and family. Consumers are relying on the doctors to give them the answers, and their doctors only listen long enough to write a prescription. We've had two or three situations here at the drop-in center where a doctor has taken a consumer off medication because they're doing well and within three to four days they go back into the hospital.

MD: I would say that the CRR [community residence rehabilitation program] and vocational program I was in were elementary and did not provide challenges for people with diverse prior life experiences and abilities. The staff treated us as if we were incapable of living independently or working in legitimate jobs. The program was designed for people to fit into its predefined limits—rather than the program adapting to the people using the services. Out of 70 people in the program, only 2 were working in jobs—and those jobs were demeaning. We did not see any signs of hope that anybody ever got out to live or work successfully outside rehabilitation services.

During the period that I was in the CRR and vocational program, I began to look for work. The OVR [Office of Vocational Rehabilitation] counselor told me that I would have to lower my standards and that I would never be able to work in my profession. I refused OVR's services from that point on and launched a job-seeking campaign on my own. I prepared and typed my own résumé. I answered want ads. My counselor had reviewed my résumé and told me that it was "all wrong" and that I should leave out any mention of my prior involvement in the Miss America Scholarship Pageant. (I had been a director, producer, and judge of local pageants and had served as field director and associate producer of the televised Miss Ohio Pageant.) I knew this experience was as relevant as my master's degree, and I ignored the counselor's advice to drop these experiences from my résumé.

In my first interview, I was considered as 1 of the top 3 finalists of 22 candidates for the position of residential director of a large residence hall on a major college campus. I came in second for the job, and I left the experience full of confidence. My next interview was at a large facility for persons labeled "[as having]" mental retardation. I was hired, I thought, as a residential counselor. When I arrived at the facility for my first day of work, I learned that I was the residential supervisor and that I was responsible for the living conditions of up to 80 adult men labeled with mental retardation and the supervision of a staff of 10. To say that my situation was unusual would be a drastic understatement: I was living in a group home for persons with mental illness while working as a supervisor in a residence for people with mental retardation. At work, I feared being found out. In my CRR, I feared being dropped out. After 3 months, I was able to afford the advance rent payment and security deposit necessary to rent a small room in center city Philadelphia.

JP: What I most often want to tell mental health professionals is that if they really care about what they are doing, then they must commit themselves to working for fundamental change in the country's approach to health care. To me, it seems almost indulgent to discuss the flaws in traditional mental health when so many people can't even access the system in the first place. I've heard numerous mental health and medical professionals bemoan the fact that insurance coverage and service availability dictate treatment. The insurance industry remains unwilling to assign the same importance to mental health as it does to medical health. That so many plans will allow costly inpatient treatment without funding less expensive outpatient treatment—therapy which could prevent hospitalization—is not only callous, but impractical.

During my first hospitalization, I can remember watching nurses prepare a pregnant woman named "Norma" for discharge. She was clearly unable to care for herself, but her benefits had run out. The nurses wrapped Norma's hand around the handle of her bag and shoved her out the door. A month later, word reached the patients that Norma and her unborn baby had frozen to death on a park bench.

We need health care, not wealth care, in this country, and professionals must commit themselves, along with consumers, to make this their primary goal before the rest.

Stigma, Stigmatizing Ourselves, Overcoming Mismanagement

The label of being *mentally ill* discourages the rehabilitation process and counters the philosophy of hope, but stigma can be transcended. People's beliefs can hold them back, and the need to overcome low self-esteem and a sense of failure is an important part of the rehabilitation process. At times, a consumer is held back by inappropriately restrictive services or an inaccurate diagnosis.

MD: Back when I took the first steps of my ongoing recovery from mental illness, I faced two major obstacles. The first was the illness itself. The second was the judgment and labels placed on me by professionals in the mental health system. The fact that I actually started to believe what they were telling me was a cause of real harm.

Back when I was in the hospital, I was feeling physically ill and was told by the staff that there was nothing physically wrong with me and that it was all in my mind. Three months later, a physical examination revealed that I had contracted hepatitis. One day, I became severely physically ill—to the point where I had to be rushed to the emergency room by ambulance. The ambulance driver asked me what medications I took. I told him I was taking lithium and an antidepressant. Upon arriving at the hospital, the emergency medical technician informed the nurse of my vital signs and completed his assessment by saying, "And he's crazy, too."

In order to be admitted to a hospital for psychiatric care, I was required to go through the hospital emergency room, where people with medical and psychiatric emergencies were combined. . . . After waiting for a while, I noticed that my gown was different from those worn by other patients. My gown was lavender. All the other gowns were light blue. I found out that the psychiatric patients had gowns of a different color. It is difficult to describe the impact which these incidents had on my self-esteem and my understanding of how I fit in society. I came to believe that I was hopeless and incapable of functioning. This kind of blatant discrimination—coupled with professionals' statements that I should expect to be in and out of psychiatric hospitals the rest of my life—took away every ounce of self-confidence. I believed that I would never get well.

JM: Right from the beginning, your family stigmatizes you—they don't understand what's happening with you. You become the black sheep, and they don't count on you anymore. They think, "Just stay away, leave me alone." They just know I'm sick, and that's all they know. If that's not a stigma, I don't know what is.

It's easy to stigmatize ourselves. When you're given repeated medications, through repeated hospitalizations, without any encouragement or education as to why you're hospitalized or why you're given medication and what it's supposed to do for you. When your medication isn't right, you're not feeling so good. It is easy to be stigmatized. Education, love, and understanding can go a long way.

JP: I find myself in a unique relationship to stigma working within the mental health system while also being a consumer/ex-patient. Several years ago, another job I held in the mental health field required that I tour a state facility with several other professionals on an official visit. Beyond the fact that the trip felt like visiting a zoo, I can remember a coworker leaning over to me at one point in the tour and whispering, "God, can you imagine living in a place like this?" The truth was that I didn't need to try to imagine hospitalization; I had exper-

ienced it myself. Rather than saying this, though, I just shrugged in agreement.

It's not important whether my inhibition about sharing my experience was the result of actual negative attitudes around me or overly sensitive fears from within—I suspect it was a combination of the two. What is significant is the fact that even within the mental health field itself, I did not feel safe at that time identifying myself as a consumer/ex-patient. I felt that my status as a professional would be endangered. I felt that I would stop being one of "us," and slip over to being one of "them," in the eyes of my colleagues.

Stigma functions in the way we understand ourselves. Identity is often formed in opposition—we understand things by looking at their opposites. The notion of *hot* has no significance without the notion of *cold*, for instance—or *high* without *low*, or *sick* without *well*. To some extent, mental health professionals may organize their sense of themselves and the role they play by drawing a line between the individual who treats and the individual who needs treatment.

The danger, of course, is that this kind of understanding can lock individuals into permanent definitions. A professional may find it hard to view a consumer as no longer "sick." Changing a label may threaten the professional's self-concept.

The Role of Empowering Friends and Professionals

Having a few people who believe in our worth and potential can be crucial in the rehabilitation process.

JP: During my last hospitalization, I spent 15 consecutive days in the quiet room. The staff felt unable to control me, and they were not satisfied with the results from the truckload of pharmaceuticals they'd given me. Finally, they decided I needed shock. I refused to agree to the treatments, and they threatened to get a court order if I did not comply. I had no way of defending or advocating for myself in the quiet room.

I wanted very much to have a psychiatrist I trusted on the outside argue against using shock, but I had no way of contacting anyone. One mental health worker helped me. She anonymously phoned a friend of mine on the outside to relay my call for help to my old psychiatrist. "I am John's only advocate," she explained to my friend. "Don't ask me who I am." Ultimately, I was able to avoid the shock treatments.

I know it sounds a little bit like mystery melodrama, but life in the hospital has an entirely different set of rules than life on the outside. Some might call what this woman did for me unprofessional or an example of staff splitting, but I assure you it meant the difference for me. I recovered without having to go through ECT [electroconvulsive therapy], and I will always be grateful for that. Professionals must remain open to acting on their best instincts in new situations and not always following the book. Human situations demand human, flexible responses.

MD: At the CRR, one staff member paid me a competitive wage to type his college papers—and that felt empowering. Earning compensation for my typing services not only supplemented my substandard welfare income, but also supplemented my substandard sense of self-worth and confidence. It occurred to me that I could go into business providing typing services, and I realized that there was no reason that my psychiatric history would interfere with my ability to make such a venture successful. The fact that I was providing a valuable service to a staff member, for which he was willing to pay, began a process in which I came to realize I was equal to [the] program staff members.

This staff member and a social worker

at the agency were two examples of mental health workers who viewed me as a person first. They regarded my mental illness as one of many parts of me.... The attitude of these two staff members was in contrast to the treatment I received from the great majority of mental health workers. These people seemed to think that my mental illness rendered me incapable of speaking or acting for myself—and that they should do so instead.

JM: The empowering therapist is something new to me. I've found very few.

It's all about being allowed to act on your own for yourself. My supervisor at the drop-in center is empowering. She gives me more and more responsibility to act on my own, to handle all kinds of situations, even a crisis—on my own.

The Importance of Advocacy

People working for positive change often make a positive impact on the rehabilitation process.

JP: People won't change their attitudes until they are confronted with an example that contradicts what they believe. The only effective way to fight stigma is to ensure that people see individuals who defy the stereotypes which have become associated with mental illness. Consumers must advocate for themselves, but they can't become advocates without the cooperation of professionals. Mental health professionals must learn to relinquish some of their authority on the subject of mental illness to consumers who can speak from direct experience. Ceding authority is never easy, but professionals should struggle to view consumer empowerment and advocacy as an asset not a threat.

MD: Knowledge is power. People need information to make choices to make their rehabilitation effective. Case management needs to be called "service management" because we are not cases.

Services need to be community based and integrated. . . . Program planners must get away from their desks, out of their offices, and into programs where they can talk to the experts: those who have been there and *are* there. Consumer advocates, working from a foundation of real-life experiences, are helpful in leading others through the system. We—family and friends, consumers of service, alumni of service, mental health professionals, and others—all have pieces of the answer to an ideal community support program. We must listen to each other and focus our energies on what we can agree on.

JM: Having been through 14 hospitalizations, I feel in a position where I can stand up and be noticed. I'm in the system, but on my job, working as a self-help advocate, I can be seen as a role model. Consumers have been there, they've been through it. They can speak for themselves, just as others can speak for them.

Self-Help

Peers often provide invaluable support and encouragement and also serve as role models.

MD: At one time, the National Mental Health Association had a brochure that said, "We speak for those who cannot speak for themselves." Self-help is helping yourself, helping others, and being able to ask for help when needed. It means speaking for ourselves rather than being spoken for. . . . Self-help involves both leaving the system and being able to return as role models for those who remain in it. It inspires us to come back to work in the system. Rather than fighting from outside, we can become involved with the solution—instead of focusing merely on the problem. Through self-help, we have resources within ourselves and with others to assure that our rights are protected, that our services are appropriate and that our lives are moving forward. Empowerment is something we take, not something that is given to us; it enables us to turn legitimate anger into constructive action.

I feel frustrated when I think of how my life would have been changed for the better if self-help services had been available to me when I was dependent on the mental health system. That frustration motivated me to use my work in the movement as an opportunity to make self-help services available to as many consumers as possible. Working with consumer groups such as Project SHARE, I often thought back to my CRR and to the attitude of its management toward client-to-client relationships. The staff said we were not to associate with certain clients because they were "sick, too"—in other words, they did not have the judgment to be friends. Despite these warnings, we met in underground self-help groups. We felt that what we were doing was beneficial and that the staff was wrong. We were unaware that we were in the grass roots of a growing national self-help movement. It was from these experts—my peers—that I received the most valuable help and support.

JM: Drop-in centers are more and more important all the time. I've never felt something on the outside like I feel here. Consumers sustain one another, it's beautiful. I've seen one consumer take three buses just to drop off a handful of quarters to someone in the hospital. (If you've ever been there, you know you need quarters in the hospital just to make a phone call to the outside.) That's the result of a self-help program. Consumers know where other consumers are coming from. In our self-help groups, we get down to the nitty-gritty of what's eating at us. That doesn't happen with professionals.

JP: The old folk wisdom that you learn more in college at the dinner table with other students than you do in the lecture hall translates directly to the mental health arena. I've often learned and felt more when interacting with other patients and consumers than I have in formal therapy or treatment. To some extent, the mental health profession already recognizes the importance of this kind of interaction—hence, its heavy reliance on group therapy.

Taken a step further, though, group therapy evolves into self-help. Consumer-run programs are the logical extension of the group approach. Groups without professional leaders have a different feel and focus. I can remember spending countless hours in AA [Alcoholics Anonymous] meetings after being discharged from my first hospitalization. Outpatient therapy couldn't pick up the slack, and AA offered a safe environment at almost any hour of the day to ease my transition back into the outside. AA was a haven, where I could quiet the noise in my head and where I didn't have to maintain a constant appearance of being okay.

Self-help groups are not perfect. They suffer from problems of dynamics and organization, like any collective endeavor. Cliques form, leaders rise and fall, but somehow the work gets done and help is given.

The Role of Therapy and Medication

Medication and therapy can help, but they can also fall short of helping adequately. Therapists can be empowering but also controlling. Medications often have disabling side effects, and some consumers choose instead to practice suppression and self-management of their symptoms.

JM: With their knowledge of medication, therapists think they have it all and don't discuss much with you. When they do discuss it, it can be inhibiting. Medication can help if you get on the right med [medication] and it works. By my twelfth

hospitalization, they had education classes about medications. If I had had this the first time around, I would have been ahead of the game. I wouldn't have needed the next 11 hospitalizations.

MD: Psychiatry and the family movement have overemphasized the medical model, and that misses the whole person, with medical, emotional, spiritual, and social needs. So many times, the medical model tries to correct what's wrong, and what gets lost is what's right about the person. The person forgets their strengths and that they have skills and talents.

When people are labeled and put into the mental health system, they are less able to practice their skills and talents. When anyone talks about spirituality or God, it can get labeled as grandiosity or delusional. People are not encouraged to explore their spiritual side.

I'm a proponent of medication, if it's the person's choice. There are a lot of services that can be explored before medication. I also think there's a great benefit in holistic approaches like nutrition, massage therapy, and chiropractic work, but these services usually aren't funded by insurance.

The roulette system of "try this, try that, try any medication" is a Band-Aid™ for the real problems of living.

JP: I take medication; I probably always will, but I have a hard time reconciling myself to this fact, and I think that that's something professionals have to keep in mind. Professionals have to become sensitized to our feelings surrounding medication. During my last hospitalization, I eventually moved to a ward that operated as a "three-quarter-way" house. This ward, unlike the locked wards in the hospital, had an optional weekly medication meeting, where professionals and residents could discuss their feelings and share information on the topic. The professionals learned as much as the residents. (It boggles me to think that a group of this kind is considered inappropriate or disruptive on a locked ward, where you are first being put on medication or being restabilized on medication. This is the time when your fears about the drugs may be the strongest, yet you have to get well to participate in treating your illness. Isn't that just a little ironic?)

Professionals naturally have a very different relationship to the medication than the consumer does. On the obvious level, professionals don't usually have experience taking the drugs they prescribe, so that tends to distance them from the people who are actually living with the chemicals and their side effects. But on a subtler level, the professional usually views the drug in terms of what it can do and what it can offer. As a consumer, on the other hand, I often think about what the drug takes away. In exchange for the leveling of my mood swings and the halting of dangerous drifts, I feel I lose a portion of my imagination; the acute, almost photographic memory I once enjoyed; and the intensity of feeling and conviction through which I know myself. My mind feels sluggish and gluey. At the same time, I feel better able to survive. This ambivalence usually keeps me in an adversarial posture with the medication.

The feeling that medication takes away a part of our essential nature is wrapped up in the part our illness plays in our identities. During my first hospitalization, I knew a woman named "Ruth." She had stopped talking and functioning during her sophomore year in college, almost a year and a half after she had survived being abducted by a stranger, held captive for several days, and repeatedly raped and abused. Over the months that I knew Ruth in the hospital, the staff tried every therapeutic approach they could to break her silence. Nothing worked.

One day, she started to speak to a few patients. We were incredibly excited by this leap forward, but within 24 hours, it became clear that something was wrong. Ruth couldn't stop talking. The staff had piled on new medications to force a change, and the medicine had gone too far. Eventually, Ruth couldn't control herself. I remember her standing in the halls in a pool of her own urine screaming over and over, "They made me talk." More medication was administered to slow Ruth down, and eventually she became sluggish and disjointed again.

The Ongoing Struggle

Rehabilitation is an open-ended process, and the work can be lifelong.

JM: I have a phrase I like. It came from one of the consumers at the drop-in center. We were sitting at a roundtable self-help group. She said my bipolar disorder and my schizophrenia are "a gift." They're a part of me, and I wouldn't be who I am without them. If I didn't have these things, I wouldn't be where I am and I wouldn't know the people I do. I would have thought they were "crazies." I would have disassociated myself from them. Recovery is lifelong. I have to keep my support system up. I rely on them.

MD: So many times, when you leave a hospital or a program, you just get filed away. Supported education and supported employment are critical. Just placing someone in a college or a training program isn't enough. There needs to be support to make sure that the person makes it through the transition. There has to be coordination of services—transitions can't be a hand-off from one service to the next.

One myth and one misconception, especially among family members, is that you aren't like other mental health consumers, "you aren't one of them." If I can look presentable and speak at a conference, then I'm miraculously cured and I'm not "one of them" anymore. The reality is something completely different.

I continue to present myself *as I am* at any given moment. My mental illness is just as much a part of me as the color of my hair or eyes. I believe that I'm in a recovering process while experiencing basic struggles associated with living. If I consider myself to be recovered, then I set myself on a pedestal, from which I can fall.

JP: Part of my problem is an inability to deal with the future. I don't like to think about the prospect, and planning more than a few weeks in advance has always agitated me. As I recover, I allow myself to look farther forward with less fear and apprehension. Part of permitting myself a future is accepting that recovery will always have to play a major and continual role in my life.

As I begin to come out of a particularly tough bout and feel more stable, I want more than anything to forget that I have an illness. This impulse puts me at risk. I deny the need to tend to my recovery, and I clear away anything that reminds me of past problems (including medication and therapy). This drive to forget is an act of self-destruction, and curbing it represents the hardest element of my ongoing struggle.

Being well, while remaining responsive to recovery from a lifelong illness, is a tough balancing act. It's a balancing act that I require not only from myself, but also from the professionals, friends, and family in my life. I want the people around me to treat me as though I'm well, when I am well, but never to assume that my illness is a thing of the past, an unfortunate stage, or a problem solved.

What Is Rehabilitation?

There is no simple answer. Consumers and professionals must recognize that rehabilita-tion can mean different things to different people.

JP: The word *rehabilitation* always makes me think of fixing up vacant houses. Consumers are not vacant houses, but the image can illustrate the way I see the rehabilitation concept. In restoring properties, the best "rehab" job will be faithful and sensitive to the original structure. Builders can't go into a house and rip everything out to start over. If they do, they sacrifice the unique character of the original.

The same can be said for psychiatric rehabilitation. In restructuring the way we live, we can't scrap everything that has come before. Personality is the sum of individual traits and past experiences, and we cannot sacrifice who we are for the sake of survival. This would be self-defeating. The best rehabilitation strategy, then, would be to incorporate the past and who we are into updated understanding and structural improvements. We have to learn to live with illness, not to start over from scratch.

JM: Consumers want love, relationships, friendships. They want a place to live, they want jobs, they want their family's approval. They have to work for these things—whereas in the mainstream, things just come. People on the outside take things for granted. Mental health consumers have to work for everything they get. They have to get Section 8 [public rent assistance], for instance. Professionals treat you like you can handle life, but there's an undercurrent of "you're always going to be sick." They don't talk to you on a self-help level.

MD: Rehabilitation is not a very positive word. It feeds into the notion that something's wrong, and you have to correct it. If people could see going through a rehabilitation process as just like going to a university or a trade school, that would be great. I began calling myself an alumnus of rehabilitation and that's when I got out of rehabilitation what I really needed.

One person's rehabilitation might be getting back into college, another person's might be a more structured program. It's a matter of having a menu of choices in which consumers actually make the choices. Professionals must recognize that those choices are valid and real, even when they differ from what the professionals would choose. I think of a continuum of challenge and support, with homelessness being the ultimate challenge and a hospital being the greatest level of support. Rehabilitation lies at different points on this continuum for different people.

I see the ideal rehabilitation professional as a kind of buddy, who is helping consumers move forward at their own pace. I'd also like to see more professionals able to share mental health experiences they've been through as an asset—not only their book learning and degrees.

When I was in high school, there was a day when the students exchanged positions with people in the community. The mayor would become a student, and a student would become the mayor for a day. This needs to be a requirement for people who are training to be mental health professionals. People need to get away from their textbooks and desks and out into the community to experience the human realities of the profession.

Conclusion

Readers of this chapter must recognize that they have heard the perspectives of three individuals who speak only for themselves. We are not mouthpieces for the consumer movement.

Clearly, three people cannot speak for the millions who are ex-patients in this country. Nor can the efforts of consumers and ex-patients be considered to represent a single,

unified movement. Self-help has grown and spread in so many directions that the ex-patient movement has become as diverse as its many participants.

Judi Chamberlin has written, "Former patients recognize numerous currents of opinion within their community. . . . There are groups whose members promote the illness metaphor (e.g., Recovery, Inc.); groups whose members see themselves as consumers (e.g., the National Mental Health Consumers' Association); and groups whose members see themselves as liberationists (e.g., the National Association of Psychiatric Survivors)" (Chamberlin, 1990, p. 336).

Like any struggle, efforts by ex-patients to organize and advocate for themselves have led to internal disagreements and to the development of differing ideologies and points of view. Debates continue over involving nonpatient supporters, accepting outside funding, and working with established mental health institutions and systems. Clashes of opinion can extend to the most basic questions, such as how exactly we conceive mental health, illness, disorders, and disabilities. The differences and diversity of ex-patients' points of view are even reflected in the comments of the three contributors to this chapter.

We hope that these comments will open new avenues of thought and discussion within the topic of rehabilitation. We also hope that our experiences and opinions will convey some sense of the flavor and context of the "ex-patient movement." Most important, though, we hope that our words will sensitize the reader to the fact that rehabilitation is only meaningful when viewed in terms of those it serves.

Acknowledgments

We would like to acknowledge the work of several consumers who assisted in conceiving and outlining this chapter and its contents.

We also thank Joseph C. Yaskin, of Project SHARE in Philadelphia, for participating in the original shaping of this work and for assisting Mark Davis in putting his thoughts onto paper.

Special thanks is given to Laura Van Tosh, a consumer/ex-patient who is the former co-ordinator of the National Mental Health Consumer Self-Help Clearinghouse located in Philadelphia. Laura convened and par-ticipated in the panel of consumer planners for this chapter and guided this project through its early stages.

References

Chamberlin, J. (1978). *On our own: Patient-con-trolled alternatives to the mental health system.* New York: McGraw-Hill.

Chamberlin, J., Rogers, J. A., & Sneed, C. S. (1989). Consumers, families, and community support systems. *Psychosocial Rehabilitation Journal, 12*(3), 93–106.

Chamberlin, J. (1990). The ex-patient's movement: Where we've been and where we're going. *Journal of Mind and Behavior, 11*(3,4), 323–336.

Mental Health Association of Southeastern Penn-sylvania. (no date). *The National Mental Health Consumer Self-Help Clearinghouse* (brochure). Philadelphia, PA: Author.

Unzicker, R. (1989). On my own: A personal jour-ney through madness and reemergence. *Psy-chosocial Rehabilitation Journal. 13*(1), 71–77.

Zinman, S., Harp, H. T., & Budd, S. (1987). *Reaching across: Mental health clients help each other.* Riverside, CA: California Network of Mental Health Clients.

Suggested Readings

Furlong-Norman, K. (Ed.). (1988). Consumer/ex-patients initiatives. *Community Support Net-work News, 5*(2), 1–15.

Ryglewicz, H. (Ed.). (1989). A self-help social movement. *TIE-Lines:* A Bulletin Concerning Young Adults with Serious Ongoing Mental/Emotional Disorders. New City, NY. *Quarterly Bulletin of the Information Exchange on Young Adult Chronic Patients, 6*(4), 1–8.

Schlageter, C. (Ed.). (1990). Consumer empow-erment. *New York State Office of Mental Health News, 2*(1), 1–16.

Chapter 2

A Family Perspective on Rehabilitation

HARRIET P. LEFLEY

Families of persons with serious and persistent mental illnesses have typically become accustomed to living with permanent stress. Although they share commonalities with other families who live with long-term disability, there are substantive differences in experience. The symptoms and behaviors of psychiatric disorders are uniquely distressing both to the persons who bear them and the relatives who live with them. In contrast to the symptomatology and functioning of persons with lifetime developmental or physical disorders, the severity of the symptomatology and its effect on functioning waxes and wanes for persons with severe mental illnesses. For their family members, there is a persistent dilemma of raised and dashed hopes, of balancing expectations that may be too high or too low at particular points in the course of the illness.

Throughout the years, moreover, families and their mentally ill loved ones have endured the effects of an overriding stressor that is basically iatrogenic, a product of wrongful thinking and treatment by professionals. Unlike families of persons with disabling developmental or physical conditions, relatives of persons with severe psychiatric illness have been implicated in the etiology or pathogenesis of these devastating disorders. There has been a presumption that family members might have been able to prevent the illness altogether, or that they may have been able to diminish the disability or even provide a cure by altering their own behavior.

The effects of these assumptions on the families of persons with mental illnesses, on the persons themselves, on professionals' attitudes and behaviors, and on societal treatment and expectations have been far-reaching and—in some cases—extremely damaging. Psychodynamic treatment models derived from these paradigms tended to exclude families from basic information and from involvement in the therapeutic process. Various family therapy models, on the other hand, have involved family members in treatment on the unlikely premise that the symptoms of schizophrenia or of major affective disorders will disappear when they are no longer needed to maintain homeostasis of a dysfunctional family system. This premise, which resulted in many families feeling frustrated and blamed (Hatfield, 1983), today is repudiated as archaic by some of the most prominent family therapists in the field (Anderson, Reiss, & Hogarty, 1986; McFarlane & Beels, 1983; Terkelsen, 1983; Wynne, 1988). As this chapter shows, these older therapeutic approaches sometimes alienated individuals with severe mental disabilities from their natural support systems and in some cases actually reinforced abandonment.

Fortunately, the current era is beginning to see dramatic and salutary changes in perceptions of families and their roles in etiology, treatment, and rehabilitation. In this chapter, we begin with the experience of mental illness in the family, describe modes of adjustment during the developmental course of the illness, and follow the history of families' experiences with mental health professionals and the service delivery system. We then go on to explore new empowering roles for families that have been generated largely by the growth of the National Alliance for the Mentally Ill (NAMI), highlighting families' roles in advocacy, public education, services, and professional training. Examples of rehabilitative resources and programs developed by family groups are described. Collaborative models with professionals, clients, and the consumer movement are traced, together with trends in service delivery and their implications for rehabilitation. We end with a discussion of families' roles in shaping new directions for research, training, and services.

Experiencing Mental Illness in the Family

The family's experience of mental illness may vary as a function of social and cultural background because these determine belief systems, degree of stigmatization, and the financial and human resources available to buffer the impact and alleviate the burden of living with the disorder. Yet, there are experiences that seem to cross all boundaries. The onset of a psychotic disorder, with its bizarre and unpredictable behavior, elicits bewilderment and concern in families throughout the world (Lefley, 1985). There are immediate appeals to healers, unrealistic expectations of a rapid cure, and a need to develop coping strategies to deal with the growing realization that this may be a lifelong disability. The nature of the unfolding disorder and the manner in which it is experienced by both patient and family are very much related to the availability, accessibility, competence, and sensitivity of societal helping resources. In order for professionals to be helpful, there must be some understanding of the realities of living with major mental illnesses.

Dimensions of Family Burden

The terms *objective* and *subjective family burden* have been used to distinguish, respectively, between the realistic demands of living with mental illness and the family members' personal suffering as a result of the disability. Examples of objective burden are the patient's economic dependency and inability to fulfill age-appropriate role functions; disruption of household routines; familial investments of time and energy in help-seeking and in negotiating the mental health system; confusing and often humiliating interactions with service providers; financial costs of the illness; deprivation of needs of other family members; curtailment of social activities; impaired relations with the outside world; and difficulties in finding appropriate alternatives to hospitalization or residential placement outside the family home.

Subjective burden of family members involves stressful effects on one's own mental and physical health; feelings of stigmatization; and frustrations at not being able to make or fulfill personal plans. Among the most painful burdens are grief and mourning for the premorbid personality, perhaps once bright with promise; empathic suffering for the pain of a loved one; and worries about the patient's future when the parents or other supportive relatives are no longer available to help.

Behavior management issues are ongoing tensions between persons with mental disabilities and their families. Household members may have to contend with verbal abuse or even assaultive behaviors based on paranoid ideation. They may have to cope with mood swings and unpredictability; socially offensive or embarrassing situations; conflicts over money likely to be ill-managed, squandered, or lost; and behaviors disturbing to household living, such as poor personal hygiene, excessive smoking, fire hazards, property damage, and sleep reversal patterns that may result in pacing or loud music at odd hours of the night. Patients' refusal to take their medications is a common area of contention, particularly when there is a known pattern of relapse.

Negative symptoms of apathy, anhedonia (inability to feel pleasure), or lack of motivation, are particularly burdensome to some families (Johnson, 1990). Attentional deficits, such as the prolonged silences and delayed reactions of schizophrenia, may be perceived as a lack of human relatedness by family members. Although they may recognize that these are not purposive distancing mechanisms, this interference with normal communication tends to further deprive family members of the rewards of human interaction and reciprocity that most people expect from their loved ones.

Family support groups indicate that one of the greatest stressors, especially for parents of disabled adults, is learning how to cope with the patient's own suffering over an impoverished life. Mentally disabled persons are often acutely aware of their lack of skills, impaired productivity, and poor future prospects. They can see that others of their own age are married, having children, or finalizing career plans. Simultaneously, they desire and fear the demands of these roles. For those previously hospitalized, community reintegration poses the threatening need to acquire or relearn vocational or psychosocial coping skills in a competitive environment. The patients' own mourning for lost developmental stages, failed aspirations, and unrealizable dreams can be extremely stressful for those who love them and can feel their pain.

Feelings of helplessness to make things better for a disabled child or sibling can generate acute distress in family members. Their suffering is compounded by guilt if sympathy alternates with frustration and rage at aversive behavior. Family members must learn to distinguish between volitional and nonvolitional behavior, recognize and deal with manipulation, and know how and when to set limits. They must learn to balance expectations that may be too high or too low, both for the ill relative and for themselves; to deal with their own legitimate anger and unjustified guilt; to tolerate the suffering of persons they love, and come to terms with their own rescue fantasies. In addition, they must learn to recognize and accept the legitimacy of their own needs.

Family burden is related to gender, age, and socioeconomic status. Females are the primary caregivers, and this is an increasingly thankless role for women in today's society (Thurer, 1983). Deinstitutionalization has created a situation in which we see many aging parents, in their 60s and 70s, as major caregivers for their psychiatrically disabled adult children (Lefley, 1987). At a time in life when they are most vulnerable to declining health, these elderly people are dealing with difficult behavior and anxieties about what will happen to their loved one if they become disabled or die. A disproportionate number of seriously mentally ill persons are from lower socioeconomic groups. Providing support to dependent dysfunctional adults adds an additional burden when the family suffers from poverty.

Experiences of individual family members may differ, depending on their role relationship as parent, sibling, wife, adult child, or other close relative. Experiences may vary according to the developmental stage of the illness and the level of disability. Tessler, Killian, and Gubman (1987) have described a typology of family response involving nine stages: (1) initial awareness of a problem, (2) denial of mental illness, (3) labelling, (4) faith in mental health professionals, (5) recurrent crises, (6) recognition of chronicity, (7) loss of faith in mental health professionals, (8) belief in the family's expertise, and (9) concerns about the future.

The family's role in rehabilitation may thus be determined by multiple factors. At a minimum, these include the patient's level of disability, the family's coping strengths, and available adaptive resources. However, this role also depends on professionals' capacity for collaborative relationships with family members. In this connection, it is important to understand the historical background of families' interactions with mental health service providers.

Overview of Family Roles in the Treatment System

Family roles in the treatment of severe mental disabilities have largely been shaped by hypotheses about etiology. For many years, untested and unproven theories not only formed the basis of various therapeutic models, but also determined professionals' attitudes and their relationships with their patients' relatives. The theories have also been instrumental in shaping confidentiality rules that are far more rigorous than those that prevail in physical illness. In some cases, confidentiality regulations have functionally prevented the discovery and reunification of homeless mentally ill persons with families who are trying to locate them (Lefley, Nuehring, & Bestman, 1992).

When patients are treated psychodynamically, therapists usually refuse to engage in any interaction with family members because this might breach the therapeutic alliance and affect the patient's trust. When noncommunication is explained in terms of maintaining confidentiality, most family members accept this and typically say they want information on medications, not therapeutic disclosures. In most situations, however, reasons for noncommunication are not explained. In many situations, there has been a clear message to families that, as Goldstein (1981) put it, "the patient's illness was their fault and they should go away, shrouded in guilt, and leave the professional to undo the damage" (p. 2). Past policies not only excluded families from any role in treatment, but also provided many exhausted relatives with grounds for separation from a problem that seemed increasingly insoluble.

The advent of family therapy brought families into the treatment process but perpetuated the view of the "identified patient" as victim and bearer of the family's psychopathology. In lieu of a psychodynamic focus on the past, family theories focused on present transactions. However, because symptoms were viewed as instrumental rather than as valid presentations of disease, families' anxious requests for information on illness management continued to be ignored or deflected.

Numerous studies have attempted to confirm the hypotheses underlying both psychodynamic and family systems theories. For the most part, theoretical models of family pathogenesis have been disputed by careful analytic reviews of the empirical literature (Eaton, 1986; Howells & Guirguis, 1985; Parker, 1982). Researchers using rigorously designed replications have failed to confirm earlier findings of deviant communication styles (Hirsch & Leff, 1975). Over the years, clinicians also began to change their appraisals. After almost a quarter century of working with persons with schizophrenia, Arieti (1981) announced that 75% to 80% of the mothers he has encountered do not remotely fit the description of "schizophrenogenic." He chastised his psychiatric colleagues for their eagerness to believe and probably reinforce any emphasis on negative maternal characteristics in the recollections of their schizophrenic patients. Writing on families in an important psychiatric textbook, Weiner (1985) pointed out that similar characteristics of parents are found in recollections of persons with bronchial asthma, ulcerative colitis, and schizophrenia.

The notion of family pathology has had damaging effects on both families and patients. Among family members, the message of culpability has generated guilt and low self-esteem, has weakened coping strengths, and has sometimes led to excessive tolerance of unacceptable behavior. Nevertheless, as Fisher, Benson, and Tessler (1990) point out, although family interaction theories and research have declined, these ideas are still quite prevalent in the field.

Types of Experiences with Mental Health Professionals

Family members have had both positive and negative experiences with mental health professionals, but the negative impact is more evident in personal accounts (Dearth,

Labenski, Mott, & Pellegrini,1986; Group for the Advancement of Psychiatry, 1986), in survey research findings (Hatfield, 1983; Holden & Lewine, 1982; Lefley, 1989, 1990), and in anecdotal data in family support groups. Some family members recalled punishing accusations that were not only hurtful, but also eroded the family's faith in its own ability to help a loved one.

> [A NAMI] member recalls being refused permission to see her newly hospitalized son, who had decompensated while away at college. Pleading to meet with the clinical director, she said: "Doctor, we love our son dearly and want to do everything possible to help him recover. Please tell us what we can do." He replied with what she recalls as icy contempt. "I think you have already done quite enough mother. After all, it was in your home that he became ill." This meeting caused her intense and long-lasting pain. No family education was given and the patient was urged not to increase his dependency by returning to the parental home. Upon discharge, the son returned to the university, decompensated within two weeks, and spent the next ten years in and out of hospitals. (Lefley, 1990, p. 132)

In some cases, professional interventions based on psychogenic hypotheses have alienated mentally disabled persons from a needed support system, leading to the patient's disintegration. Two accounts exemplify how this can happen:

> A young wife and mother of two small children described life with a disabled husband who suffered from paranoid schizophrenia. Her marriage was punctuated by crisis emergency admissions, delusional outbursts and threats, fears for the safety of the children, and severe economic stress. As the sole support of the family, she worked long hours to pay for child care outside the home, and when her husband was finally admitted to the state hospital, made time for long-distance hospital visits. There, her husband received psychotherapy from a young psychology intern who suggested to the patient that psychotic behavior has functional value in the family system. When the wife visited, she was informed by the patient that "My shrink thinks I'm here because you need me to be sick. He thinks you get something out of my symptoms."

> Instead of being offered support, education, counseling, or respite help from the treatment system, the exhausted wife was now given the message that she was the cause of her husband's illness. This provided a good reason to separate herself from a thankless and difficult situation, allowing her to get on with her life, but stripping the husband of his most valuable human resources. (Lefley, 1990, p. 133)

Parents are often given the message that they are impeding separation and individuation by allowing a mentally disabled adult to live with them. There is an implicit premise that once free of the family, the person will become motivated to seek independent solutions for survival. With seriously mentally disabled persons, this expectation is both naïve and potentially life-threatening.

> A young man had a pattern of stopping medications and revolving-door crisis admissions. When his desperate mother sought guidance from a psychiatrist, she was advised to evict her son from their apartment and to refuse his nightly importuning for readmission. After her son spent weeks of homeless wandering in the cold and rain, and was subjected to severe assaults, infection, and sickness, the mother realized this was "a crazy solution to a difficult problem." Today, ten years later, Mrs J. is haunted by the terrible experience of seeing her son on the street . . . feels terribly guilty, and has lost trust in a mental health profession that could offer no better solution to her son's problems. (Hatfield, Farrell & Starr, 1984, p. 288)

Today, the system is likely to offer more options in the way of psychosocial rehabilitation programs, case management, and alternative housing options, although these resources vary widely from place to place. Some systems also make an effort to offer family education and counseling. Among these are interventions that have been developed largely within the past decade in response to the needs following deinstitutionalization.

Family Education and Counseling

New modes of interventions with families began to evolve in the late 1970s and early 1980s. These were largely responsive to the failures of older models of family therapy, to a growing literature on family burden (Lefley, 1989), and to the pragmatic needs of deinstitutionalization because many families were now confronting a caregiver role for which they were untrained and ill-prepared. According to Ryglewicz (1989), a major source of the new interventions was also a body of expressed emotion (EE) research that suggested an association between the expression of hostile criticism toward or emotional overinvolvement (high EE) with the mentally ill family member and that patient's relapse. The studies indicated that members of low-EE families lacked these negative qualities and were described by major investigators as calm, empathic, accepting, and respectful. Cross-cultural research ultimately demonstrated that in studies throughout the world, most families of persons with schizophrenia showed low EE, thereby negating the stereotypes of schizophrenogenesis (Leff & Vaughn, 1985).

The EE researchers categorically denied any implication that families or high EE cause mental illness (Falloon, 1988; Leff, 1989). They suggested instead that ordinary expressions of anger or criticism based on justified but unrealistic behavioral expectations might be overstimulating for people with the core deficits of schizophrenia. As Ryglewicz (1989) notes, corollary research on information processing deficits in schizophrenia broadened the EE concept as an "attention/arousal" model and suggested that both families and professionals would benefit from education aimed at providing a low stress environment.

The psychoeducational interventions that emerged were finally responsive to families' requests for information, support, and illness-management techniques. Developed by a number of different practitioners (see Anderson, Reiss, & Hogarty, 1986; Falloon, Boyd, & McGill, 1984; Goldstein, 1981), they share a biologically based vulnerability/stress model of major mental illnesses. All approaches deal with illness education and medication management, identification of stressors and strategies for dealing with them, crisis intervention and behavior management techniques, communication and problem-solving skills, and methods for lowering anxiety and helping family members to value and take care of their own needs, as well as those of others in the household. Multiple family groups, espoused by Beels and McFarlane (1982) offer a sharing experience, information exchange, role-modeling, and socialization. Well-designed research has indicated a significant relationship between specific psychoeducational approaches, combined with low dose neuroleptics, and lower relapse rates among persons with schizophrenia (Anderson, Reiss, & Hogarty, 1986; Falloon, 1988).

There are concerns about embedding family education in a treatment model, administered by people who are trained as therapists rather than as educators. Thus, excellent models of family education have been developed that differentiate skills training from the idea of a therapeutic intervention (Hatfield, 1990). When treatment is desired, models that seem to be favored by families are supportive family counseling or individual family therapy that deals with very specific family situations. In the supportive counseling model of Bernheim and Lehman (1985), the goal is to buttress the family's supportive relationship with the mentally ill person while making life easier for the family. This involves understanding the family's agony, communicating acceptance, educating the family about treatment options, and helping families to set realistic expectations, deal with areas of potential conflict, and develop strategies for daily living. A model used by Selzer, Sullivan, Carsky, and Terkelsen (1989) goes "beyond psychoeducation" to raise the family's consciousness about how their relative actually experiences the illness. Families are taught to understand behaviors as personal reactions to being mentally ill, as well as indicators of functional disabilities.

Implications for Practitioners

Family advocates have objected to the social policy implications of orienting psychoeducational interventions toward relatives as major caregivers and restricting EE research to families alone (Hatfield, Spaniol, & Zipple, 1987). Most interventions focus on how to diminish stress, and as the EE researchers have pointed out, psychobiological vulnerability to stress can be manifested in many nonfamilial environments including the treatment system (Falloon, 1988; Leff, 1989); Pepper and Ryglewicz (1987) have called for studies of "interactional intensity" or "II" as an analogue of EE in clinical and rehabilitative programs. They suggest that high demand treatment environments are motivating for some clients but may be overstimulating and toxic for others.

Both the EE research and the psychoeducational approaches may ultimately prove more important for practitioners than for families. The growth of the family movement has focused attention not only on the rights and needs of families, but also on the value of their expertise at case-centered and programmatic levels. In this connection, family organizations have highlighted training and service issues in system improvement. Major efforts of the family advocacy movement have included specialized training for clinicians working with persons who have serious mental disabilities, and updated technology of the treatment system to respond to the needs of a heterogeneous patient population.

The Rise of the Family Movement

Prior to the advent of NAMI, families had few resources. Although some local mental health associations had family support groups, there was no national advocacy group focusing on the needs of persons with severe mental disabilities, and there were few participatory roles for families in the rehabilitation process. NAMI was initiated in 1979, when 300 family members from various states convened at the University of Wisconsin, Madison, with backing from the Community Support Program of the National Institute of Mental Health (NIMH). In a little over a decade, this movement has grown into over 100,000 families

with over a thousand local affiliates in all fifty states.

NAMI has multiple activities and functions. They include advocacy; mutual support and self-help groups; resource development; education of professionals, themselves, and the public; participation in mental health planning, policy, and governance boards; and training NAMI members as effective lobbyists and consumer advocates. The organization has been extremely active in legislative advocacy for mentally ill persons at both national and state levels. NAMI has been instrumental in obtaining increased congressional funding for research and services and has helped to develop private research foundations for mental illness, such as the National Alliance for Research on Schizophrenia and Depression (NARSAD), in addition to other awards for scientific research. NAMI groups have developed an array of rehabilitative resources, including housing, psychosocial rehabilitation centers, sheltered workshops, vocational training and employment programs, social programs, and drop-in centers that are consumer staffed or operated.

Concerned about what will happen to loved ones "when I am gone," some NAMI groups have begun to develop pooled monetary trusts and surrogate parent programs, often in joint planning with parents of mentally retarded persons (Lefley, 1987). They have developed national educational and antistigma campaigns, generated television programs, and in general have tried to effect massive social changes with respect to how the public views serious mental illness. There are numerous national AMI networks that range from finding missing and homeless mentally ill persons to forming liaisons and educating with the clergy.

A major initiative has been to influence clinical training in the core mental health professions. The NAMI Curriculum and Training Network works at both state and national levels to make sure that new generations of mental health professionals will become more interested in working with seriously mentally disabled persons, and that they will view families as allies in the treatment process. The network tries to ensure the inclusion of both state-of-the-art biomedical research and psychosocial rehabilitation philosophy and techniques in the core curriculum. The Curriculum and Training Network, with NIMH cosponsorship, has held two National Forums on "Training Mental Health Professionals to Work with Seriously Mentally Ill Persons and Their Families." These have generated multiple documents, curriculum materials, and spin-off conferences, as well as two books for the professions (Lefley & Johnson, 1990; National Institute of Mental Health, 1990). Curriculum and Training Network members have also become increasingly active in lecturing and delivering grand rounds in professional training programs, and they have involved primary consumers in these efforts as well. In some programs, affirmative action initiatives have emerged to train both family members and primary consumers as mental health professionals.

NAMI members support and participate as subjects in biological, genetic, and psychosocial research on serious mental illness. Currently, NAMI is sponsoring a major mental health services needs assessment conducted by a group at Johns Hopkins, which is surveying families, and by a group at Rutgers, which is surveying consumers. To increase the knowledge of its members, NAMI is also publishing a new journal, *Innovations and Research in Clinical Services, Community Support, and Rehabilitation*, in conjunction with the Center for Psychiatric Rehabilitation at Boston University. The new publication abstracts information from professional journals on new developments, research, and service models, reviews current books, and presents dialogues on important policy issues in the field.

A major problem in the development of both family and consumer movements is that they have been composed primarily of persons of white middle class background. This is especially troubling because some members of ethnic minorities, particularly African Americans and American Indians, are overrepresented in inpatient psychiatric ser-

vices, in relation to their population distributions, while others are underserved (Rosenstein, Milazzo-Sayre, MacAskill, & Manderscheid, 1987). NAMI has had a strong minority outreach campaign since its inception. The former Ethnic Minority Concerns Network, now retitled the Language and Cultural Concerns Network, has expanded its activities considerably over the years. NAMI affiliates are more ethnically heterogeneous than in the past, and a number of affiliates have developed that are predominantly African American, Hispanic American, Asian American or American Indian. For example, as of this writing, there are four Spanish-speaking affiliates in the Los Angeles area. New York City, Chicago, and various areas in Texas also have Hispanic American affiliates. Predominantly African American affiliates are found in New York, Washington DC, and Florida. Ohio has a People of Colors affiliate, most of whom are African American or Hispanic American. American Indian groups are found in Washington state, on the Colville reservation, and in New Mexico, with an outreach program to Native American families in the Pueblo, Navajo, and Apache tribes. Also, Asian American family groups are found in the San Francisco area.

Although some of these ethnically homogeneous affiliates also tend to have a disproportionately high number of members of middle class or higher educational background, there is continuous outreach to lower socioeconomic families. Videos have been developed regarding how to organize Spanish-speaking support groups and on multicultural AMI families. A minority outreach training manual is currently being developed for all NAMI affiliates. NAMI state affiliates have also been active in coordinating a number of state conferences on minority mental health and in other collaborative activities with mental health professionals.

Collaborative Roles in Rehabilitation

It is noteworthy that most clinicians seem to conceptualize families' roles in rehabilitation in terms of reducing high EE or otherwise altering their relationships with patients. Even noted researchers such as Fisher, Benson, and Tessler (1990), in a chapter section entitled "Families as Agents of Patient Rehabilitation," speak only of psychoeducation and the research demonstrating its effectiveness. In fact, however, family roles in rehabilitation are far more extensive and proactive than as recipients of psychoeducational training. They encompass roles at societal, programmatic, and case-centered levels.

We have already indicated some of these proactive collaborative roles at the societal level: joint legislative advocacy for services and research; national initiatives for professional training; collaborative public education, such as mental illness awareness week; antistigma campaigns; active roles in mental health systems planning at state and local levels; and encouragement and support of consumer programs and education. Many NAMI groups dispense resource information through telephone hotlines, and some have solicited and received private funding for local information centers and libraries offering the most recent scientific information on mental illnesses.

At the individual program level, family members serve on governance and advisory boards of community mental health centers. Many local AMI groups develop family support groups that are run independently of or in conjunction with a mental health facility, which offer support services to needy families regardless of AMI affiliation. Similarly, AMI groups have developed residential, vocational, and other rehabilitative resources that are available to all patients of a particular agency or locale. At the programmatic level, AMI members may offer volunteer assistance, help consumers to develop social programs, staff mobile crisis teams, contribute to in-service training, participate in program evaluation, and help with fund raising.

At the case-centered level, families' roles are reciprocal rather than reactive. They both learn from and teach the professionals who are working with their loved ones. Family members now have far greater participation in treatment goals and discharge planning. They typically know the developmental history of the illness and the rhythms and cycles of disability. They monitor medication and know the patient's response to medications—the ones that work best and those that seem to be harmful, the types of side effects, and the factors that affect medication compliance. Like many patients, household members often recognize precipitants and prodromal or early cues of decompensation. Over the years, they have learned adaptive strategies in coping with the disability, and they can speak about their own problem-solving and behavior management techniques—coping patterns that worked and those that have failed. Many therapists have found that in addition to giving valuable input on the case, family members provide information that is helpful for their other patients. Resource information and illness management techniques are also shared in multifamily support groups. Additionally, patients' relatives often offer help with case management.

These increasing roles are usually satisfying to the families involved and are helpful to service providers. However, as noted previously, they largely reflect the efforts of educated middle class persons who do not represent the large number of individuals found in the inpatient, outpatient, and crisis emergency caseloads of our treatment system. The adjunctive resources offered by nonprofessional volunteers also have social policy implications for future service delivery.

Future Trends and Issues

Directions in mental health services are invariably interrelated with events in the larger society. These include changes in federal policy and administrative infrastructure, availability and distribution of government funding, third party restrictions that affect the locus and duration of treatment, expanded numbers and differential needs of consumers of services, and changes in social and professional thought regarding the parameters and the priorities of mental health services (Lefley,

1988). These factors affect clinical training and determine the type of professionals who will come into the field, as well as the ratio of professionals to paraprofessionals and to consumer providers. The latter are former patients who provide mental health services to their peers.

The growth of the family movement has influenced and become coterminous with the growth of the primary consumer movement of former and current patients of the mental health system. These developments are strongly related to and are generating changing trends in service delivery. Among these is the emergence of consumer-operated services, including crisis intervention, residential programs, and drop-in centers. Many of these have been funded as research and demonstration grants by NIMH. The emerging data may ultimately provide an empirical basis for peer-supported services as replacements or enhancements of existing services.

Consumer services are highly desirable because they provide peer support, role models, and social outlets for persons who might otherwise lead lonely and impoverished lives. In providing these outside of the officially designated mental health system, consumer providers also offer a destigmatizing and empowering message to persons who for years have felt diminished and powerless because of their illnesses. Yet, in some cases, these services may be embedded in a philosophy that aims to dismantle the professional care system, including those components that serve the most seriously disabled clients. Although the family movement has supported consumer groups and peer-operated services, there are disagreements between some consumer organizations and family members regarding the future of mental health service delivery.

Family and Consumer Movements

Both family and consumer movements have been supported in principle and have been helped developmentally by the Community Support Program (CSP) of NIMH. They share similar agendas in wanting to improve and expand community-based care, and both are committed to protection and advocacy, with a focus on preventing any abuse of patients by the system. NAMI has a Consumer Council and has indicated its commitment to consumer issues by twice electing a president who is a primary consumer, as well as a family member. Consumers have served on NAMI boards and have had a strong role in shaping policy.

Nevertheless, there are clear divisions in outlook and priorities between the family movement and the primary consumer advocacy groups, such as the National Association of Psychiatric Survivors (NAPS) and the slightly less radical National Mental Health Consumers' Association (NMHCA). NAPS has traditionally been antipsychiatry and has categorically opposed all involuntary treatment, while NMHCA has suggested instead that any involuntary intervention be permitted only on the conditions of imminent, visible threat of suicide or bodily harm to self or others. Isaac and Armat (1990) claim that since 1990, both organizations have taken the same stand of complete opposition. Although NMHCA attests to the validity of mental illness and was organized to improve rather than invalidate the treatment system, both organizations focus heavily on issues of psychiatric abuse rather than on provision of services. In contrast to other types of patient organizations defined by a particular disability, there is little emphasis on seeking clues to etiology and to long-range prevention.

Although many consumers accept their illness as biologically based, others have accepted the political view of mental illness as a social construct. It is frequently suggested that families have embraced biological theories because these absolve them of blame (Fisher, Benson, & Tessler, 1990). However, other reasons for embracing a biological model are far more salient. For many years now, NAMI families have consistently been given biogenic explanations and have been informed that families do not cause mental illness by the most important scientists and researchers in the field, including all directors of NIMH. To families, this opinion of the experts is also intuitively reasonable, because in most cases, they have an intimate knowledge of a developmental history that simply does not warrant a psychogenic disorder of such devastating proportions (Johnson, 1990).

Perhaps the most important reason for biogenic explanations is that an investment in biological research is a way for families to abstract some meaning from a central tragedy of their lives. Those who looked for change through modifying their own behavior have learned that at best, this may effect some modest improvements in relationships and outlook, but it offers no hope of a cure. Basic biological research solves no current problems but may assure mentally ill persons and their families some control of the future and may prevent the disease in unknown sufferers.

The ideological differences between family members and some members of the consumer movements will undoubtedly continue because the difference in agendas is very clear. For NAMI families, most of whose mentally ill relatives are severely dysfunctional, the need for ongoing treatment and symptom stabilization is an absolute necessity if their relative is to have any potential for rehabilitation or even for survival. Although they may share a libertarian philosophy that places the highest value on personal empowerment, it is family members—not legal advocates, not ex-patients, and not professionals—who endure the emotional suffering if a loved one decompensates or dies.

NAMI members have multiple stories about missing loved ones who were discharged to the street. They describe experiences with victims of self-neglect, beatings, rape, severe infections; barriers to treatment for floridly psychotic persons who could easily be stabilized on medications; and adversarial commitment hearings in which they are pitted against a psychotic loved one whose return to the streets will generate untold anguish for the client and themselves (see Dearth et al.,1986; Group for the Advancement of Psychiatry, 1986; Isaac & Armat, 1990). Indeed, this author has heard defense attorneys in involuntary commitment proceedings privately admit that they often defended mentally ill clients who were so sick or suicidal that they prayed they would lose the case.

The most commonly heard explanation of the division between family advocates and consumers is a presumptive difference in disability level of the two patient constituencies. Consumers remember the terror and humiliation of their own involuntary commitments and are legitimately outraged by any minimization of the horror of those memories. However, in opinions expressed at numerous meetings and conferences, NAMI members see a world of difference between the irrational, dysfunctional people whom they see at home and the articulate speakers and fluent writers they see in the consumer movement. Many have expressed the view that the consumer leadership is composed primarily of persons with affective disorders, who generally do not deteriorate in functioning, whereas there are many more regressed people with schizophrenia represented by NAMI families. They feel that most members of the consumer movement suffered fewer involuntary commitments, and longer ago, than their own relatives, who frequently are in a revolving door pattern because of legal barriers. Some family members suggest that consumers remember a more repressive system than exists today, and that they are reacting to their own pain rather than considering the treatment needs of their more severely disabled peers.

These are hypotheses that easily could be tested empirically. They are unlikely to be tested because there are philosophical barriers against suggesting that persons who have experienced mental illness may be differentiated by diagnosis, levels of disability, or need for intervention. As indicated, some members of the consumer movement do not accept the idea of mental illness per se, and they view all people so categorized as political victims of an oppressive system. On this basis, they firmly oppose the institution of involuntary treatment under any conditions.

Attempts to find alternatives to involuntary treatment have been generated on several fronts. The CSP of NIMH has convened conferences of consumers, family members, and psychiatrists on this issue. A dialogue between family and consumer viewpoints appeared in a 1991 issue of *Schizophrenia Bulletin*, addressing the issue of prior consent; in it, Rosenson and Kasten called for a type of contract in which persons whose illness is stabilized may voluntarily contract for enforced medication if they should later become too psychotic to be capable of rational informed consent. They suggested that "the most authentic expression of autonomy may be the decision by a patient whose psychiatric symptoms are in remission to plan for treatment in the event of a crisis" (p. 1).

A rejoinder by two prominent consumers (Rogers & Centifanti, 1991) agreed in principle but emphasized "the right to say no as well as yes to any and all treatment" (p. 10). In lieu of the self-paternalism of giving up rights in advance, they advocated a type of will that would include treatment history and reasoned arguments for and against a range of treatment choices. Both family advocates and consumers agreed on empowering competent persons to give prior informed consent for treatment that they might reject in a state of decompensation, thereby leaving the ultimate decision in the patient's hands.

Families and a Changing Service-Delivery System

Current trends are altering the mental health system, including changes in structure of formerly comprehensive community mental health centers. Many centers are trying to attract private fee-paying clients, contracting with industry for employee assistance programs, or affiliating with managed care plans as mental health services providers. Community facilities that were built with tax monies to meet the needs of deinstitutionalization are showing much less interest in providing services to a Medicaid funded severely mentally disabled clientele.

Meanwhile, case management and supported housing are beginning to replace the centralized residential and treatment facilities of the community mental health centers. Mobile crisis teams try to defuse psychiatric emergencies on site, without admitting patients to crisis stabilization or inpatient units. Free-standing psychosocial rehabilitation centers and a range of consumer-operated alternatives are reducing the need for partial hospitalization or day treatment programs.

Although many of these are salutary developments, they are important additions rather than replacements for the known continuum of care. Despite ongoing and increasing waiting lists, state hospitals continue to close beds and shift monies to less expensive community sites that offer a different level of services and considerably less protection for persons who may need continuing oversight and management.

Families voice fears that without carefully planned case management, persons in supported housing may stop taking medications, abandon the treatment system, and decompensate. There are concerns that people will mismanage their money, stop paying rent, or receive rent increases that they cannot manage and thus be evicted into homelessness. Case managers are overworked and underpaid, with commensurate turnover. Their resignations result in functional abandonment of the person on whom the patient has become most dependent. In many situations, case managers simply cannot handle their caseload, and family members become surrogate or actual case managers. This once again shifts responsibility for patient care to family members who may have multiple competing demands on their time and attention, including the right to lead their own lives.

Families have an emotional and vested interest in a comprehensive system of care that will enrich their relatives' lives, enhance their relatives' potential for autonomous living, and reduce their relatives' dependency on kinship networks. This means strong support of the best in rehabilitative services for their loved ones, including services operated by and for consumers. Indeed, many AMI groups have spearheaded consumer-run endeavors precisely because they recognized the limitations of the professional mental health system to provide friendship and role models in a normalized atmosphere. However, it is evident that AMI members will also continue vigorously to support a professionally driven system that will provide the latest in psychopharmacological treatment and psychosocial rehabilitation. NAMI members will also continue to press for federal funding and to offer their personal contributions to support biological and services research on the major psychotic disorders.

In sum, families' roles in rehabilitation involve collaborative efforts with providers, legislators, researchers, systems planners, and primary consumers at all levels. The indications are clear that families will continue to provide legislative and human rights advocacy, promote public education, enhance clinical training to make sure it contains the most state-of-the-art rehabilitative technology, help develop adjunctive resources, and monitor the system to make sure it continues to serve the needs of mentally ill people of all functional levels. Families will continue to press vigorously for resources that will increase the potential for independent living of capable clients. They will also make every effort to ensure that the system does not devalue its most disabled clients by dismantling any of the basic services needed for survival, treatment, and rehabilitation.

References

Anderson, C. M., Reiss, D. J., & Hogarty, G. E. (1986). *Schizophrenia and the family.* New York: Guilford.

Arieti, S. (1981). The family of the schizophrenic and its participation in the therapeutic task. In S. Arieti & K. H. Brodie (Eds.), *American handbook of psychiatry* (2nd ed., Vol. 7, pp. 271–284). New York: Basic Books.

Beels, C. C., & McFarlane, W. R. (1982). Family treatments of schizophrenia: Background and state of the art. *Hospital & Community Psychiatry, 33,* 541–549.

Bernheim, K. F., & Lehman, A. F. (1985). *Working with families of the mentally ill.* New York: Norton.

Dearth, N., Labenski, B. J., Mott, M. E., & Pellegrini, L. M. (1986). *Families helping families: Living with schizophrenia.* New York: Norton.

Eaton, W.W. (1986). *The sociology of mental disorders* (2nd ed.). New York: Praeger.

Falloon, I. R. H. (1988). Expressed emotion: Current status. *Psychological Medicine, 18,* 269–274.

Falloon, I. R. H., Boyd, J. L., & McGill, C. W. (1984). *Family care of schizophrenia.* New York: Guilford.

Fisher, G. A., Benson, P. R., & Tessler, R. C. (1990). Family response to mental illness: Developments since deinstitutionalization. In J. R. Greenley (Ed.), *Research in community and mental health: Mental disorder in social context* (pp. 203–236). Greenwich, CT: JAI Press.

Goldstein, M. J. (1981). *New directions for mental health services: 12. New developments in interventions with families of schizophrenics.* San Francisco: Jossey-Bass.

Group for the Advancement of Psychiatry. (1986). *A family affair—Helping families cope with mental illness: A guide for the professions* (Report No. 119). New York: Brunner/Mazel.

Hatfield, A. B. (1983). What families want of family therapists. In W. R. McFarlane (Ed.), *Family therapy in schizophrenia* (pp. 41–65). New York: Guilford.

Hatfield, A. B. (1990). *Family education in mental illness.* New York: Guilford.

Hatfield, A. B., Farrell. E., & Starr, S. (1984). The family's perspective on the homeless. In H. R. Lamb (Ed.), *The homeless mentally ill* (pp. 279–300). Washington DC: American Psychiatric Press.

Hatfield. A. B., Spaniol, L., & Zipple, A. M. (1987). Expressed emotion: A family perspective. *Schizophrenia Bulletin, 13,* 221–226.

Hirsch, S. R., & Leff, J. P. (1975). *Abnormalities in parents of schizophrenics.* London: Oxford University Press.

Holden, D. F., & Lewine, R. R. J. (1982). How families evaluate mental health professionals, resources, and effects of illness. *Schizophrenia Bulletin, 8,* 626–633.

Howells, J. G., & Guirguis, W. R. (1985). *The family and schizophrenia.* New York: International Universities Press.

Isaac, R. J., & Armat, V. C. (1990). *Madness in the streets.* New York: Free Press.

Johnson, D. L. (1990). The family's experience of living with mental illness. In H.P. Lefley & D.L. Johnson (Eds.), *Families as allies in treatment of the mentally ill: New directions for mental health professionals* (pp. 31–63). Washington DC: American Psychiatric Press.

Leff, J. P. (1989). Controversial issues and growing points in research on relatives' expressed emotion. *International Journal of Social Psychiatry, 35,* 133–145.

Leff, J. P., & Vaughn, C. (1985). *Expressed emotion in families: Its significance for mental illness.* New York: Guilford.

Lefley, H. P. (1985). Families of the mentally ill in cross–cultural perspective. *Psychosocial Rehabilitation Journal, 8*, 57–75.

Lefley, H. P. (1987). Aging parents as caregivers of mentally ill adult children: An emerging social problem. *Hospital & Community Psychiatry, 38*, 1063–1070.

Lefley, H. P. (1988). Linked changes in mental health service delivery and psychiatric education. *Psychiatric Quarterly, 59*, 121–139.

Lefley, H. P. (1989). Family burden and family stigma in major mental illness. *American Psychologist, 44*, 556–560.

Lefley, H. P. (1990). Research directions for a new conceptualization of families. In H. P. Lefley & D. L. Johnson (Eds.), *Families as allies in treatment of the mentally ill: New directions for mental health professionals* (pp. 127–162). Washington DC: American Psychiatric Press.

Lefley, H. P., & Johnson, D. L. (Eds.), (1990). *Families as allies in treatment of the mentally ill: New directions for mental health professionals.* Washington DC: American Psychiatric Press.

Lefley, H. P., Nuehring, E., & Bestman, E. W. (1992). Homelessness and mental illness: A transcultural family perspective. In H. R. Lamb (Ed.), *Treating the homeless mentally ill.* Washington DC: American Psychiatric Press.

McFarlane, W. R., & Beels, C. C. (1983). Family research in schizophrenia: A review and integration for clinicians. In W. R. McFarlane (Ed.), *Family therapy in schizophrenia* (pp. 311–323). New York: Guilford.

National Institute of Mental Health. (1990). *Clinical training in serious mental illness.* H. P. Lefley (Ed.), (DHHS Publ. ADM 90–1679). Washington, DC: Superintendent of Documents, U.S. Government Printing Office.

Parker, G. (1982). Re-searching the schizophrenogenic mother. *Journal of Nervous & Mental Disease, 170*, 452–462.

Pepper, B., & Ryglewicz, H. (1987). Is there expressed emotion away from home? Interactional intensity ("I-I") in the treatment program. *Tie-Lines, 4*(1), 1–3.

Rogers, J. A., & Centifanti, J. B. (1991). Beyond "self-paternalism": Response to Rosenson and Kasten. *Schizophrenia Bulletin, 17*, 9–14.

Rosenson, M. K., & Kasten, A. M. (1991). Another view of autonomy: Arranging consent in advance. *Schizophrenia Bulletin, 17*, 1–7.

Rosenstein, M. J., Milazzo-Sayre, L. J., MacAskill, R. L., & Manderscheid, R. W. (1987). Use of inpatient services by special populations. In S. A. Barrett, & R. W. Manderscheid (Eds.), *National Institute of Mental Health: Mental health, United States, 1987* (DHHS Publ. No. ADM 87-1518) (pp. 59–97). Washington, DC: Superintendent of Documents, U.S. Government Printing Office.

Ryglewicz, H. (1989). Psychoeducational work with families: Theme and variations. *Tie–Lines, 6*(3), 1–3.

Selzer, M. A., Sullivan, T. B., Carsky, M., & Terkelsen, K. G. (1989). *Working with the person with schizophrenia.* New York: New York University Press.

Terkelsen, K. G. (1983). Schizophrenia and the family: II. Adverse effects of family therapy. *Family Process, 22*, 191–200.

Tessler, R. C., Killian, L. M., & Gubman, G. (1987). Stages in family response to mental illness: An ideal type. *Psychosocial Rehabilitation Journal, 10*(4), 3–16.

Thurer, S. L. (1983). Deinstitutionalization and women: Where the buck stops. *Hospital & Community Psychiatry, 34*, 1162–1163.

Weiner, H. (1985). Schizophrenia: Etiology. In H. I. Kaplan & B. J. Sadock (Eds.), *Comprehensive textbook of psychiatry* (4th ed., pp. 650–680). Baltimore: Williams & Wilkins.

Wynne, L. C. (1988). Changing views of schizophrenia and family interventions. *Family Therapy News*, May–June, 3–4.

Chapter 3

A Modern Perspective on Psychiatry in Rehabilitation

BERYL LAWN
ARTHUR T. MEYERSON

During the past several decades, psychiatry's approach to the diagnosis, prognosis, and treatment of disabling, severe, and persistent mental illness has undergone major advances. Some of these changes include (1) the growing realization that schizophrenia need not invariably result in lifelong dysfunction; (2) the increasing acknowledgment that medication is only one of many aspects of therapy and that a team approach to rehabilitation similar to that used for physical disability is crucial in maximizing the skills and functioning of persons with serious and persistent mental illness; and (3) the development of new medications, most notably clozapine, which have resulted in clinical improvement in patients previously refractory to antipsychotic medication. In addition, the fourth formulation by the American Psychiatric Association of the *Diagnostic and Statistical Manual* (third edition, revised) *(DSM-III-R)*, which specifies diagnostic criteria, including those for the various disabling mental syndromes, has helped to increase uniformity in diagnosis in both clinical and research settings. This chapter elaborates further on these developments.

Definition of Serious and Persistent Mental Illness

The serious and persistent mentally ill population encompasses persons who experience "certain mental or emotional disorders (organic brain syndrome, schizophrenia, recurrent depressive and manic depressive disorders, and paranoid and other psychoses, plus other disorders that may become chronic) that erode or prevent the development of their functional capacities in relation to three or more primary aspects of daily life— personal hygiene and self-care, self-direction, interpersonal relationships, social transactions, learning, and recreation" (Goldman & Manderscheid, 1987, p. 13). Individuals who are the subject of this text most often have an illness that frequently "prevents the development of their economic self-sufficiency. Most such individuals have required institutional care of extended duration, including intermediate-term hospitalization (90 days to 365 days in a single year), long-term hospitalization (1 year or longer in the preceding 5 years), or nursing home placement" (Goldman & Manderscheid,

1987, p. 13) or numerous intermittent short-term hospitalizations.

Terms in common use, which are important in understanding the concept of serious and persistent mental illness, as well as in conceptualizing its treatment, include *impairment, disability, and handicap* (Anthony & Liberman, 1986). *Impairment* refers to a sign or symptom of mental illness—for example, hallucinations or delusional thinking. *Disability* refers to functional loss resulting from the impairment—for example, inability to relate appropriately to others and, therefore, difficulty in obtaining and maintaining a job. *Handicap* refers to the societal response to a disability—for example, societal discrimination accentuates the impact of a given disability, further limiting the autonomy and function of a disabled person.

Of the three terms (*impairment, disability,* and *handicap*), *disability* has been the most difficult to define. Consequently, *disability* has been defined in different ways with little consensus. The Americans with Disabilities Act of 1990 "refers to disability as substantial limitation in a major life activity" (National Institute of Mental Health [NIMH], Program Announcement, Research on disabilities and rehabilitation services for persons with severe mental disorders, July 1991). Similarly, the World Health Organization defines "disability as inability to participate or perform at a socially desirable level in such activities as self-care (e.g., activities of living), social relationships, work and situationally appropriate behavior" (NIMH, 1991).

The Social Security Administration pinpoints four key areas of function (or dysfunction) in their definition of *disability*: (1) activities of daily living (e.g., grooming/hygiene, maintaining a household, managing finances); (2) social functioning (including functioning with family, neighbors, and in the workplace); (3) concentration, pace, and task persistence (the ability to perform routine tasks 6 to 8 hours per day, at a reasonable pace, and without excessive supervision); and (4) the ability to tolerate the increased emotional and mental demands of competitive work. Duration is also important in the

Social Security Administration's definition of *disability*: That is, the disability must have been present or be expected to be present continuously for at least 12 months (Goldman & Manderscheid, 1987, p. 14). Thus, severe mental illness, whether it be persistent and long-term or episodic, has a profound impact on an individual's ability to function in one or more spheres of daily living, which results in significant disability (NIMH, 1991).

The recent report by the Institute of Medicine, *Disability in America*, indicates that the disparity between an individual's mental and/or physical capabilities and demands placed on this individual by the environment result in disability. Individuals are not inherently disabled, but it is the interaction of an individual's limitations and social and environmental factors that determine whether one is disabled. In many instances, disability is preventable (Pope & Tarlov, 1991).

The population of those who are severely psychiatrically disabled has been defined in terms of diagnosis, disability, and duration. The Community Support Program (CSP) of the NIMH, which is a federal initiative to promote the development of community support systems (CSSs) for the severely mentally ill population has a definition of this target population.

This definition includes the following:

1. **Severe Disability Resulting from Mental Illness**

   CSP clients typically meet at least one of the following criteria:
   - Have undergone psychiatric treatment more intensive than outpatient care more than once in a lifetime (e.g., emergency services, alternative home care, partial hospitalization or inpatient hospitalization).
   - Have experienced a single episode of continuous, structured, supportive residential care other than hospitalization for a duration of at least 2 years.

2. **Impaired Role Functioning**

   CSP clients typically meet at least *two* of the following criteria on a continuing or intermittent basis for at least 2 years.
   - Are unemployed, are employed in a shel-

tered setting or have markedly limited skills and a poor work history.

- Require public financial assistance for out-of-hospital maintenance and may be unable to procure such assistance without help.
- Show severe inability to establish or maintain a personal social support system.
- Require help in basic living skills.
- Exhibit inappropriate social behavior, which results in demand for intervention by the mental health and/or judicial system.

(This definition is adapted from National Institute of Mental Health [1980]. Announcement of community support system strategy development and implementation grants [pp. iii, iv]. Rockville, MD: Author. In Anthony, Cohen, and Farkus [1990], *Psychiatric Rehabilitation*, Psychiatric Rehabilitation Center, Boston University, p. 5)

Demographic Profiles of Persons with Serious and Persistent Mental Illness

Who and where are those with severe and persistent mental illness? Goldman and Manderscheid (1987, p. 16) estimate that there are between 350,000 and 800,000 individuals with severe emotional disabilities, and an additional 700,000 individuals with moderate disabilities living in the community. Based on diagnosis, disability, and duration, Goldman and his colleagues (Goldman, Gatozzi, & Taube, 1981) estimated that 1.7 to 2.4 million Americans are considered to be severely mentally disabled. Estimates are that about two thirds of discharged patients return to families (Minkoff, 1978). Many persons with serious mental illness, however, are in institutions, hospitals, special care facilities, and nursing homes (Kaplan & Sadock, 1989, p. 2091). Increasing numbers of persons with serious and persistent mental illness are also considered to be street people, either chronically or episodically homeless; and some are also being found among the jail population (Teplin, 1984).

Schizophrenia, affective illness, and senile dementia represent the largest diagnostic categories of those with disabling mental illness (Kaplan & Sadock, 1989, p. 2091). The adult seriously mentally ill client is more likely to be female, older, currently unmarried, and African American, when compared with nondisabled individuals (Goldman & Manderscheid, 1987, p. 19). There is also increasing concern that many of those with serious mental illness use or abuse alcohol and other drugs, which tend to exacerbate their illness and complicate treatment (Ridgely, Goldman, & Talbott, 1986). The presence of a personality disorder may also complicate diagnosis and treatment of major Axis I disorders and may affect prognosis.

Diagnosis of Psychiatric Disorders That May Become Chronic

The American Psychiatric Association's DSM-III-R codes psychiatric diagnoses on five separate axes, each of which focuses on a different aspect of the patient's clinical picture. Axis I represents the major psychiatric diagnosis (e.g., schizophrenia, affective [i.e., mood] disorders, substance abuse); Axis II specifies any personality disorder; Axis III denotes concomitant medical diagnoses (e.g., diabetes mellitus, hypertension); Axis IV indicates current stressors and their severity (e.g., "death of spouse: severe"); and Axis V specifies highest level of function over the preceding year (coded numerically from a Global Assessment of Function Scale). This multiaxial approach allows for a more inclusive view of the patient's current situation than would the indication of psychiatric diagnosis alone. Two patients with identical Axis I psychiatric diagnoses, for example, might have very different clinical presentations and treatment needs, based on the presence and severity of associated medical illness (e.g., recent amputation of a limb or diagnosis of cancer); the presence and severity of life stressors (such as death of a parent, recent eviction from a boarding home, or breakup of a primary relationship); and what their baseline level of function has been (i.e., relatively high or low functioning, at baseline). Axes IV and V represent crucially important aspects of the patient's current situation.

DSM-III-R lists the diagnostic criteria for all Axes I and II disorders. Succinctly stated, a diagnosis of schizophrenia is based on the presence of active psychotic symptoms (hallucinations and/or delusions and/or markedly disorganized thinking or behavior) for at least a week, which is preceded, followed, or accompanied by residual psychotic symptoms (e.g., apathy/withdrawal, unusual thinking [such as magical thinking], or unusual behavior [such as collecting and saving garbage]) for at least 6 months. Implicit in the diagnosis of schizophrenia is that no known physical cause of the symptoms is present (e.g., brain tumor, medications, illicit drug use) and that the patient does not have a mood disorder, such as mania or depression.

Mood (or affective) disorders may be either unipolar (i.e., recurrent episodes of major depression) or bipolar. The latter are characterized by recurrent episodes of mania and depression, or sometimes episodes in which mania and depression occur together. The major signs and symptoms of a person with mania are distractibility, irritability, grandiosity, flight of ideas (rapid, tangential speech), hyperactivity, sleeplessness, and talkativeness. Both mania and depression may occur with or without psychotic symptoms such as hallucinations or delusions. If psychotic symptoms do occur in a patient with a mood disorder, the mood disorder usually precedes the development of the psychotic symptoms. The psychotic symptoms are also relatively brief in relation to the overall duration of the clinical illness. Both of these features help differentiate mood disorders from schizophrenia, in which psychosis (not a mood disorder) dominates the clinical picture. Schizoaffective disorder manifests symptomatology of both schizophrenia and affective illness, and may in fact represent a heterogeneous group of patients manifesting atypical forms of either schizophrenia and/or affective disorders.

Etiology of Severe Mental Disorders

The etiologies of the major psychiatric disorders that may become chronic and disabling are still incompletely understood. *Schizophrenia*, *schizoaffective disorder*, *major depression*, and *bipolar illness* may actually be umbrella diagnoses for a number of different diseases with similar clinical presentations, with each disease within a given syndrome having a multifactorial etiology. Genetic predisposition is one important factor in the etiology of all of these disorders; that is, they all "run in families." Yet genetic predisposition is only part of the picture. In identical twins (who by definition are *genetically* identical), if one twin develops schizophrenia, there is only a 50% likelihood that the second twin will be similarly affected (Kaplan & Sadock, 1989, p. 738). This fact highlights both the importance of genetics and the fact that genetics does not tell the whole story.

One mechanism by which genetic predisposition may cause illness is by sensitizing the person to stress. Although the role of a pathological maternal–child relationship (the so-called schizophrenogenic mother) is no longer favored as an important cause of stress-induced schizophrenia, stress per se is still regarded as important in both the precipitation and the exacerbation of schizophrenia. That stress may include separating from parents in late adolescence (a common time of onset for schizophrenia); living in a family in which emotions are expressed often, loudly, and critically; or a variety of other situational or interpersonal stresses to which an individual may be subjected. Thus, environment may play a role in the course of schizophrenia but appears to be less related to etiology than the field once believed.

One final common pathway by which genetic predisposition and stress express themselves is through changes in brain function. Ultimately, all thought, behaviors, and moods are mediated by these brain functions. Derangement of brain anatomy, physiology, and chemistry in various psychiatric disease states continues to be the focus of intensive research.

Kaufmann and Weinberger (1987) have reviewed current thinking about the neurobiological basis of psychiatric disability. They classify psychiatric symptoms that result in chronic psychiatric disability within two broad categories: excesses and deficits. *Excesses* include symptoms such as hallucinations, delusions, or aggression (i.e., so-called *positive* symptoms of psychosis), while *deficits* include deficiencies in cognitive abilities, interpersonal skills, or initiative (i.e., the negative psychiatric symptoms). Kaufmann and Weinberger (1987) emphasize the fact that psychiatry has traditionally focused much of its attention on positive symptoms, while negative symptoms are more closely correlated with prognosis (although often less responsive to medication). Negative symptoms are usually associated with a diagnosis of schizophrenia and are persistent or progressive over time, unlike positive symptoms, which tend to be more episodic. Negative symptoms correlate with a poor prognosis, including more residual symptoms, more hospitalizations, and poorer work histories.

Kaufmann and Weinberger (1987) cite evidence from research linking positive symptoms with *increased* central nervous system (CNS) activity of dopamine, a vital chemical messenger produced by the brain, and negative symptoms are linked with *decreased* dopamine activity in *other* dopaminergic CNS pathways. Kaufman and Weinberger (1987) speculate that "depletion of cortical dopamine results in persistent negative symptoms and in disinhibition of subcortical dopamine pathways. This disinhibition, in turn, results in vulnerability to intermittent (stress-induced) increases in subcortical dopamine neurotransmission, and positive symptoms" (p. 28).

Neuroradiological studies (such as computerized axial tomograms [CAT scans] of the brain) in schizophrenia cited by these same authors (Kaufman & Weinberger, 1987) revealed cortical atrophy, as shown by lateral ventricular enlargement, in large numbers of persons with schizophrenia (the *lateral ventricles* are the large cavities containing cerebrospinal fluid, which form the interior of both cerebral hemispheres); lateral ventricular enlargement correlated with both cognitive impairment and negative symptoms. Lateral ventricular enlargement also correlated

with decreases in cerebrospinal fluid dopamine metabolites, tying in anatomy with neurochemistry.

Neurophysiological studies (regional cerebral blood flow [rCBF], positron emission tomography [PET scanning]) in chronic schizophrenia have demonstrated a pattern of frontal lobe dysfunction, both at rest and in response to cognitive challenge. "Cognitive impairments are associated with negative symptoms, and like negative symptoms, may not respond to neuroleptics [antipsychotic medication]" (Kaufman & Weinberger, 1987, p. 31).

Kaufmann and Weinberger (1987) conclude that negative symptoms, cognitive impairment, cortical and subcortical atrophy, prefrontal-lobe brain dysfunction, and neuroleptic refractoriness identify a group of persons with schizophrenia who have both poor prognoses and persistent disabilities. Despite intensive psychosocial/vocational rehabilitation and judicious use of medication, these individuals may continue to have moderate to severe impairment in social, vocational, and self-care functioning.

That the anatomical changes seen in the brains of persons with schizophrenia (especially enlargement of the lateral and third ventricles) are not purely genetic in origin was shown in a recent article by Suddath and colleagues (Suddath, Christison, Torrey, Casanova, & Weinberger, 1990). In this study, identical twins discordant for schizophrenia were studied with magnetic resonance imaging, and in most cases, the twin with schizophrenia had significantly larger lateral and third ventricles. Because the twins were genetically identical, the anatomical changes appear to have had some other cause. Across schizophrenic twins, however, the enlarged ventricles did not seem correlated to length of illness or to neuroleptic dose. Whether the changes are etiologically related to schizophrenia or merely associated findings is not currently clear.

That there is a biological predisposition for the development of schizophrenia has been clearly shown. What that biological predisposition might be is less clear. "Is it a gene, toxin, auto-antibody, or virus? . . . is it the only determinant of the disease, or [is] its role to provide an abnormal vulnerability to triggering factors that can in turn be biological or psychological?" (Mesulam, 1990, p. 842). The results of ongoing research will be necessary to fully answer these questions.

As far as affective illness is concerned, the neurobiological correlates of depression have been reviewed (Gold, Goodwin, & Chrousos, 1988). Like schizophrenia, affective illness is a multifactorial syndrome; genetic predisposition, childhood stress, and (in the case of depression) a complex interaction of these factors with current environmental stressors are all important. The body's system for releasing hormones and brain messengers such as norepinephrine are believed to be involved in the recurrent episodes of affective illness. (See Gold et al., 1988, for a further elaboration of this complex topic.)

Prognosis and Course of Major Psychiatric Illness

Schizophrenia

Traditionally accepted good prognostic indicators in schizophrenia include good prior social and work history, late onset, acute onset, a clear precipitant, affective symptoms (e.g., depression), a good support system, and positive symptoms. Poor prognostic indicators are the obverse: early, insidious onset without clear precipitants; poor premorbid functioning; poor support systems; negative symptoms; and neurological signs and symptoms (such as cognitive impairment) (Kaplan & Sadock, 1989, p. 768). Recent longitudinal outcome studies of schizophrenia include the Vermont Longitudinal Study (Harding, Brooks, Ashikaga, Stauss, & Breier, 1987), the NIMH Longitudinal Study (Breier, Schreiber, Dyer, & Pickar, 1991), and that of Carone and colleagues (Carone, Harrow, & Westermeyer, 1991).

In the recent NIMH Longitudinal Study, only 20% of a sample of persons with chronic schizophrenia had a good outcome at 6-year follow-up (Breier et al., 1991). Outcome was determined by level of self-care, social and work histories, and presence and degree of psychotic symptoms, as determined by a variety of rating scales. During the 6-year follow-up period, 78% of the patients had a relapse, 38% attempted suicide, and 24% had episodes of affective illness. Once patients were optimally medicated, their levels of positive and negative symptoms predicted outcome, although their degree of symptomatology prior to medication did not. The authors concluded that response to medication treatment is therefore an important predictor of outcome.

They also examined results of outcome studies with longer follow-up periods, such as the Vermont study, which showed that 60% of chronic, backward patients with schizophrenia released into the community in the mid-1950s had a good global outcome, with no or only mild impairment, 32 years later (Harding et al., 1987). Using these and their own data, they speculate that schizophrenia may be a three-phase illness: an early phase marked by deteriorating course for 5–10 years; a stable middle phase; and a third phase of gradual improvement with age. They further speculate that these three phases may be related to dopamine concentrations in significant brain areas, which are at their peak in adolescence (the deteriorating phase), and which decrease with age (perhaps explaining the improvement seen on very long-term follow-ups, i.e., with advanced age).

Citing again the correlation between negative symptoms and poor social and work performance, Breier and colleagues (1991) suggest that treatments addressing these negative symptoms might have the greatest effect on outcome in schizophrenia. They specifically mention the newly released neuroleptic clozapine, which affects both positive and negative psychotic symptoms (unlike traditional neuroleptics, which mainly affect positive symptoms), and wonder whether ongoing research into its use will demonstrate meaningful improvements in outcome in these patients (see further discussion in the subsequent section, "Medications for Treatment of Major Psychiatric Illness").

Carone (Carone, Harrow, & Westermeyer, 1991) looked at the likelihood of complete remission in young adults with nonchronic schizophrenia, and concluded that the number of patients who have a complete remission is small: 10% after a 2 to 5-year follow-up period, and 17%, 5 years post follow-up. Mesulam (1990) states that "even with the most up-to-date management, about half of patients [with schizophrenia] have chronic deterioration" (p. 842). As these studies indicate, however, what one can predict about prognosis in schizophrenia is largely dependent not only on the population studied, but also on the point in their illness at which the patients are studied.

Affective Illness

The prognosis for patients with affective illness is considerably better than for those with schizophrenia. Within the affective category, patients with unipolar depression do better than those with bipolar illness (Harrow, Goldberg, Grossman, & Meltzer, 1990), who in turn do better than those with schizoaffective disorder. Persons with schizoaffective disorder, furthermore, do better than those with schizophrenia (Coryell, Keller, Lavori, & Endicott, 1990).

In later life, affective episodes tend to develop more rapidly, with less clear relationship to environmental stressors, and such episodes tend to be more severe (Gold et al., 1988). Thus, the more episodes one had in early life, the more likely one is to have others with poorer response and prognosis.

Bipolar illness usually begins in the early 20s, and if *untreated*, a patient would be expected to have 7 to 15 affective episodes over the course of a lifetime (Gold et al., 1988, p. 349). Unipolar depression often begins in midlife, and if untreated, it might be expected to produce 3 to 5 affective episodes in a lifetime (Gold et al., 1988, p. 349). "Untreated

episodes usually last from 7 to 14 months, although 20% last 2 years or more. Although some patients report no symptoms between affective episodes, as many as 30% describe intercurrent depressive symptoms" (Gold et al., p. 349). "Before drug treatment for major depression became available, studies showed suicide rates of 15%–30%. Recent studies show an inverse relation between the vigor or dose of antidepressant therapy and the risk of suicidal behavior and suicide" (Gold et al., 1988, p. 349).

A 1990 posthospital outcome study of patients with mania who had required hospitalization showed a greater degree of work disruption, rehospitalization, and recurrent affective episodes than expected (Harrow et al.). These authors concluded that patients requiring hospitalization may have "a more severe, recurrent and pernicious disorder than many have realized" (p. 670). These findings occurred despite the use of lithium in this group of patients; lithium generally has a 70% to 80% response rate in bipolar patients, both in treating the symptoms of acute mania, and in decreasing the frequency and severity of recurrent affective episodes.

Biopsychosocial Model as Applied to Persons with Persistent and Disabling Mental Illness

The conceptual model that describes the multifactorial etiology of mental illness discussed earlier in the chapter is the biopsychosocial model. The biopsychosocial model of health and illness was first described by George Engel in 1977. The clinical application of the model was further described by Engel in 1980. The essential conceptual thesis of the model is that illness in general, including mental illness, results from an interplay of factors derived from the biological, social, and psychological realities of the individual who is diagnosed with the given illness.

Thus, in the medical sphere, an individual with cardiovascular and/or pulmonary disease may have inherited a biological vulnerability to heart attacks at an early age, but psychological factors may render the individual subject to increased stress, with dramatic changes in pulse and heart rate, where another individual with a different psychology might experience the same stress (e.g., boss's criticism) as a matter of less threatening significance and, therefore, have less physiological change. Clearly, smoking is an example of a cardiovascular-related factor that may be a function of the person's psychology but is also a function of the social environment, as is exposure to cardiotoxins, which some societies will tolerate and others will not. Thus, the health or illness of the individual is seen as a result of the complex interaction of all three factors: the biological, social, and psychological.

Serious and persistent mental illness is subject to conceptualization involving these same factors. Anthony and Liberman (1986), utilizing Engel's general conceptual notion of a biopsychosocial model, put forth a model of mental illness, which they called the "vulnerability, stress, coping and competence model." Their model was designed to focus on mental disorders and to include rehabilitation outcomes as well as the rehabilitation-relevant states of impairment, handicap, and disability. In this model, an individual with a mental disorder is seen as subject to a biological vulnerability and/or a psychological vulnerability. This vulnerability, when coupled with individual specific socio-environmental stressors, might move an individual from a relative state of stability toward exacerbation of illness and increased impairment, handicap, and disability. Anthony and Liberman (1986) point toward a number of mediating, protective factors which include social support, skill building, transitional programs, and medication. These protective factors may interrupt the movement toward decompensation despite the psychobiological vulnerability and increased socioenvironmental stressors. Thus, if the protective factors are active, the individual may experience less decompensation, impairment, handicap, and disability.

Rehabilitation, which acts to improve such factors as social support, skill building, medication compliance, self-esteem, and family functioning, is seen as bolstering and enhancing these protective factors and thus reducing the impact of psychobiological vulnerability and socioenvironmental stressors. In this model, antipsychotic medicine is seen as a modulator or reducer of biological vulnerability, which helps to decrease the rates of relapse and thus improves the prognosis for schizophrenic disorders. Medications are also seen to protect against environmental stressors that may precipitate psychotic symptoms, so that a greater degree of stress may be required to cause a relapse in a medicated individual than in a nonmedicated individual. The reduction of biological vulnerability by medication does not, unfortunately, completely protect an individual against decompensation when severely stressed or suffering a loss of environmental social supports. People may decompensate when underlying biological vulnerabilities are increased, which is more likely when patients are unmedicated. Stressful life events may then overwhelm the individual's coping skills and social competence, and the social support network may also weaken, due to the network members' lack of ability to cope with the individual.

Implications of the Biopsychosocial Model for Treatment

The biopsychosocial model of health and illness, as applied to disabling mental disorders, leads to a model of integrated and comprehensive biopsychosocial treatment and rehabilitation. This entails an appropriate treatment plan for a disabled schizophrenic individual (or a person diagnosed with any disabling psychiatric disorder) and might require a combination of medication, building of social and vocationally related skills, rehabilitation approaches, and family interventions along the psychoeducational spectrum, as well as other interventions. This complex treatment plan requires integration across programs and professionals. The psychiatrist must communicate with the rehabilitation program staff to obtain feedback as to the patient's behaviors, which may be relevant to the dose or type of medication prescribed. The rehabilitation workers will need to know the possible side effects and time course profiles of the medications that the physician is prescribing. The family or other individuals in the patient's social support system (e.g., residence counselors) need to understand the implications of the illness and the treatment, in order to provide an informed, supportive environment. Treatment plans will only become truly effective if the plans are both integrated and comprehensive, touching on all elements of the biopsychosocial model and all persons involved in applying that model to the individual's treatment.

Anthony and Liberman (1986) combine the biopsychosocial approach with their impairment/disability/handicap model of rehabilitation mentioned earlier. They visualize psychiatric rehabilitation as encompassing both client skills development and environmental resource development. Rehabilitation in their model begins with a comprehensive medical/psychiatric evaluation, which results in a psychiatric diagnosis and an assessment of the person's current level of function (and by implication, his or her skills and skill deficits) and his or her other social and environmental supports. Using the concepts of impairment, disability, and handicap, the rehabilitation begins by addressing the impairment. In the case of schizophrenia, for example, this would be done by using major tranquilizers (neuroleptics) to treat the hallucinations or delusional thinking. In their example, medication would be treating the impairment by addressing the biological substrate of the disorder (in this case, probably the dopaminergic neurotransmitter system in the brain). With psychotic thinking reduced, the individual becomes more amenable to other aspects of the rehabilitation process, especially skills building (the psychosocial part of the biopsychosocial model).

Skills training is intended to lessen the degree of disability associated with any residual psychiatric impairment, following aggressive treatment of the impairment. Because many severely and persistently mentally ill individuals have been ill during crucial developmental periods (often adolescence and early adulthood), they may have failed to develop the skills normally mastered at these times, including social, vocational, and self-care skills. Tools such as specific instruction, therapist modeling, and patient role playing can be used to help individuals learn various skills, such as how to dress for and behave on a job interview, how to ask someone out on a date, or how to take public transportation to a predetermined destination.

If skills training and treatment of the impairment do not abolish all deficits, disability can still be further decreased by providing living, working, and social environments that accommodate to the deficit, to maximize the client's function and autonomy. Examples of such environmental supports include supervised living situations and modified work settings. Environmental modifications and skills building are viewed by Anthony and Liberman (1986) as complementary in treating the person with serious mental illness.

Finally, some of the client's limitation may be based less on impairment or disability than on societal discrimination (i.e., handicap). Anthony and Liberman (1986) envision "societal rehabilitation" as being crucial in addressing this facet of the problem.

Because environmental support is so important for persons with serious and persistent mental illness, and because stress in that environment is a key predictor of relapse, a family approach to treating these persons is essential. This is not to suggest that families are to blame for these complex illnesses, however. The emphasis is on the helpful role they can play. Ingredients in such an approach include educating the family about the signs and symptoms of a given disorder (negative schizophrenic symptoms, for example, are often perceived as laziness by uninformed families); reviewing the signs of early relapse, and possible causes (e.g., medication—noncompliance and illicit drug use) of early relapse; discussing prognosis and realistic expectations for the individual; and emphasizing the role of high expressed emotion in the family as a predictor of relapse. *High expressed emotion* families are those where there is frequent expression of intense emotions, particularly those of a hostile or critical nature. Referring families to lay-led support groups, such as the National Alliance for the Mentally Ill (NAMI), is also often helpful.

The rehabilitation program also needs a captain, and this individual should be the patient/client's primary therapist (often, *not* a physician). A consistent, predictable therapist is crucial for developing a trusting relationship with the patient/client. This relationship can be healing in itself and also crucial in obtaining the client's willingness to participate in many other aspects of the rehabilitation process. The importance of the stability of this interpersonal relationship is underscored by how difficult it is for many seriously mentally ill clients to form relationships or learn to trust. In our zeal to provide adequate psychopharmacological, skills building, and environmental intervention, let us also not forget the needs of the seriously mentally ill client to *talk* (see "Can we talk?" by "A recovering patient," 1986), the personal plea of a person with serious mental illness). Once again, the role of the trusted therapist is highlighted.

If the psychiatrist is not the primary therapist, he or she will be paying particular attention to the patient's medication management in the context of the overall treatment plan and biopsychosocial assessment. Relevant questions here are: Is the medication working? Is the patient getting enough medication? Is the patient getting too much medication? The answers to these questions may not be as obvious as they seem. Major tranquilizers (neuroleptics) often have side effects such as akathisia (restlessness, insomnia), which erroneously appear to be signs of worsening psychosis and therefore incorrectly suggest the need for *more* (rather than less) medication. Due to the uncomfortable nature of akathisia, this may result in noncompliance with prescribed medication for some clients. Also, apathy and social withdrawal may simply be assumed to be negative symptoms of schizophrenia, and therefore relatively untreatable, when in fact they may represent neuroleptic side effects and therefore respond to a change in the dose or type of medication or to the addition of an *anticholinergic agent* (i.e., a drug used to alleviate motoric slowing and other undesirable neuroleptic side effects). Alternatively, apathy and withdrawal can also be seen as manifestations of a superimposed affective disorder (i.e., depression), again with implications for medical management. Psychiatrists will often try to use medication side effects to advantage by prescribing more energizing medications for withdrawn patients and more sedating medications for agitated patients (Andreasen, 1984).

With some psychopharmacological agents such as lithium (commonly used for bipolar or schizoaffective disorder) or cyclic antidepressants, blood levels of the drug often must be monitored in addition to continuing clinical evaluation. This is mandatory for lithium and often relevant for a number of antidepressants. Blood levels complement clinical assessment by addressing questions such as "Is the patient really taking the drug?" "Is he or she getting enough medication?" "Is he or she getting too much medication?" These questions are vital in rehabilitation, because a patient who is over- or undermedicated or experiencing medication side effects will not be able to participate optimally in the rehabilitation process.

Medications for Treatment of Major Psychiatric Illnesses

Classes of medications commonly used in treating persons with serious and persistent mental illness include neuroleptics (antipsychotic medication or "major tranquilizers"), benzodiazepines ("minor tranquilizers"), lithium, and antidepressants. Each of these classes of medications (except lithium) contains many drugs; which one is chosen usually depends on the patient's previous (favorable) response and the medication's side effect profile. Neuroleptics are used for psychotic symptoms such as hallucinations, delusions, or grossly disorganized thought or behavior. There are five major classes of neuroleptics: phenothiazines (e.g., chlorpromazine, thioridazine, fluphenazine), indolic compounds (e.g., molindone), dibenzoxazepines (e.g., loxapine), thioxanthenes (e.g., thiothixene), and butyrophenones (e.g., haloperidol). Benzodiazepines can supplement neuroleptics in the acutely psychotic patient, as well as being used adjunctively with other medication in acute mania; they sedate and calm acute agitation but do not definitively treat psychosis in the way that neuroleptics do. Lithium is used to treat acute mania and to prevent mood swings in bipolar and schizoaffective disorder; its mechanism of action is still controversial. Carbamazepine (an anticonvulsant) is sometimes used instead of (or with) lithium, for the same indications. Antidepressants are used for treating depression.

Clozapine, a newly released neuroleptic alluded to earlier, appears to hold some promise for psychotic patients who have not responded to other neuroleptics, or who cannot take them due to severe side effects. It may also help with the recalcitrant negative schizophrenic symptoms, such as apathy and social withdrawal. Clozapine has been demonstrated to be effective for about 30% of refractory patients with schizophrenia (Honigfeld & Patin, 1990). It is not a panacea, however; patients still may require extensive rehabilitation even if the drug is successful. Clozapine's high cost (approximately $8000 to $9,000 per year, which includes cost of drug and laboratory tests) and potentially fatal toxicity (due to lowering of the white blood cell count) preclude its use except when clearly indicated. As with all psychotropic medications, it both alleviates patients' suffering and makes them more amenable to other rehabilitative therapies. However, due to possible fatal toxicity, the drug requires monitoring, which results in its high cost. It also necessitates that patients be extremely compliant with appointments. Therefore, this is not the medication of choice for a number of persons with serious mental illness who tend not to be compliant with medication monitoring appointments. However, there has been much controversy concerning the availability of clozapine for all patients who could possibly benefit. Its high cost causes problems for the public mental health system, which has limited financial resources (Griffith, 1990).

Because neuroleptics are the most commonly used type of medication for treating serious mental illness, and because their side effects are often troublesome to patients, some of these side effects are briefly reviewed here. Neurological side effects include dystonic reactions, akathisia, drug-induced Parkinson's disease, and (one of the most feared) tardive dyskinesia. The other group of side effects most bothersome to patients are the anticholinergic side effects: sedation, blurred vision, dry mouth, constipation, and (sometimes) urinary retention.

Of the neurological side effects, dystonic reactions are often seen as soon as hours-to-days after beginning neuroleptic therapy, and consist of involuntary contractions of muscles of the jaw, neck, and throat (usually only on one side of the face). They can be rapidly reversed by intramuscular injections (diphenhydramine, benztropine); however, they are so frightening to patients that they are a common cause for subsequent medication refusal.

Akathisia begins in the first weeks to months of neuroleptic use and is characterized by pacing, insomnia, and constant restless leg movements. As mentioned earlier, it wrongly can be confused with increasing psychotic agitation. Decreasing the neuroleptic dose, changing to a less potent neuroleptic, or adding beta blockers or benzodiazepines are the usual approaches to treating akathisia.

Drug-induced Parkinson's disease is characterized by tremor, muscle rigidity, slowness of movement, a characteristic shuffling gait, and an expressionless face. It usually begins in the first weeks to months of neuroleptic use. Its manifestations can mimic depression, but unlike depression, they respond quickly to the addition of anticholinergic medication (e.g., benztropine).

Tardive dyskinesia is one of the most feared neuroleptic side effects because it is often irreversible, even when the neuroleptic is stopped. It is rarely seen before 6 months of continuous neuroleptic use. It is characterized by involuntary movements of the tongue and face (e.g., tongue-protusion, lip-smacking, grimacing), which are unattractive and embarrassing to the client. There may also be involuntary movements of the extremities and trunk. There is no good treatment for tardive dyskinesia. Clozapine has been reported not to cause tardive dyskinesia. The best approach is prevention (i.e., using the lowest dose of neuroleptic possible) because tardive dyskinesia may be related both to dose of medication and duration of use.

The Role of the Psychiatrist in the Rehabilitation Process

What is the role of the psychiatrist in the care and treatment of those with serious and persistent mental illness? Clearly, pharmacological management is required. However, this alone is insufficient, in most, if not all cases. The psychiatrist must also continually monitor the observations of the family, the nonphysician therapists, and the rehabilitation workers, in order to provide the best use of psychotropic medication to maximize function and minimize disruptive side effects. The psychiatrist may teach the patient, the family, and service providers the means for recognizing the early signs and symptoms of relapse. The psychosocial team requires a sophisticated assessment of signs and symptoms (impairments) and their implications for rehabilitation readiness and responsivity. This will help in selecting those most likely to benefit from psychosocial rehabilitation and those less amenable. With scarce resources, this selection and monitoring process is essential for high quality, state-of-the-art, effective care. The psychiatrist must be a well-trained integrated part of the treatment team in outpatient management of these illnesses,

as much as he or she is in the acute phases of inpatient treatment. The psychiatrist's skills in evaluation, assessment, and monitoring of the patient are essential components of the rehabilitation process.

Conclusion

Care of persons with serious and persistent mental illness spans a continuum from inpatient hospitalization, in order to contain behavior that is out of control and to begin definitive pharmacological and other treatments; psychosocial and vocational rehabilitation to maximize adaptive functioning, once the patient has been stabilized psychiatrically and is therefore amenable to rehabilitation; and maintenance and follow-up therapy when a patient is either in remission or has achieved his or her maximum potential. In all of these situations, a team approach, which involves rehabilitation workers, psychiatrists, social workers, mental health workers, psychologists, and the patient and his or her family, results in optimal care. The conceptual model that underlies such a treatment approach is the biopsychosocial model.

References

"A recovering patient" [Author]. (1986). "Can we talk?" The schizophrenic patient in psychotherapy. *American Journal of Psychiatry, 143*(1), 68–70.

Americans with Disabilities Act of 1990. Public Law No. 101-336, title 42, United States Code, Section 12101 (1990).

Andreasen, N. (1984). *The broken brain.* New York: Harper & Row.

Anthony, W., Cohen, M., & Farkus, M. (1990). *Psychiatric rehabilitation.* Boston: Psychiatric Rehabilitation Center, Boston University.

Anthony, W. A., & Liberman, R. P. (1986). The practice of psychiatric rehabilitation: Historical conceptual and research base. *Schizophrenia Bulletin, 12*(4), 542–559.

Breier, A., Schreiber, J. L., Dyer, J., & Pickar, D. (1991). National Institute of Mental Health longitudinal study of chronic schizophrenia: Prognosis and predictors of outcome. *Archives of General Psychiatry, 48*, 239–46.

Carone, B. J., Harrow, M., & Westermeyer, J. F. (1991). Post hospital course and outcome in schizophrenia. *Archives of General Psychiatry, 48*, 247.

Coryell, W., Keller, M., Lavori, P., & Endicott, J. (1990). Affective syndromes, psychotic features, and prognosis. *Archives of General Psychiatry, 47*, 651.

Engel, G. L. (1977). The need for a new medical model. *Science, 196*, 129–136.

Engel, G. L. (1980). The clinical application of the biopsychosocial model. *American Journal of Psychiatry, 137*, 535–544.

Gold, P. W., Goodwin, F. K., & Chrousos, G. P. (1988). Clinical and biochemical manifestators of depression: Relation to the neurobiology of stress. *New England Journal of Medicine, 319*, 348–353, 413–420.

Goldman, H. H., & Manderscheid, R. W. (1987). The epidemiology of psychiatric disability. In A. T. Meyerson & T. Fine (Eds.), *Psychiatric disability: Clinical, legal and administrative dimensions* (pp. 13–21). Washington, DC: American Psychiatric Association Press.

Goldman, H. H., Gatozzi, A. A., & Taube, C. A. (1981). Defining and counting the chronically mentally ill. *Hospital and Community Psychiatry, 32*, 21–27.

Griffith, E. (1990). Clozapine: Problems for the public sector. *Hospital and Community Psychiatry, 41*(8), 437.

Harding, C. M., Brooks, G. W., Ashikaga, T., Stauss, J. S., & Breier, A. (1987). The Vermont longitudinal study of persons with severe mental illness. *American Journal of Psychiatry, 144*, 718–735.

Harrow, M., Goldberg, J. F., Grossman, L. S., & Meltzer, H. Y. (1990). Outcome in manic disorders. *Archives of General Psychiatry, 47*, 665–671.

Honigfeld, G., & Patin, J. (1990). A two-year clinical and economic follow-up of patients on clozapine. *Hospital and Community Psychiatry, 41*(8), 882–885.

Kaplan, H. I., & Sadock, B. J. (1989). *Comprehensive textbook of psychiatry* (5th ed.). Baltimore: Williams and Wilkins.

Kaufmann, C. A., & Weinberger, D. R. (1987). The neurobiological basis of psychiatric disability. In A. T. Meyerson & T. Fine (Eds.), *Psychiatric disability: Clinical, legal and administrative dimensions* (pp. 23–47). Washington, DC: American Psychiatric Association Press.

Mesulam, M. M. (1990). Schizophrenia and the brain. *New England Journal of Medicine, 322*, 842.

Minkoff, K. (1978). A map of the chronic mental patient. In J. Talbott (Ed.), *The chronic mental patient.* Washington, DC: American Psychiatric Association.

National Institute of Mental Health. (1991, July). Program Announcement. *Research on disabilities and rehabilitation services for persons with severe mental disorders.* Rockville, MD: Author.

National Institute of Mental Health. (1980). *Announcement of community support system strategy development and implementation grants.* Rockville, MD: Author.

Pope, A., & Tarlov, A. (Eds.) (1991). *Disability in America: Toward a national agenda for prevention.* Washington, DC: National Academy Press.

Ridgely, S., Goldman, H., & Talbott, J. (1986). *Chronically mentally ill young adults with substance abuse problems: A review of relevant literature and creation of a research agenda.* Baltimore, MD: Mental Health Policy Center, University of Maryland.

Suddath, R. L., Christison, G. W., Torrey, E. F., Casanova, M. F., & Weinberger, D. R. (1990). Anatomical abnormalities in the brains of monozygotic twins discordant for schizophrenia. *New England Journal of Medicine, 322*, 789.

Teplin, L. (1984). Criminalizing mental disorder: The comparative arrest rate of the mentally ill. *American Psychologist, 39*(7), 794–803.

Chapter 4

Rehabilitation in Community Support Systems

BETH A. STROUL

Since the 1960s, there has been a rising tide of concern regarding the treatment of persons with severe, disabling, and long-term mental illness. No longer are persons with long-term mental illness isolated in the back wards of mental institutions. Increasingly, they are living in community settings and receiving community-based care. However, critics have noted that conditions in the community often are as bad as those in institutions—people with mental illness are isolated, neglected, stigmatized, untreated, and, in some cases, abused. The need for improved care is evidenced by the very visible and growing problem of homelessness among mentally ill individuals.

Clearly, mental health treatment alone is not enough. There is general agreement that persons with long-term mental illness require a range of basic community services and supports, which has become known as a community support system (CSS). The CSS concept was designed by the National Institute of Mental Health (NIMH) Community Support Program (CSP), in collaboration with state mental health officials, family groups, consumer groups, researchers, citizen advocates, and others from across the nation. The concept was first described by Turner (1977) and has been revised and updated, according to accumulating evidence and experience (NIMH, 1980; Stroul, 1984, 1988, 1989; Turner & Shifren, 1979; Turner & TenHoor, 1978).

Additionally, the CSS concept formed the basis for a model mental health plan designed by NIMH to offer guidance to states and communities in planning for community-based mental health systems (NIMH, 1987).

The CSS concept recognizes that traditional mental health services are not sufficient and includes the entire array of treatment, life support, and rehabilitation services needed to assist persons with severe, disabling mental illness to function at optimal levels within the community. Accordingly, the CSS concept delineates an array of essential components that are needed to provide adequate services and support, including client identification and outreach, mental health treatment, crisis response services, health and dental care, housing, income support and entitlements, peer support, family and community support, rehabilitation services, protection and advocacy, and case management. Each community should have arrangements to perform these essential functions (NIMH, 1987). This chapter describes the CSS concept in detail, including the components that compose a CSS, the principles that guide CSSs, and the ways in which CSSs may be provided and organized.

What Are the Needs?

In the past, persons with serious mental illness were confined to institutions for long periods of time. These institutions typically were far from the person's home community and provided little more than custodial care. Over the past 30 years, reliance on public mental institutions for the care and treatment of persons with long-term mental illness has been reduced dramatically. The development of new drugs and treatments, court decisions mandating an individual's right to treatment in the least restrictive setting, fiscal incentives, and other factors enabled many persons to be released from institutions to receive care in their home communities.

This trend of deinstitutionalization brought with it a corollary trend of noninstitutionalization. This is reflected in the practice of admissions diversion, whereby persons are kept out of the hospital if at all possible and are referred instead for community care. Thus, mentally disabled persons who spent much of their lives in public mental institutions now live in the community, and many younger persons, who at one time might have resided in these institutions, now remain in the community as well. To meet their needs, community-based services, including community hospitals, were envisioned.

Despite these trends, most communities are not prepared or equipped to meet the needs of persons with long-term mental illness. In many cases, resources are not available to meet their basic human needs for shelter, food, clothing, income, and medical care. Supportive and rehabilitative services are largely unavailable in many areas, leaving persons with little or no ongoing care. While some persons are able to gain access to needed community services and supports, there are many tragedies due to lack of access, including some ex-patients wandering the streets and sleeping outdoors and others living in squalid, single room occupancy dwellings. Continual readmissions to hospitals, overuse of emergency rooms, repeated encounters with the correctional system, and overwhelming burden on families are all problems that result from insufficient community services and supports. The current, tragic problem of homeless persons who are mentally ill points out the especially critical need for housing for mentally ill individuals.

The fundamental problem is a severe shortage of supportive and rehabilitative programs in the community to meet the needs of persons discharged or diverted from hospitals. Today, most agree that community-based care is more humane, more therapeutic, and less stigmatizing than institutional care. Nationwide, however, there has not been enough progress in developing adequate community-based services for persons with long-term mental illness.

What are the needs of persons with long-term mental illness? What services and supports are needed to ensure an optimal quality of life within the community? Institutional care, despite its many negative aspects, provided for all aspects of a person's life. Shelter, food, clothing, structured activities, companionship, medical care, therapy, and rehabilitation were all, theoretically, part of the services of a "total institution." In order for individuals to function and thrive within the community, all aspects of their lives also must be considered—their basic human needs, as well as their needs for treatment and rehabilitation. This recognition reflects the understanding that a person with mental illness is a person first, with basic needs and goals similar to other members of the community (Anthony, Cohen, & Kennard, 1990). A place to live, a job, and friends are fundamental needs common to all people, while specialized interventions and supports are needed in response to psychiatric symptoms and resulting functional disabilities. Thus, there is widespread agreement that an array of services, supports, and opportunities (i.e., a CSS) is needed in order to maintain the community tenure and to enhance the quality of life of persons with long-term mental illness.

It has been estimated that approximately 2.8 million individuals have severe, disabling, long-term mental illness (NIMH, 1985). More recent estimates suggest that the population may actually number 3.3 million or more (NIMH, 1989). It is important to recognize that the population of concern is diverse. Each individual has unique concerns, abilities, strengths, preferences, problems, and limitations. Further, the population comprises a variety of subgroups, each having different characteristics and service needs. These include mentally ill persons belonging to racial or ethnic minority groups, elderly persons, young adults and youths in transition to adulthood, persons with both mental illness and substance abuse problems or both mental illness and mental retardation, and mentally ill individuals within the criminal justice system.

A major subgroup requiring specialized, intensive services comprises severely mentally ill homeless individuals. This is a multineed population, often with substance abuse, physical, and mental health problems, as well as social and vocational deficits; specialized interventions are needed to engage and assist homeless individuals. Despite the heterogeneity and divergent subgroups within the population of concern, the CSS concept includes the basic range of services and supports needed within the community by most persons with long-term mental illness.

What Principles Guide Community Support Systems?

A CSS represents more than a network of service components. Rather, it represents a philosophy about the way in which services should be delivered to persons with long-term mental illness. Although the actual components and organizational configuration of a CSS may differ from state to state and from community to community, all CSSs should be guided by a set of basic values.

The CSS ideology embraces the notion that services should maintain the dignity and respect the individual needs of each person. Individuals with mental illness are seen, first and foremost, as persons with basic human needs and aspirations and as citizens with all the rights, privileges, opportunities, and responsibilities accorded other citizens. They should have access to the supports and opportunities needed by all persons, as well as to specialized mental health services. Further, the CSS concept is based on creating opportunities for individuals to develop their potentials—for growth, improvement, and movement toward independence—rather than fostering a life of dependency, disability, and "chronic patienthood."

The CSS ideology has further evolved to champion the philosophy of consumer empowerment. At the service delivery level, this means that the consumer's own goals and preferences should be the most significant determinants of the services and supports to be provided. At the system level, this means that the goals and preferences of consumers should serve as the basis for system planning and that both consumers and families should be full participants in all phases of policy making and of planning, implementing, and delivering services.

Another basic value inherent in the CSS concept is that the community is the best place for providing long-term care. Inpatient care is a part of the array of needed community-based services and should be used for short-term evaluation and stabilization and for the small percentage of individuals who require long-term hospitalization.

The CSS philosophy is embodied in a set of guiding principles as follows:

> *Services should be consumer centered.* Services should be based on and responsive to the needs of the client rather than the needs of the system or the needs of providers.
>
> *Services should empower clients.* Services should incorporate consumer self-help approaches and should be provided in a manner that allows clients to retain the greatest possible control over their own lives. As much as possible, clients should set their own goals and decide what services they will receive. Clients also should be actively involved in all aspects of policy making and of planning and delivering services.

Services should be racially and culturally appropriate. Services should be available, accessible, and acceptable to members of racial and ethnic minority groups and to women.

Services should be flexible. Services should be available whenever they are needed and for as long as they are needed. They should be provided in a variety of ways, with individuals able to move into and out of the system as their needs change.

Services should focus on strengths. Services should build on the assets and strengths of clients in order to help them maintain a sense of identity, dignity, and self-esteem.

Services should be normalized and should incorporate natural supports. Services should be offered in the least restrictive, most natural setting possible. Clients should be encouraged to use the natural supports in the community and should be integrated into the normal living, working, learning, and leisure time activities of the community.

Services should meet special needs. Services should be adapted to meet the needs of subgroups of severely mentally ill persons, such as elderly individuals in the community or in institutions; young adults and youths in transition to adulthood; mentally ill individuals with substance abuse problems, mental retardation, or hearing impairments; mentally ill persons who are homeless; and mentally ill persons who are inappropriately placed within the correctional system.

Service systems should be accountable. Service providers should be accountable to the users of the services and monitored by the state, to ensure quality of care and continued relevance to client needs. Primary consumers and families should be involved in planning, implementing, monitoring, and evaluating services.

Services should be coordinated. In order to develop CSSs, services should be coordinated through mandates or written agreements that require ongoing communication and linkages among participating agencies and among the various levels of government. In order to be effective, coordination must occur at the client, community, and state levels. In addition, mechanisms should be in place to ensure continuity of care and coordination between hospital and community services.

What Is a Community Support System?

A *CSS* is defined as "an organized network of caring and responsible people committed to assisting persons with long-term mental illness to meet their needs and develop their potentials without being unnecessarily isolated or excluded from the community" (Stroul, 1984, p. 8). The goal of a CSS can be characterized simply as helping people to function better so that they can become more successful and satisfied in their various living, learning, working, and social environments (Anthony, Cohen, & Kennard, 1990). NIMH (1987) characterized the mission of CSSs as the provision of

> Programs and services that assist adults with severe, disabling mental illness to control the symptoms of the illness; to develop the skills and acquire the supports and resources they need to succeed where they choose to live, learn, and work; and to maintain responsibility to the greatest extent possible, for setting their own goals, directing their own lives, and acting responsibly as members of the community. (p. 12)

In order to achieve these broad goals, the CSS concept includes the entire array of treatment, support, and rehabilitation services needed to assist persons with severe, disabling mental illness to function at optimal levels within the community and, ultimately, to become more successful and satisfied. A graphic representation of a comprehensive CSS is provided in Figure 4.1, and each specific service component is described briefly in the following subsections.

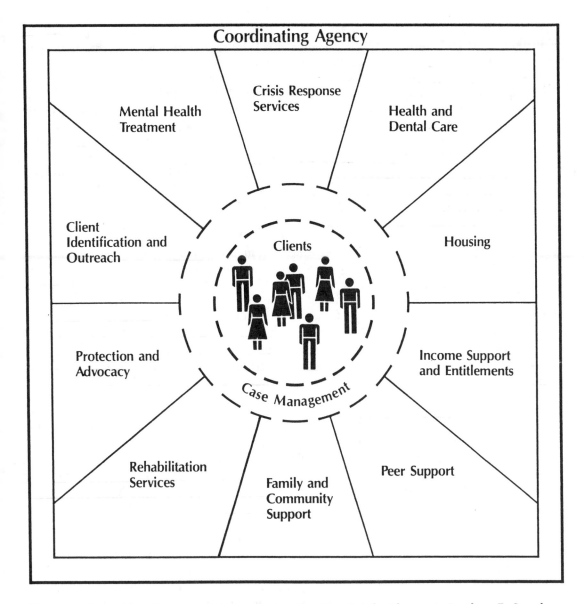

Figure 4.1. Comprehensive community support system. Reprinted with permission from B. Stroul, (1989), Community and support systems for persons with long-term mental illness: A conceptual framework, *Psychosocial Rehabilitation Journal, 12*(3), pp. 9–26.

Client Identification and Outreach

Mentally ill individuals often <u>have difficulty seeking out services</u>. As a result, mechanisms are needed to <u>locate potential clients</u>, regardless of where they reside, and <u>to inform them of available services.</u> For example, linkages with boarding homes, emergency rooms, inpatient facilities, police departments, fam-

ily groups, and consumer organizations may be used to identify persons in need of community support services.

Some individuals decline to attend a formal treatment program or center or are unable to do so. Outreach services should be provided to assist these individuals in their own environments. Such outreach services might include crisis intervention, medication checks, assistance in meeting basic human needs, skill training, and referral to appropriate health or welfare agencies. *Assertive outreach services, often delivered by multidisciplinary teams of staff*, are proving to be highly effective in delivering intensive treatment and support services to many high-risk and difficult-to-reach clients.

Effective outreach is particularly critical for homeless mentally ill persons who are among the least able to locate appropriate agencies, programs, and resources and who tend to reject traditional mental health and social services. Outreach to shelters, soup kitchens, drop-in centers, or people on the streets can reach many homeless individuals who otherwise would be overlooked by the mental health system. Outreach provides a more flexible approach, which is often effective in gradually and patiently engaging the hardest-to-reach clients.

Many clients, particularly those in rural areas, have difficulty taking advantage of needed support services because of the lack of transportation. Transportation assistance should be provided to clients to enhance their access to needed services and community resources. Such assistance may be provided through a variety of mechanisms, including special arrangements with public transportation systems or through use of vans, buses, taxis, private automobiles, or volunteers.

Mental Health Treatment

Mental health treatment is a critical component of a CSS. The clinical conditions of persons with serious, disabling mental illness change over time, and they experience periodic relapses or flare-ups of acute symptoms. Clinical management of psychiatric disorders should be an integral part of service delivery and should be provided continuously on a long-term basis.

Accordingly, mental health treatment for persons with long-term mental illness should be directed at helping clients to manage symptoms, recognize signs of relapse, and cope with daily living. Specifically, mental health care should include both diagnostic evaluation and ongoing assessment and monitoring of psychiatric conditions. Accurate diagnosis of psychiatric and medical problems is essential for the development of an individualized treatment plan, including appropriate medications. A second component of mental health care is supportive counseling and therapy. Counseling can be provided on an individual and/or group basis and generally is directed at helping clients to cope with a variety of life problems and stresses.

Another essential aspect of mental health treatment is medication management. Medication management services include prescribing medications, ensuring that needed medications are available to clients, carefully monitoring medications to ensure maximal therapeutic effectiveness and minimal adverse side effects, and educating the client and family regarding the nature of medications, their benefits, and potential side effects.

Specialized treatment services are needed for the increasing numbers of mentally ill persons who also have substance abuse disorders. In addition to services provided to the general population, these individuals often require detoxification and other interventions to address alcohol and other drug abuse problems. Programs should accept and provide services to persons with mental illness and substance abuse problems and should either provide or help in providing access to the needed specialized services. Linkages and collaborative service delivery with the substance abuse treatment system in the community have become an indispensable aspect of a CSS.

Crisis Response Services

Persons with serious and long-term mental illness tend to experience recurrent crises even when comprehensive and continuous community support services are available. As a result, the capacity to provide crisis assistance is a critical aspect of a CSS. Crisis services are needed to provide an immediate response to individuals in crisis and to members of the individual's support system on a 24-hour-a-day, 7-day-a-week basis. In many cases, crisis services can assist the client to stabilize and to readjust to community living. Further, crisis services often can be effective in averting hospitalization.

The primary goal of crisis services is to assist individuals in psychiatric crises to maintain or resume functioning in the community. Crisis response services should enable the client, family members, and others to cope with emergencies while maintaining the client's status as a functioning community member to the greatest possible extent. The availability of crisis services should be known to providers, families, clients, community agencies, law enforcement agencies, and the community at large.

Crisis assistance can be conceptualized as a range of responses to be used in crisis situations. These include 24-hour crisis telephone services (such as hotlines), walk in crisis intervention services at mental health agencies, and mobile crisis outreach services, which involve going to the client and providing services in the setting in which the crisis is occurring. Outreach workers may stay with the client and significant others as long as is necessary to intervene successfully in the crisis—initiating necessary treatment, resolving problems, providing high levels of support, and making arrangements for ongoing services.

With intensive crisis intervention and support, many clients in crisis can be maintained and assisted in their natural environments. When such approaches are not sufficient to achieve stabilization and crisis resolution, crisis residential services should be available. These services involve providing crisis intervention in the context of a residential, nonhospital setting on a short-term basis. A variety of settings or approaches can be used to provide crisis residential services, including family-based crisis homes; staffed residences for small groups of clients in crisis; crisis apartments, which are staffed on an as-needed basis; and sometimes crisis beds within longer term residential facilities.

Inpatient beds in a protective environment should be provided for crises that cannot be handled in the natural setting or in crisis residential settings. Hospitalization is needed for the most severe crises, in which clients need intensive support, structure, and supervision during the period of stabilization. Persons who are acutely dangerous to themselves or others, or who retain little impulse control, or who have complicating medical conditions may require inpatient care. These inpatient beds may be provided in a psychiatric unit of a general or community hospital or in a nearby state hospital and serve as a backup to other community support services.

Health and Dental Care

Persons with long-term mental illness frequently lack proper health and dental care. This results from the difficulty in locating medical and dental practitioners who are willing to serve this population, coupled with the inability to pay for such services. Severely mentally ill persons have been found to have significantly higher rates of physical illness than the general population. Further, a significant number of persons with long-term mental illness have undetected physical diseases that may contribute to their mental disorders. Adequate health care services for this population is, therefore, particularly important.

Creative arrangements and procedures may be needed to ensure that persons with long-term mental illness have access to adequate health and dental care services. First, the CSS should have mechanisms to ensure that clients who are entitled to medical assistance benefits, such as Medicaid or Medicare, receive these benefits. Further, mechanisms and procedures to ensure access to medical and dental services for clients should be in place. These may include the establishment of linkages and agreements with private practitioners, hospitals, clinics, or other medical organizations and facilities to provide services to clients. Services may be provided by bringing clients to medical and dental resources in the community or by bringing such services to clients at the mental health program or agency. For example, some programs have contracts with community physicians to perform physical examinations and provide medical care to clients on a regular basis. Assistance with transportation to medical and dental appointments may be needed for many clients.

Housing

Adequate housing is essential to the well-being of any person. Many persons with long-term mental illness do not have stable, affordable housing and have difficulty locating, securing, and maintaining housing. The lack of housing options for persons with mental illness contributes to inappropriate and prolonged hospitalization, enormous stress and burden on families, and, of course, homelessness. Housing problems are closely related to economic and social problems that affect persons with mental illness, such as poverty, discrimination, and lack of affordable housing in general. CSSs should include a range of residential options for clients, offering the opportunity for decent, affordable housing in the community. Without an appropriate range of housing options, the success of other treatment and rehabilitation approaches is jeopardized.

Stability in housing is a crucial factor that often has been overlooked in the care of persons with long-term mental illness. Long-term, stable housing should be a goal of rehabilitation, rather than requiring clients to progress through a series of time-limited, transitional housing environments. Frequent moves create dislocation and the need for readjustment, thereby requiring the learning of new skills—all of which create stress for mentally disabled individuals. Further, mechanisms should be devised to ensure that a client's housing is protected when he or she is absent due to a crisis or a period of hospitalization.

An array of residential alternatives that provide varying levels of support and supervision should be offered within a community. An individual consumer's preferences, values, and goals with regard to housing, along with the person's functional level, should be primary considerations in determining an appropriate housing arrangement. Recent philosophical and service delivery shifts suggest that the emphasis should be on the most normalized housing options, and that training, supports, and services should be provided to enable individuals to reside successfully in these more normalized community residential settings. Reliance on normalized living environments maximizes the opportunity for individuals with mental illness to become integrated into community life and to function as independently as possible. Known as "supported housing," this approach involves helping each individual to choose, acquire, and maintain a home in the community. A broad range of flexible and individualized services and supports—such as case management, on-site crisis intervention, and rehabilitation—are provided in these natural settings, enabling clients to succeed in the community living environments of their choice. Thus, the supported housing approach rests on the major principles of consumer choice in selecting housing from available community housing alternatives, use of normalized housing environments, and provision of ongoing and flexible supports.

A variety of more specialized or structured residential settings may be used for individuals who require a greater degree of attention, supervision, or structure. These include congregate settings such as group homes and residential treatment programs of various types. Particularly for some extremely disabled clients, a range of residential treatment settings can provide alternatives to institutional care. These types of programs are not necessarily long-term, permanent housing options, but rather offer more specialized, facility-based programming. Other options, which often are part of the array of available housing options, include family foster care homes, board and care homes, apartments with varying levels of staff supervision, and other settings. An individualized approach to housing is needed, whereby the client's needs and choices dictate the selection and development of housing options.

Special residential assistance for homeless mentally ill persons is an essential aspect of the housing component. These individuals require a range of additional living situations, with varying degrees of supervision and structure. Emergency shelters are needed to provide an immediate, short-term alternative to the streets. Shelters should have mechanisms to identify persons who are mentally ill and to link them with needed mental health and support services. Drop-in centers should be provided in locations that offer street people easy access. These centers may offer daytime refuge, daytime and evening programs, counseling, vocational training, recreational activities, and housing, or some combination of these services.

Crisis residential services are needed for homeless individuals who are in periods of acute stress and who require intensive treatment and close supervision. Such crisis residential settings can serve as alternatives to hospitalization for homeless individuals and can focus on both treatment and housing needs. Transitional housing also is needed for homeless mentally ill individuals because it is often impossible to make permanent living arrangements during the short stay permitted at emergency shelters. Temporary residences allow time for homeless mentally ill persons to receive the treatment and assistance needed to make the physical and emotional transition from a shelter to long-term housing. Finally, as for all persons with psychiatric disabilities, long-term, permanent housing linked to supportive services is essential for homeless persons and is the ultimate goal. In order to fulfill this goal, it is essential that CSSs broaden their focus to encompass the activities and linkages, within the public and private sectors, needed to promote the availability of stable, affordable, normalized housing for persons with psychiatric disabilities.

Income Support and Entitlements

Severe and persistent mental disorders interfere with an individual's functional capacities in daily life. Thus, many persons with long-term mental illness have sporadic employment histories and have difficulty securing and maintaining stable jobs. In addition to suffering from psychiatric disabilities, many individuals also must endure poverty and are unable to earn the money needed for basic necessities such as shelter, food, clothing, and medical care.

A variety of public assistance and entitlement programs are available to persons with mental disorders to help with subsistence and medical expenses, such as Supplemental Security Income, provided by the Social Security Administration, and Medicaid. Many persons, however, have difficulty locating the appropriate agencies, communicating effectively with agency personnel, understanding complex eligibility requirements, and completing cumbersome application forms and procedures.

Assistance should be available to help clients obtain income supports and other entitlements they may need in order to live in the community. Staff members might screen clients for eligibility, provide transportation to the appropriate agencies, accompany clients to the various locations, assist in the completion of application procedures, and serve as advocates for the client with the agency in question. Efforts must be devoted to ensuring that clients receive the benefits to which they are entitled and which are critical factors in successfully remaining in the community.

Peer Support

Peer support or self-help is rapidly becoming an important force in the mental health arena, with increasing numbers of consumers coming together to share their common experiences, pain, problems, and solutions. Peer support can counter feelings of loneliness, rejection, discrimination, and frustration, by offering mutual support, companionship, empathy, sharing, and assistance. Emotional support and practical help for dealing with common problems foster a sense of community, as well as a sense of empowerment. Self-help groups are the most common form of peer support and involve groups that meet regularly on a formal or informal basis, to share ideas, information, and mutual support.

Consumer operated services are service programs that are planned, administered, delivered, and evaluated by consumers. Consumer run service programs are an outgrowth of the self-help movement and provide a variety of services in nonthreatening atmospheres. Such services are voluntary and are based on the values of freedom of choice and consumer control.

Consumer-operated services are often organized around a drop-in center. The peer-run drop-in center provides an open, comfortable setting and often serves as the nucleus for a wide variety of support, service, and socialization activities. Services provided by consumer operated programs include self-help groups; training in independent living skills; advocacy and assistance in locating needed community resources and services such as housing and financial aid; education about patients' rights, psychiatric drugs, and other topics of interest; social and recreational activities; and community or public education on mental illness. Consumer-run programs may also provide services, including housing, job counseling and employment assistance, employment in consumer operated businesses, crisis assistance services, and respite care. Consumers also successfully serve as case management aides and, in some communities, as case managers. The programs generally supplement the services of the formal mental health system and may meet a variety of social and life support needs.

Self-help and consumer-run programs should be part of each CSS, to provide opportunities for peer support, consultation, education, and assistance. Peer support opportunities can provide social supports that the formal system is unable to provide and can assist persons who decline to use formal mental health services or who have moved beyond the need for intensive, formal services.

Family and Community Support

Many mentally ill individuals live at home with their families. Families often must fend for themselves while coping with persistent symptoms, unpredictable behavior, and inadequate community support services. In the past, families often were blamed and ignored by mental health professionals. Currently, the need for family involvement in services, as well as support and education for families, is increasingly recognized. Families are no longer seen as part of the problem, but rather as resources to the helping effort and partners in the service delivery process.

Families should be involved appropriately in the treatment planning process and in service delivery. In addition, a variety of types of support and assistance should be provided to families, as they often do not possess the skills and resources needed to adequately assist their disabled family member. One of the most important of these services is education regarding topics such as the nature of mental illness, medication effects and side effects, signs of relapse, coping strategies, and community resources. Consultation and supportive counseling should be provided to assist families in handling daily problems and intermittent crises, and respite care should be available to offer families a much needed break from the stress and demands of coping with a mentally ill relative. Additionally, opportunities for mutual support among families of persons with mental illness should be encouraged and promoted by the CSS. Families should be apprised of and referred to family support and advocacy organizations, and the development of such groups should be encouraged.

Support and education for the community is another essential aspect of a CSS. In order to promote community integration and acceptance of persons with long-term mental illness, backup support, consultation, and education should be provided to key individuals and agencies within the community. Landlords, employers, friends, community agencies, law enforcement agencies, and others who come into frequent contact with mentally ill individuals should be the focus of such educational and supportive efforts. In addition, there should be efforts to educate the general public about mental illness, to reduce stigma and to promote community acceptance. Consumers, family members, and providers all should be involved in efforts to educate the public. Media campaigns and presentations to civic organizations, schools, agencies, and the community at large are among the strategies that may be used for community education purposes.

Rehabilitation Services

Despite the symptomatic improvement resulting from medication and other mental health treatment, many persons with long-term mental illness experience continuing social and vocational handicaps. Rehabilitation services address these social and vocational deficits, helping persons with psychiatric disabilities to learn the social and vocational skills and to acquire the supports needed for survival in the community. This two-pronged focus on skill development in the individual and development of supports in the individual's environment complements the focus on symptom control, through mental health treatment interventions. Thus, improved functioning is the desired outcome of rehabilitation services.

Rehabilitation services traditionally have been provided by psychosocial rehabilitation centers, but many other programs and settings are changing their service delivery to a rehabilitation orientation, and such services are provided in clubhouses, hospitals, day treatment programs, community residences, supported work settings, educational settings, and elsewhere. Rehabilitation services are based on a process that involves helping the client to set goals, completing a functional assessment of the client, teaching skills to the client, and linking the client to services and supports. Both social and vocational rehabilitation should be integral parts of a CSS, with the goals of building the skills and providing access to the supports needed in order to function as actively and independently in society as possible.

Social rehabilitation is directed at helping the client to gain or regain the practical skills needed to live and socialize in the community. Services should include activities that teach daily and community living skills based on individual client needs and potentially addressing diet, personal hygiene, cooking, shopping, budgeting, housekeeping, use of transportation, and use of other community resources in the natural settings where clients live, learn, work, and socialize. Educational approaches should teach clients how to cope with and compensate for their disabilities, how to manage medications, recognize danger signs, and utilize professional resources when necessary.

Social rehabilitation also involves assistance in developing interpersonal skills and leisure time activities and interests that provide a sense of participation and personal satisfaction. Opportunities should be provided for age appropriate, culturally appropriate daytime and evening activities that offer the chance for companionship, socialization, and enjoyment. The use of social and recreational opportunities available in the community should be maximized.

Because of the importance of productive activity in any person's life, vocational services are an essential ingredient of a CSS. The goal of vocational rehabilitation is to help clients to become productive, contributing members of society by achieving the best possible vocational outcome. The assumption is that successful involvement in some type of meaningful work is essential to develop independence, self-esteem, social recognition, and community integration. There should be a range of vocational services and educational and employment opportunities available to assist clients to prepare for, obtain, and maintain employment. These may include vocational assessment and counseling, prevocational work experiences, vocational training, job trials or transitional employment opportunities, training in job seeking and job keeping skills, assistance in the development of work adjustment skills, job development with local employers, job placement, and even small businesses operated by the mental health or rehabilitation agency, which provide employment opportunities for clients. In addition, mechanisms often are needed to offer support and assistance to both clients and employers to enhance job retention. Supervision and support can assist clients in handling the stresses or demands that may be inherent in employment situations.

An approach showing great promise as a vocational rehabilitation option for persons with psychiatric disabilities is called "supported employment." Adapted from models designed for persons with mental retardation, the approach rests on the assumption that all persons, even those with severe disabilities, are capable of meaningful, productive work in normal settings, given the necessary supports. The approach is characterized by the goal of paid employment (either full-time or part-time), the use of integrated work settings, and the provision of ongoing supervision, training, transportation, crisis intervention, and other supports. Job coaches from the mental health or rehabilitation agency typically provide the supportive services, working with clients for as long a period of time as is necessary to ensure job stability and maintenance. Supported employment slots should include a variety of skilled jobs commensurate with client abilities and interests, as well as entry level jobs, ideally with the possibility of advancement. The wide array of vocational rehabilitation services allows most persons with long-term mental illness to be productive and to make a contribution in accordance with their interests and abilities.

Another promising approach in rehabilitation is called "supported education." This approach has been applied to postsecondary environments and involves providing a range of support services to students with psychiatric disabilities on college campuses. The goal of supported education is to provide whatever supports are needed to enable students to achieve their goals in the context of normalized, integrated educational settings. In addition to working directly with students, staff members may provide consultation and training to college faculty and staff. Supported education can be instrumental in assisting young adult clients, in particular, to achieve their career aspirations.

Protection and Advocacy

The protection and advocacy function of a CSS should be evident in several areas. First, the CSS should include mechanisms to ensure the personal safety and protection of client rights in both residential and nonresidential settings. Among the basic rights of all clients are the right to treatment in the least restrictive, appropriate environment and the right to informed consent to treatment. Safeguards are necessary to ensure that these rights are upheld, as well as safeguards to protect clients' rights upon admission to hospitals and upon consideration of involuntary commitment to inpatient or outpatient treatment settings.

CSSs should adopt mechanisms for protection of client rights, which may include ongoing inspections and monitoring for violations by internal and external groups; oversight of admission, discharge, and service delivery procedures on an individual case basis; ombudsman programs; grievance procedures; oversight by client-elected representatives; oversight by consumer and family groups; and protection and advocacy systems. Mechanisms to enable immediate and prompt reporting of abuse and neglect, as well as prompt in house investigations of such complaints, also are necessary. Additionally, there should be procedures for informing clients and families of their legal rights and of how to gain access to the resources available to assist them in upholding those rights and of procedures for redressing grievances and ensuring appropriate investigations of complaints of abuse and neglect.

In addition to personal safety and rights protection, the CSS should actively promote advocacy activities on behalf of clients. Advocacy activities involve efforts to ensure that individual clients and families receive appropriate services, benefits, and protections. Advocacy efforts are also needed at the systems level, to seek improvements in services, benefits, or protections of safety and rights on behalf of all persons with long-term mental illness.

The Protection and Advocacy for Mentally Ill Individuals Act of 1986 requires states to establish protection and advocacy systems to protect persons with mental illness who are residents in facilities providing 24-hour mental health care or treatment. These systems are intended to protect and advocate the rights of mentally ill individuals, to ensure compliance with constitutional, federal, and state mandates, and to investigate incidents of abuse and neglect of mentally ill individuals within such public and private residential settings. The act also contains the "Bill of Rights for Mental Health Patients," which Congress included as a guide and urged states to use as a basis for state law. CSSs should be based on the principles contained in this bill of rights and should promote the adoption of these principles at the state level, as well as advocate for appropriate state statutes and regulations regarding protection and advocacy.

As a result of the legislation, each state and territory now has an operational protection and advocacy system designed to protect mental health clients from abuse and neglect and to ensure that their rights as citizens and as recipients of care are fully respected. The protection and advocacy systems typically take the form of private, nonprofit entities designated by the state for this purpose. They are authorized to pursue administrative, legal, and other appropriate remedies on behalf of their clients and are encouraged to coordinate with other mental health advocacy organizations. In addition to serving individual clients, these protection and advocacy systems have become involved in class actions, public education and training, organization of consumer groups, and advocacy for legislation and for community-based services. CSSs should ensure that their protection and advocacy activities are consistent and well coordinated with the state protection and advocacy system.

Case Management

Case management services should be available for all clients who receive services supported through public funds. Case management is intended to ensure that clients receive the services they need, that services are coordinated, and that services are appropriate to their changing needs over time. *Case management* involves providing either a single person or a team to assume responsibility for maintaining a long-term, caring, supportive relationship with the client on a continuing basis, regardless of where the client is residing and regardless of the number of agencies involved. The case manager serves as a helper, service broker, and advocate, assisting clients and families to negotiate the system in order to meet their needs.

Among the specific functions performed by case managers are identifying the clients to be served, assessing the client's needs, coordinating and assisting in the development of a comprehensive service plan based on the client's needs and goals, helping the client to make informed choices about services, assisting the client to obtain needed services and resources, monitoring the adequacy and appropriateness of services, ensuring the continuity of service provision, advocating for treatment and services for the client, and providing interpersonal support. Some case management approaches combine clinical interventions with the other case management functions of resource acquisition, service planning and coordination, and support. Most of these functions cannot be accomplished in an office or behind a desk. Case managers must work in natural environments within the community with clients, families, and agencies, to manage, coordinate, and unify the many components of the CSS.

Many communities are providing *intensive case management services*, which involve an aggressive, comprehensive approach to ensuring that clients obtain services and supports. Also referred to as *assertive outreach* or *assertive community treatment*, this approach typically involves such features as a specific focus on preventing hospitalization and homelessness, intervention in natural environments, a focus on the resolution of everyday problems, assertive advocacy to secure a wide variety of services and supports, and easy accessibility for crisis intervention. In these programs, staff members typically are available 24 hours a day, 7 days a week, and they are prepared to see clients as often as necessary to provide services and support, even daily if indicated. Intensive case management services are delivered through an outreach mode and allow case managers the flexibility to implement highly individualized strategies for treatment and community support. In all case management approaches, the long-term, continuous relationship with the client is central to providing effective services.

Particularly for homeless mentally ill individuals, effective case management must be intensive and ongoing and must take place in shelters or on the streets. Case management activities must be based on an aggressive outreach approach in order to engage clients, build trust, and prepare clients to receive needed services.

Table 4.1 lists the components of a CSS. It should be recognized that a small percentage of individuals are profoundly disabled as a result of their mental illnesses. Regardless of the level and continuity of services and supports, they may have difficulty functioning in community settings. These individuals may require the highly specialized treatment and supervision that only can be provided in a hospital setting. Thus, in some cases, long-term hospitalization may be needed.

How Should Community Support Systems Be Organized?

The CSS model is flexible, in that it does not prescribe how states or communities should provide or organize its essential components. The concept includes the range of functions that should be performed to meet the needs of mentally ill individuals and leaves states and communities to decide how this might best be

Table 4.1 Components of a Community Support System

Client identification and outreach
Client identification
Outreach
Transportation assistance
Mental health treatment
Diagnostic evaluation
Supportive counseling
Medication management
Substance abuse services
Crisis response services
Crisis telephone services
Walk-in crisis services
Mobile crisis outreach services
Crisis residential services
Inpatient services
Health and dental services
Housing
Supportive housing
Residential assistance for homeless mentally ill persons
Income support and entitlements
Peer support
Self-help
Consumer-operated services
Family and community support
Support, education, and assistance to families
Support and education for the community
Rehabilitation services
Social rehabilitation
Vocational rehabilitation
Protection and advocacy
Case management

accomplished. Thus, the CSS concept is not a prescription, but rather a guide.

The CSS model also avoids specifying the type of agency that should provide a particular type of service. States and communities are encouraged to make effective use of resources and facilities that are in place, such as community mental health centers, psychosocial rehabilitation agencies, community residences, a variety of public and private human service agencies, and psychiatric hospitals. In defining and implementing the ideal CSS, states and communities can use different approaches and configurations, depending on geographic, political, socioeconomic, and ethnic factors. For example, in rural areas, it may not be financially possible to develop a comprehensive CSS in each locality. Alternative approaches, such as shared services among several communities, with accompanying transportation capability, may be needed under these circumstances. The CSS model itself, and the way the model is implemented, can easily be adapted to the needs, circumstances, and resources of each state or community.

While the CSS concept leaves considerable flexibility for implementation, a CSS is more than just a collection of discrete programs or service components. The components must be organized into a coherent, integrated system. Only by organizing a system of care can the community ensure that the necessary array of human services will be made available. In order to constitute a system, there must be formal arrangements in a community for planning, developing, financing, coordinating, monitoring, and evaluating community support services. This involves the designation of one agency or entity as the managing agency. This agency should have both broad authority to convene other agencies and primary responsibility for ensuring the delivery and coordination of all services for clients in a geographically or politically defined area. The most logical structure and process for these management functions must be determined by each state and community. The managing agency could be a unit of local government or another agency. Regardless of the type of entity assigned this role, there should be a single focal point of authority, responsibility, and accountability for community support services at the local level.

In considering the organization and development of CSSs, it is important to distinguish between *community support services* and *community support systems*. Community support *services* are the specific, discrete services needed by persons with mental illness, such as mental health treatment, rehabilitation, and housing. These are the components that make up a comprehensive system of care. A *system* includes all essential components, along with mechanisms to ensure proper management and coordination. Unfortunately, all too often, much attention is devoted to the development of indivi-

dual service components, while the concept of a comprehensive, coordinated system of care is neglected. The needs of persons with severe, disabling mental illness will remain unmet until states and communities develop both the full range of services and the community level focal points for management and accountability.

Most states have made significant strides in improving services for persons with long-term mental illness. This can be seen most clearly in the high priority that most state governments now place on the population of persons with long-term mental illness and on CSS development. CSS concepts have been introduced into state legislation, plans, guidelines, and regulations. States also have made important strides in educating mental health and other human service providers about CSS concepts. While the majority of state mental health funds still support the operation of state mental hospitals, increasing resources are being allocated to CSS development. In sum, most state mental health systems are in the process of reorienting to focus on community care as the highest priority for persons with severe, disabling mental illness.

On the whole, states and communities report an increased availability of community support services resulting from two primary factors. First, new community support services have developed. Many states, for example, have selected priority CSS components and have concentrated their efforts on developing these on a statewide basis. Psychosocial rehabilitation and housing programs are two such components. Second, many existing services have been reorienting toward CSS concepts and principles. This shift in philosophy is particularly evident in day treatment programs, which increasingly are adopting a rehabilitation orientation and are providing more meaningful and appropriate rehabilitation opportunities for mentally disabled individuals.

No discussion of progress at the community level would be complete without mention of the many excellent model programs that have been developed to provide community support to persons with long-term mental illness

(Stroul, 1986). These models have been replicated and adapted widely in many communities. Many psychosocial rehabilitation programs have evolved from Fountain House in New York City, which provides a model comprehensive psychosocial rehabilitation center. The Fairweather Lodge model includes transitional programs at hospitals, followed by community-based lodges or group homes, to teach persons the skills needed for community living. The training in community living model, which originated in Madison, Wisconsin, focuses on teaching the basic coping skills necessary to live as autonomously as possible in the community. This assertive-outreach approach has become the basis for community support activities in numerous and diverse localities. The community worker model, developed in Rhinelander, Wisconsin, uses lay citizens of the community to provide extensive support and case management to persons with long-term mental illness. This model has been adopted by many communities, particularly in rural areas with shortages of resources and professional staff. Thus, at the local level, a wide variety of approaches to serving persons with mental illness have been tested. Evaluation results consistently demonstrate the effectiveness of these community services. New approaches also have been developed, and community support services of all types have begun to proliferate across the nation (Grusky et al., 1985). Further, there is growing attention to the important role of self-help, consumer operated services, and family involvement in a CSS.

Despite clear progress, much remains to be done. The task of creating systems of community-based services for persons with mental illness is complex. Although many community support services and programs have been developed, we are not yet close to having comprehensive systems of care in each community. The gaps in local systems are apparent. The lack of safe, affordable housing linked to treatment and supportive services is perhaps the most significant gap in CSS development. This shortage of housing has resulted, in some areas, in pressure to reopen institutions to care for homeless mentally ill persons. In communities where services exist, often these services are not organized into systems of care. Leadership and accountability at the local level generally are weak or nonexistent. In some communities, comprehensive CSSs are beginning to emerge. However, many communities must develop additional community support services and must create a focal point for system management.

One of the impediments to the large-scale development of CSSs has been the lack of financial resources. Over the past years, shrinking service dollars have hampered efforts to develop the mental health and other health and human services needed by persons with long-term mental illness. Current funding mechanisms for clients' multiple service needs are fragmented and complex. There has been experimentation with various approaches, but to date, there is no coherent financing strategy for CSSs. Further, there has been a clear reluctance on the part of federal, state, and local governments to provide sufficient financial resources to build adequate CSSs for persons with mental illness. Strategies must be directed at promoting more appropriate and judicious use of limited resources, as well as obtaining other resources, to provide a stable funding base for CSSs. In addition, the current fiscal crises facing many states have placed existing community support services in grave jeopardy and have curtailed the development of new services, despite compelling needs and mounting political pressures to serve homeless and substance abusing populations in particular. An ever present danger is that our society will once again come to rely on institutional care rather than committing the resources needed to properly develop and operate comprehensive, community-based systems of care.

In addition, because human resources account for more than 70% of the total costs of community support services, states and communities must address the need for training, recruiting, and retaining qualified personnel. The curricula at colleges and universities in all mental health related disciplines have not kept pace with the rapidly developing field of community support. Persons preparing to work in programs serving persons with long-term mental illness need training in the CSS philosophy and in new technologies for service delivery. Both preservice and in service training activities must be devoted to creating skilled and dedicated personnel who are knowledgeable about the operation of community support services and systems.

Public Law 99-660, passed by Congress in 1986, was intended to hasten the development of CSSs for adults with long-term mental illness and for children with serious emotional disorders. The legislation requires states to submit plans for the development of community-based systems of care and annual progress reports to document the implementation of their plans. It is hoped that the legislation will serve to increase the attention and resources devoted to creating comprehensive CSSs.

We have learned a great deal about developing community-based systems of care, and the technology for providing comprehensive services to persons with long-term mental illness is evolving. It is important to regard the CSS concept as a dynamic one, which will evolve and change as continued research and experience dictate. Still, the most up to date technology regarding community support is not as yet being implemented on a sufficiently broad scale.

Perhaps the most heartening sign of progress has been the development of a network of individuals and organizations, a national coalition of concern, dedicated to promoting the development of CSSs. The ever growing network includes policymakers, providers, researchers, family members, consumers, and citizens who work in their own states and communities, as well as at the national level, to advocate for CSSs and for the resources needed to develop CSSs. The vision shared by members of the network is to have a CSS in every community in the nation.

References

Anthony, W., Cohen, M., & Kennard, W. (1990). Understanding the current facts and principles of mental health systems planning. *American Psychologist, 45*(11), 1249–1252.

Grusky, O., Tierney, K., Holstein, J., Anspach, R., Davis, D., Unrah, D., Webster, S., Vandewater, S., & Allen, H. (1985). Models of local mental health delivery systems. *American Behavioral Scientist, 28*(5), 685–703.

National Institute of Mental Health. (1980). *Announcement: Community support systems strategy development and implementation grants.* Rockville MD: National Institute of Mental Health, Community Support Program.

National Institute of Mental Health. (1985). Unpublished tabulation. Rockville, MD: Division of Biometry and Applied Sciences, Statistical Research Branch.

National Institute of Mental Health. (1987). *Toward a model plan for a comprehensive community-based mental health system.* Rockville, MD: U.S. Department of Health and Human Services; Alcohol, Drug Abuse, and Mental Health Administration.

National Institute of Mental Health. (1989). [Mental health supplement to 1989 National Health Interview Survey]. Unpublished estimate. Rockville, MD: Division of Biometry and Applied Sciences, Statistical Research Branch.

Stroul, B. (1984). *Toward community support systems for the mentally disabled: The NIMH Community Support Program.* Boston, MA: Center for Psychiatric Rehabilitation Research and Training in Mental Health.

Stroul, B. (1986). *Models of community support services: Approaches to helping persons with long-term mental illness.* Rockville, MD: National Institute of Mental Health, Community Support Program.

Stroul, B. (1988). Community support systems for persons with long-term mental illness: Questions and answers. Rockville, MD: National Institute of Mental Health, Community Support Program.

Stroul, B. (1989). Community support systems for persons with long-term mental illness: A conceptual framework. *Psychosocial Rehabilitation Journal, 12*(3), 9–26.

Turner, J. C. (1977). Comprehensive community support systems for mentally disabled adults: Definitions, components, guiding principles. *Psychosocial Rehabilitation Journal, 1*(3), 39–47.

Turner, J. D., & Shifren, I. (1979). Community support systems: How comprehensive? *New Directions for Mental Health Services, 2*, 1–13.

Turner, J. C., & TenHoor, W. J. (1978). The NIMH Community Support Program: Pilot approach to a needed social reform. *Schizophrenia Bulletin, 4*(3), 319–348.

Chapter 5

An Interdisciplinary Team Approach to Rehabilitation

ROBERT BAER
GENE GOEBEL
ROBERT W. FLEXER

Interdisciplinary team process is an approach to individual evaluation, planning, and program implementation in which the individual, mental health professionals, and when appropriate, the individual's family and other support persons meet as a team to plan and coordinate a wide range of services (Chase, Wright, & Ragade, 1981). Interdisciplinary planning should be *focused on the goals of the individual* rather than on the services of an agency. Agency services are then tailored to fit the individual's vocational, residential, and quality of life goals, cutting across disciplines and agencies. Interdisciplinary planning therefore requires a new way of thinking for mental health administrators and professionals trained in organizing services according to organizational functions and professional affiliations.

The trend toward psychiatric rehabilitation and ecological approaches has created a trend toward the use of more disciplines and supports in mental health services (Anthony, Cohen, & Farkas, 1990). Interdisciplinary planning can be seen as an extension of the concept of case management, which has traditionally been oriented to the coordination of a wide range of services, but it goes beyond this concept to include the coordination of the *planning* of these services. The advantage

of this approach becomes most apparent for persons with severe mental disabilities, who require a complex array of services, which are often outside the expertise of the case manager. Through interdisciplinary team process, the case manager can bring in expertise relevant to the preferences and needs of the participant and can bring that expertise to bear in solving a wide range of problems. This provides the service recipient the benefit of knowledge and resources beyond those of the case manager alone.

While interdisciplinary team approaches can increase the power and breadth of mental health interventions, implementation of *effective* team processes requires a considerable scope of knowledge and expertise. Interdisciplinary team process is multidimensional and complex, involving knowledge about (1) the parameters of interdisciplinary planning, (2) individual concerns, and (3) group processes. In addition, the team leader needs to understand how each of these factors can affect the others (Flynn & Harbin, 1987; Levine & Perkins, 1987).

The *parameters of interdisciplinary planning* define the limits imposed on the interdisciplinary team by the service system and the professional environment in which it is developed. These parameters can be defined in terms of the service system and the team models. *Mental health service systems* range from psychiatric and psychosocial rehabilitation approaches that focus services on a broad range of individual preferences and needs to medical models that focus highly specialized clinical services on specific individual needs. *Team models* determine which parts of the service and support system directly intervene with the individual. They include methods for determining the team composition, which team members make contributions in defining participant needs, the relationship of professions to the team, and whether the team functions in an interdisciplinary, multidisciplinary, or transdisciplinary fashion. The impact of these parameters of interdisciplinary planning is discussed in the first section of this chapter.

At the core of the complex system, however, is the *individual*, who happens to have a psychiatric disability and to be in need of assistance to move from dysfunction and dependence to personal effectiveness and independence. Prerequisite to planning with the individual is the collective value base of the team—that asks," What are belief structures about the individual and how do services relate to individual preferences and needs?" In order to define the individual's plan, it is necessary to identify a common point of reference for problem definition and strategies to increase participant involvement. The second part of this chapter discusses these and other issues related to preparing the individual for greater participation on the team.

Group process, the final component of the complex system, is what happens when team members sit around a table to plan with the individual. How do they interact with the individual? How do they interact with each other? What impact do interactions have on what is planned? In order for the team to be effective, there must be leadership and an understanding of the stages of group development. In addition, there must be an understanding of how to deal with group dysfunctions that arise due to overlapping professional roles and differing individual and agency agendas. This aspect of interdiscipli-

nary planning is discussed in the third and final section of this chapter.

Parameters of Interdisciplinary Planning

Service System Trends

The use of interdisciplinary team process is highly related to a number of service system trends. These include trends toward individual participation, psychiatric rehabilitation, and interagency collaboration. The trend toward individual participation in community mental health services can be attributed in part to transitional programs such as Fountain House and Fairweather Lodge, which demonstrated the efficacy of involving clients in their own rehabilitation (Fairweather, 1980). A related service trend toward psychiatric rehabilitation has created a growing rationale for the use of interdisciplinary team process as a way of addressing individual needs in multiple and interrelated service and support environments (Anthony, Cohen, & Farkas, 1990). A third related service trend is the trend toward interagency collaboration. Collaborative agreements among the National Institute of Mental Health (NIMH), the Rehabilitation Services Administration (RSA), and the National Institute on Disability and Rehabilitation Research (NIDRR) were initiated in 1980. This paved the way for interagency cooperation at the local level and for passage of Public Law (P.L.) 99-506, which recognized interagency collaboration as a mental health service priority (Anthony & Blanch, 1988).

While the need for interdisciplinary planning and coordination of services has become apparent as a result of policy changes, implementation has been described as slow and variable (Pierce & Blanch, 1989). The development of community mental health centers and the NIMH linkage initiatives have been largely unsuccessful in coordinating services for persons with the most severe disabilities (Dowell & Ciarlo, 1983; Goldman, Burns, & Burke, 1980: Tischler, Henisz, Myers,

& Garrison, 1972). Additionally, attempts to coordinate services have been hampered by conflicts between primary care physicians and the providers of mental health and rehabilitation services (Burns, Burke, & Kessler, 1981) and by a lack of involvement of family caregivers and consumers (Grusky & Tierney, 1989).

The success or failure of efforts to address these problems is often a matter of allocating the necessary staff resources to interdisciplinary planning and related service coordination. Studies indicate that the case manager is often the coordinator of services in the community (Goering, Huddart, Wasylenki, & Ballantyne, 1989), while the mental health attendant is usually the coordinator for hospital-based services (Craig, Peer, & Ross, 1989). These staff members are generally not able to address agency and interagency barriers to the effective coordination of services—including barriers to the adoption of interdisciplinary planning. Therefore, in order for interdisciplinary team planning to be effectively implemented, administrators and agency directors will have to become involved or delegate the authority to develop interagency linkages and interdisciplinary teams.

The multidisciplinary emphasis of staff training can also be a barrier to implementation of interdisciplinary planning. Clinical and diagnostic approaches are still taught in most mental health disciplines (Mowbray & Freddolino, 1986), and studies indicate that professionals in mental health and rehabilitation agencies tend to deliver services based on their own professional orientations rather than on an interdisciplinary approach (Mowbray & Freddolino, 1986). In order for interdisciplinary team process to be implemented in most agencies, staff will need to be retrained to think of their profession in the context of an interdisciplinary plan rather than an individual professional approach.

Retraining of professionals will not be a simple process. Interdisciplinary team process differs from multidisciplinary approaches in its willingness to work toward common goals rather than a number of individually pre-scribed goals. This requires professional flexibility in regard to assessment and provision of services, with the interdisciplinary professional presenting recommendations in a way that can be understood and criticized by both lay and professional team members. Professionals (i.e., social workers, occupational therapists, rehabilitation counselors, physicians, nurses, psychologists, and psychiatrists) are often not prepared or inclined to exhibit this flexibility (Anthony, 1979; Marshall, 1989; Minkoff, 1987; Stern & Minkoff, 1979). Even professionals willing to participate in interdisciplinary team process are ill equipped by their training to use functional assessments or to discuss services in lay terms (Marshall, 1989). Mental health administrators must therefore commit to training their professionals in functional problem-solving approaches and the value of team planning, if interdisciplinary team process is to be effective.

Team Models

The provision of services by a team may be *multidisciplinary*, provided separately; *interdisciplinary*, coordinated among professions; or *transdisciplinary*, with professionals sharing roles and responsibilities (Lyon & Lyon, 1980; Sands, Stafford, & McClelland, 1990). Interdisciplinary and transdisciplinary team processes are often referred to interchangeably; however, transdisciplinary proponents refer to "role release" as the major difference between interdisciplinary and transdisciplinary approaches. Role release allows professionals and other team members to reinforce each other's treatments (Lyon & Lyon, 1980). For example, a speech therapist could participate in a psychologist's behavioral interventions while providing communication training, or the psychologist could follow through on the communication specialist's interventions during counseling. The primary advantage of transdisciplinary approaches is an increase in the consistency and reinforcement density of mental health interventions. Because professionals usually only see their clients intermittently, transdisciplinary approaches can be particularly helpful for interventions requiring frequent and consistent implementation. Table 5.1 shows how services would differ among multidisciplinary, interdisciplinary, and transdisciplinary approaches.

Studies of interdisciplinary teams suggest that the core team should consist of the participant, service providers, and, if appropriate, family and friends who have the most direct contact with the participant (Anthony, Cohen, & Farkas, 1990; Campbell, 1987; Sadler & Hulgus, 1990). If professional assessments or consultations are needed, the core team can exercise the option of inviting other professionals for their input. Basing team membership on involvement with the participant rather than representation of professional functions of the agency has two major advantages: (1) The participant becomes the focus rather than the professional service, and (2) professional resources are not needlessly used up in meetings where input is not essential (Campbell, 1987).

The team composition can have a significant impact on interdisciplinary team outcomes. Physicians and psychiatrists, due to their status, have been found to have the greatest influence on team decisions. One study found that physicians as members of an interdisciplinary team affected practically all treatment decisions and that mental health teams developed on medical models tended to be more autocratic than consensual (Fiorelli, 1988). Another study found that physicians, on the whole, were less inclined to value participant autonomy, consider subjective data, or compromise with other professionals (Roberts, 1988).

Psychologists may represent a broad range of orientations to the interdisciplinary team process. Typically, psychology has been oriented more to improving individual coping skills than to social and systems interventions. However, the emergence of community psychology has led to a recognition that psychological interventions must include consideration of supports, as well as individual coping. Community psychologists recognize the value of working with various professions and community supports in bringing about positive outcomes for participants and can be strong advocates for interdisciplinary approaches (Moxley, 1988). On the other hand, the field of psychology has strong roots in diagnostic approaches, which can make communication and coordination with other team members difficult.

Social workers, like psychologists, come with a wide range of orientations. Social work has grown out of two schools of thought. One school has been heavily oriented to social support, systems change, and advocacy, while in much of psychiatric social work (the second school) training has been oriented to counseling and psychotherapy (Borenzweig, 1974). Many social workers in the mental health system have been heavily influenced by psychodynamic models, which are often hard to distinguish from psychological models of private practice (Anthony, Cohen, & Farkas, 1990). However, support- and advocacy-oriented social workers can be instrumental in supporting self-help and the empowerment of persons with psychiatric disabilities. Social workers are also effective in the organization of support and family groups, social skills training, and training in responsible self-advocacy.

Psychiatric nursing has also been heavily influenced by psychology. In the past, psychiatric nursing internships have been oriented to providing services in hospital and office-based settings, removing graduates from the social context of persons with severe psychiatric disabilities (Anthony, Cohen, & Farkas, 1990). However, as psychiatric nurses have become involved in outreach and home-based programs, they have become advocates for family involvement and collaboration with mental health and community service providers (Gerace, 1988). The psychiatric nurse working with participants in their homes can therefore be instrumental in identifying actual and potential support systems, and in linking the participant with these systems.

With the recognition of the community living and vocational potential of persons with psychiatric disabilities, rehabilitation

Table 5.1 Comparison of Service Models

Multidisciplinary	Interdisciplinary	Transdisciplinary
Participation of the client is limited to a professional–client relationship	*Participation* of the client is as a member of a team	*Participation* of the client is as a member of a team
Assessment is done or interpreted by the professional seeing the individual client	*Assessment* is based on needs and preferences as seen by the client and each team member, including nonprofessionals	*Assessment* is based on needs and preferences, as seen by the client and each team member, including nonprofessionals
Planning is confined to organization of individual treatments provided by the professional	*Planning* is based on functional needs within professions, coordinated to obtain outcomes desired by the client	*Planning* is based on functional needs and preferences, across disciplines, in which activities are shared to obtain outcomes
Implementation consists of a series of individual treatments	*Implementation* consists of interventions coordinated by professionals and team members	*Implementation* consists of interventions shared by professionals and team members
Evaluation is based on progress in regard to individual treatments	*Evaluation* is based on progress within each intervention, toward common goals set by the team	*Evaluation* is based on progress in overall function toward goals set by the team

counselors have assumed a larger role in the mental health system. However, there continues to be a paucity of rehabilitation counselors with a specialty in psychiatric rehabilitation with less than 12% of graduate programs offering this specialty up to 1982 (Weinberger & Greenwald, 1982). While rehabilitation counselors may lack training in psychiatric rehabilitation, they can be a valuable asset in developing functional assessment, skills training, and resources for the participant moving into employment and community settings. Rehabilitation counselors should be considered in gaining access to transition programs for school-age youths (age 16 or over) and for participants entering the work force and community settings from hospitals or family homes.

In summary, interdisciplinary team process is an approach to individual evaluation, planning, and program evaluation, which can increase the power and breadth of mental health interventions. The parameters of interdisciplinary planning are defined in terms of the service system and various team models. In order for interdisciplinary planning to become a reality, the service system must allocate resources to planning and coordination of services, adopt a common language for professionals and lay persons, and develop teams according to the needs of the individual. For persons with severe disabilities, the team may need to adopt a more transdisciplinary approach, so that professionals and support persons can go beyond their traditional roles to supplement the efforts of one another. Orientations of the members of the team may be varied and—at times—at odds with each other, but the orientation of the team to the individual is paramount.

The Individual's Plan

The key concepts behind developing the individual's plan are participant-defined preferences (what is and is not happening in the person's important environments), appropriate goals (what has to happen in those environments, from the participant's frame-

work), and discipline contributions (how is assistance rendered to move the person toward these goals). Interdisciplinary teams need to evaluate services, starting with the outcomes desired by the individual. The goals for individuals in the psychiatric rehabilitation process should reflect independence and increased participation in community life. The trick in the planning process is to individualize the goals, the outcomes, and the assistance provided, and to identify processes which maximize the inputs and control by the person for whom the plan is being developed.

An Ecological Framework for Individual Planning

The conceptual framework underlying service provision has a profound impact on whether the planning of services is *interdisciplinary* and structured around client *preferences and needs,* or is multidisciplinary and defined in terms of agency functions. A conceptual framework compatible with a focus on individual preferences and needs is the ecological open system/social systems approach, in which the individual is seen as part of larger social systems—the individual in his or her family, the family and the extended family and friends, and the community. This *ecological view* states that people, in order to survive and thrive, must adapt to their environment. Individual functioning cannot be understood without examining individual–environment relationships. The focus of the ecological approach is less on individual problems than on maximizing the helping forces in the environment to aid the individual and his or her family. By doing an ecological analysis, it is possible to identify supports that tie the person into the specific environment.

The ecological model has four major principles that should be reflected in the makeup and function of interdisciplinary teams:

1. *The principle of interdependence—* which assumes that any change brought

about in the participant, or any of the participant's environments, is likely to affect other aspects of his or her life. This principle emphasizes the importance of coordinating services and including representatives from all relevant environments on the interdisciplinary team.

2. *The principle of transference*—which assumes that resources must follow the participant throughout the rehabilitation process. As the participant moves into the community and employment, the interdisciplinary team needs to reflect this change, by soliciting membership from receiving agencies prior to transfer.

3. *The principle of adaptation*—which assumes that a behavior intervention that may work well in one setting may require adaptations as settings change. This principle emphasizes the importance of re-examining the individual plan when changes in the participant's environment are anticipated.

4. *The principle of succession*—which assumes that the participant's needs and environment are growing and ever-changing. This principle emphasizes the need for the interdisciplinary team to continually look for new resources and supports (Kelly, 1966).

Normalization as a Framework for Individual Planning

Normalization is a conceptual framework that can be used in planning as a basis for defining the individual as a valued member of the team. *Normalization*, as applied to mental health services, suggests that they need to provide roles and experiences for the participant that are similar to those of the individuals in the community at large (Wolfensberger, 1972). Applying this criterion suggests that the person with a psychiatric disability should be perceived like any other person who needs professional assistance, including assistance in making informed consent. His or her role would be similar to the role given to a person seeking medical

services who needs professional assistance in choosing those services best suited to treat his or her condition. This conceptualization puts the participant with mental health concerns in a more culturally normative and socially valued role than that of a "psychiatric case" or a "mental patient." This allows participants to obtain richer and more varied experiences from the mental health system by offering them the opportunity of exercising greater control over the rehabilitation process (Levine & Perkins, 1987).

The role of the interdisciplinary team leader can also be viewed within the theoretical framework of normalization. In normal social situations, all community members assume responsibility for managing their own services or depend on those closest to them to assume responsibility for managing their affairs when they lose the capacity to do so for themselves. Normalization would suggest that the interdisciplinary team should follow a hierarchy of closeness when designating a team leader. While the complexity of the mental health system will often require appointing the case manager or the mental health attendant as the coordinator of services because of their knowledge of the service system, the team leader could be the participant, a family member, or a member of a support group. In order to assume the role of team leader, the participant would need to be given training and opportunities to make decisions in regard to treatments and supports. This role would need to be flexible, to compensate for changes in mental status and rehabilitation progress (Levine & Perkins, 1987).

The Individual with a Disability as a Team Member

Research suggests that individuals with psychiatric disabilities generally know what is needed for them to live in the community. This is supported by studies showing that the types of services requested by persons with psychiatric disabilities are generally those that have been found to work in promoting community integration (Ewalt & Honeyfield,

1981). However, there is a common misconception that persons with psychiatric disabilities do not achieve success because they cannot make realistic choices. This may be due to the fact that persons with psychiatric disabilities often lack vocational and community living experience from which they can develop goals. Gaining participant input may require exposure to vocational, educational, and community living options (Anthony, Cohen, & Farkas, 1990). Once these options are presented, participants are generally able to decide best what course their rehabilitation should take. Anthony, Cohen, and Farkas (1990) note,

> It has been our experience that, when given the opportunity, most persons with psychiatric disabilities can be helped to set reasonable goals. This is not to deny that at times persons with psychiatric disabilities will set unrealistic or even destructive goals. Rather, over time, as they become engaged in a process geared toward understanding what they want out of life, rather than what their pathology has done to their life, their symptoms will become less dominating. (p. 249)

The question becomes how to give persons with psychiatric disabilities the knowledge to make realistic choices and the experience to make vocational, educational, and community-living choices. Danley and Anthony (1987) suggest that a "Choose-Get-Keep" model is a way of fostering decision-making for persons with psychiatric disabilities entering employment. The key concepts of this model involve working with participants on choosing to work and setting work goals that are realistic. The choice comes from the participant, but is tested by the professional. Once the choice to work has been made, participants can move into specific vocational programs or employment relevant to their preferences and needs. A transitional employment approach can further foster informed choice, by allowing the participant to try out jobs for limited duration and to make choices based on personal preferences and job success. The key in both of these approaches is participant action, involvement, and professional feedback.

Strategies in Decision-Making and Participation

Teaching participants with psychiatric disabilities to assert themselves is another important aspect of teaching them to participate on interdisciplinary teams. The use of consumer groups has been found to be effective in helping persons with psychiatric disabilities to advocate for their choices through the use of positive patient role models (Chamberlin, 1984). Although the concept of advocacy can include anyone who speaks on behalf of participants, advocacy works best when the participants are able to speak for themselves (Turner & Tenhoor, 1978).

Another way of supporting self-advocacy in the interdisciplinary team is to schedule preparatory meetings prior to formal planning meetings (Anthony, Cohen, & Farkas, 1990). During these meetings, the team leader/coordinator can discuss possible goals and services needed by the participant, and can discuss strategies for advocating these requests through role play with the participant or by asking whether the participant would like anyone to advocate on his or her behalf. For participants unable to represent themselves, the team leader may want to meet with family members, or significant others, to discuss goals for the participant and to elicit their involvement in planning, if appropriate.

A number of barriers unique to the mental health system are likely to be encountered in giving the participant enhanced status in planning services. As opposed to other disability systems, the mental health system is dominated by high-status professions oriented to diagnosis and treatment rather than service and support (Anthony, Cohen, & Farkas, 1990). The very existence of these high-status professions tends to make the participant relatively more powerless. Anthony and Blanch (1988) note that

> In general, the client with a psychiatric disability has more often been in a medically based, symptom focused treatment as opposed to a developmental, skill based approach. The client with a psychiatric disability is treated in a system . . . populated by practitioners with more

perceived status and treatment failure is more apt to be attributed to deficiencies in the client rather than the treatment technology. (p. 9)

The role of the participant on the interdisciplinary team can be viewed from the perspective of social learning theory, which suggests that behavior is a function of expected positive outcomes and avoidance of expected negative outcomes (Feather, 1982; Sarbin, 1970). For the participant with a psychiatric disability, these expectations may severely limit effective participation in the team process. Studies indicate that individuals subjected to repeated failure are prone to withdraw from participation (Feather, 1982). To counter the effect of this learned helplessness, the team may need to provide considerable support and reinforcement to elicit participant involvement in the early stages of team planning (Fairweather, 1980).

The family may also be considered as a resource in advocating for the participant with a severe psychiatric disability (Stroul, 1989). While the role of the family member on the interdisciplinary team must be carefully considered, especially if the family is in conflict with the participant (Lefley, 1988), the family can be a good source of information about participant needs and abilities (Chamberlin, 1989). This is demonstrated by the fact that self-help organizations have used families effectively in advocating for their relatives with mental illness for more than 20 years (Nemec & Furlong-Norman, 1989).

In summary, the key questions to be addressed in regard to interdisciplinary team process and the individual relate to the role of the individual in the planning process, how that role can be enhanced to improve outcomes, and what conceptual framework is most useful in establishing a view of the participant that minimizes negative stigmas. The ecological model and the normalization concept are two conceptual frameworks that maximize the use of community supports and individual resources. The key orientation of these concepts is an individual-based, outcome-oriented, community-supported plan. The empowerment of the individual is paramount and is facilitated by the interdisciplinary team by preparing the individual to decide and advocate for him- or herself.

Group Process: Team Building and Functioning

Once the interdisciplinary team has been established, and the role of the individual has been determined, the team leader is faced with the problem of how the interdisciplinary team and the participant all work together. To understand the dynamics of the team, the leader should have a working knowledge of group process. This includes an understanding of (1) proper functions of the team, (2) stages of team development, (3) leadership and power, and (4) group dynamics.

Proper Functions of the Team

For more than two decades, in business settings and in the behavioral sciences, it has been maintained that group decision-making is superior to individual decision-making in most instances. Teams can develop more ideas than can an individual, and teams can develop consensus, coordinate activities, and organize resources. These strengths can be particularly helpful for an individual with a psychiatric disability, who requires a wide range of services from diverse professions in a fragmented and underfunded system of services.

Team decision-making does have certain drawbacks, however. Teams are often characterized by role ambiguity, duplication of effort, and confusion concerning responsibility for decisions (Hefferin & Katz, 1971; Pluckman, 1972; Wallace, 1976). When decisions must be made quickly, when options are extremely limited, or when information is not understandable by nonexperts, team decision-making may be less effective than more autocratic approaches. Consequently, in an agency where crisis management is the norm, it may be futile to try to implement team process until a more proactive approach to service provision is possible. Additionally, agencies that are constrained by a narrow definition of service (e.g., psychotherapy in the office) may find the additional service ideas generated by a team more of a threat than a help.

However, in the context of psychiatric rehabilitation, these aspects of team functioning can be viewed as benefits. For example, role ambiguity can be viewed as prerequisite to role release, in which disciplinary approaches are blended and reinforce one another. Duplication of team roles may help the members realize where they are duplicating services and may lead them to work with their respective agencies to develop a more efficient allocation of resources. Confusion concerning responsibility for decisions can result in development of a shared responsibility in decision-making. Because the person with a severe psychiatric disability needs many different kinds of services, requires a broad range of expertise (including community supports), and benefits from long-range planning, it can be expected that the team process will be more effective in meeting his or her preferences and needs than the more autocratic and traditional treatment approaches.

The benefits of teaming are not always realized, however, even in this context. To be effective, a team must manage its decision-making process so that the strengths of group decision-making are not lost (Abelson & Woodman, 1983). Three interlocking aspects of the team's life are critical: (1) gaining a sense of shared responsibility (team development), (2) moving toward consensus (leadership and participation), and (3) harnessing the team's resources to solve problems (group dynamics).

Stages of Team Development

The stages of team development have been conceptualized in the work of Tuckman and Jensen (1977). They assert that groups go through five rather predictable basic stages of development: forming, storming, norming, performing, and adjourning. The team leader needs to understand that his or her role

changes as the team goes through each of these phases. In the first stage, *forming*, the team leader needs to deal with all the uneasiness that people experience in any new situation. This initial period of caution is followed by a period of *storming*, as people react to the demands of the tasks, question authority, and attempt to resolve any dissonance. In the third stage, *norming*, the leader has to help the team develop constructive rules of behavior appropriate and necessary for the team to accomplish its mission. In the fourth stage, *performing*, the leader needs to help members focus their energies on the task. The team is now free to develop working alternatives to the task(s) confronting it, and an atmosphere of support tends to remain from the norming stage. Finally, with the task nearing completion, the team moves into *adjourning*, in which closure to the task and a changing of relationships is anticipated.

Tuckman finds it helpful to view each of the stages of forming, storming, norming, performing, and adjourning from two points of view—group maintenance and task behavior. *Group maintenance* concerns itself with interpersonal relationships, with the team moving through predictable stages of testing and dependency (forming), tension and conflict (storming), building cohesion (norming), and finally, establishing functional role relationships (performing) before the team adjourns. At each of these stages, movement to the next stage requires adequately dealing with the interpersonal problems encountered in the previous stage.

At the same time the team is struggling with these interpersonal problems, it is being asked to fulfill its mission or task. *Task behavior* concerns itself with a team's mission, with the team moving through predictable stages of defining the task (forming), generating ideas and solutions (storming), sharing interpretations and narrowing focus (norming), and acting on solutions (performing). As before, successful task behavior in each stage is largely dependent on completion of the tasks of the previous stage.

The twin pillars of team process are therefore building a team and focusing the team's energies toward its task or mission. The team leader addresses team building (interpersonal relations), as well as task behaviors, because communication among team members is the primary means to move toward task goals (which are the individual goals for the person with a psychiatric disability). Team members who have an understanding of the tasks of the team, and who are comfortable with its interpersonal context, are now able to improvise both individually and as a group.

Leadership and Power

When one person does what another wants him or her to do, we would say that the one has power over the other. Leadership intuitively involves *power*—that is, the ability to influence what other people say and do. A person may be very influential and have a great deal of power in one team and may be considered the leader because the team accepts his or her direction. The point is, that power is not universal, it is limited by the persons being influenced. Discussion of leadership therefore usually evolves into a discussion of power and vice versa. One of the most important issues of team process concerns the meaning of leadership. It is necessary to draw a distinction between *leader* and *leadership*. A leader may be a person in a position of authority; he or she is given the right to make decisions for others. From that position, leaders may influence others who look to them for clues or who seek to emulate them. From another perspective, it might be said that whoever influences the group is the leader; that is, any person who influences the group (whether in a position of leadership or not) exhibits leadership behavior. Leadership behavior has to do with influence on the team, regardless of position. In some groups, different leaders may emerge in the different stages of group development or when the group is in either the task or the group-maintenance modalities. Therefore, power may be defined differentially, according to attributes that may qualify the team member to take leadership at a particular point.

In addition to personal factors that define leadership, there are expertise factors that contribute to leadership and power. As far back as the seventeenth century, Francis Bacon formulated that "knowledge is power." Expertise defines the extent to which the individual participant is able to contribute in a way that facilitates meeting the group's goals (Bailey, Helsel-DeWert, Thiele, & Ware, 1983). According to a study by Gilliam and Coleman (1981), the participants of an interdisciplinary team meeting that are most influential in decision-making are (1) the psychologist/psychiatrist, (2) directors, (3) supervisors, and (4) consultants. The problem is that these are the participants who have the least contact with the client. This means that there is a power dichotomy between those who are in expert positions with little contact with the client and those who are in nonexpert positions (families and direct-care workers) with considerable contact with the client. The effect of this dichotomy is that the people with the most contact with the client often defer their decision-making in interdisciplinary team meetings to those they perceive to have expert power. While deference to professionals may at first glance appear appropriate and beneficial, it is also counterproductive to the most efficient delivery of services.

In addition to underutilizing the leadership of persons with greater client contact, low participation by direct service providers also results in the loss of much of their effort and enthusiasm in regard to team decisions (Yoshida, Fenton, Maxwell, & Kaufman, 1978). In a series of experiments, Bass and Leavitt (1963) found that persons have a higher probability of carrying out decisions that they have helped to make than decisions that others have made for them. What leads to such commitment may be the individual's participation in and satisfaction with the group process and their acceptance of the decision (Vroom, 1969). Cooper and Wood (1974) studied groups of college students and found positive relationships between participation and satisfaction—higher levels of satisfaction were found for groups who were allowed to generate, evaluate, and make final decisions about items to be included in an attitude survey than for groups who were limited to only generating, evaluating, or finalizing decisions. In short, the degree of a team member's participation on a team is directly related to that member's commitment to execute the decisions of that team.

In order to achieve interdisciplinary solutions to the myriad decisions concerning people with chronic mental illnesses, all members of the planning team must participate in and feel satisfaction with the decision-making process. This is particularly true for decisions that must be carried out by those not possessing the expert power in the decision-making process. Organizational theorists note,

> If people hope, through participation, to realize their aim of contributing to the decision-making of their groups or organizations on important issues, certain requirements must be fulfilled with regard to their level of motivation and expertness. (Mulder & Wilke, 1970, p.445)

It may be assumed, therefore, that in many instances, learning processes are necessary to make it possible for people to fulfill these requirements. One possibility is learning before, during, and through the interdisciplinary process. Thibaut and Kelley refer to two opposing possibilities for a person to use his or her expert power: either by giving expert advice to the extent that the other people become expert or by not teaching the relevant knowledge at all (Thibaut & Kelley, 1959). While we do not advocate the latter, we do advocate, whenever possible, using expert knowledge to educate and not to dictate. This may take the form of speaking in nontechnical terms, explaining concepts, showing patience, and possibly providing background information before, during, or after the interdisciplinary meeting. Table 5.2. shows the contrasting behaviors that illustrate misuse of authority and expert power.

Group Dynamics

Leadership is just one of many roles assumed by members of a team. Each member may exhibit behaviors, which—taken in aggregate—create complex dynamics that influence the productiveness of the team. Studies by Bales (1950, 1970) and others (Benne & Sheats, 1948; Rieken & Homan, 1954) have identified two types of team behaviors, or roles, which influence group dynamics: team-task roles and team-maintenance roles.

The first role that influences group dynamics is related to the team's orientation to its task. Roles of members here are to help the group select and define the common goals and to work toward solution of those goals. For example, suppose that representatives from mental health and human service agencies decide to work together to facilitate transition from the hospital to the community for a person with a psychiatric disability. Members whose actions would be categorized in the task realm would initiate discussion of what could be done or how the problem might be approached, or they may *suggest different methods* for getting the family involved. Someone may *offer information* on what other agencies in the state are doing and what other resources may be available for more help. Another may *offer opinions* on the subject. Others may *elaborate* from their experience, or conferences they may have attended. With this variety of opinions and suggestions, someone can coordinate or *clarify* the various suggestions in terms of which are appropriate for the team to work on. One person may *summarize* what has happened and perhaps point out departures from the original goals. There may be critics or evaluators who *question* whether there is a need to deliver a service. An energizer may prod the group to reconsider its potential and may *stimulate* members to greater activity. There may be a procedural technician who can direct the group to where information and materials can be obtained. That person also may have *access* to materials and speakers who could help clarify some of the technical questions being raised. Another member may *record* or write down the suggestions or otherwise keep a record of group decisions.

Although task roles focus on the problem-solving aspects of achieving movement to-

Table 5.2 Misuse of Authority/Expert Power

Sets up barriers: The person with authority begins to wall himself or herself off from others more than is necessary.

Uses people as tools: The person with authority relates to others as if they were instruments to be used in carrying out his or her will. Such behavior is impersonal and dehumanizing.

Does not check self: The person acts arbitrarily and sees no need for checking because of feelings that he or she can do no wrong. The validity of his or her behavior becomes self-evident and, hence, the person does not solicit the advice of others.

Sticks to his or her own level: The person with authority relates to others in terms of their positions in the hierarchy, glorifying the elite and condescending to subordinates.

Uses special language: The person with authority uses words, abbreviations, and labels in special ways, as in jargon or slang. He or she talks around a point.

Eliminates opposition: The person with authority does not tolerate serious disagreement. He or she demolishes or overwhelms a dissenter, offering no long-range solution.

Shows pseudohumility: The person is patronizing and sweet at one time and indifferent at another time.

Stresses rules and conformity: The person insists on an evergrowing body of rules and regulations, emphasizes conventional ways and conformity, and tends to avoid the risks of change.

Dichotomizes: The person considers things right or wrong, good or bad. He or she is intolerant of ambiguity.

Enjoys no real relationships with subordinates: The person selects women or men who will not rock the boat. He or she prefers adulation and seeks out sycophants.

Gets tough when anxious: The person calls for hard work, cracks down, uses power as a convenient way to deny anxieties and buries himself or herself in work, although he or she is not genuinely productive.

Is anti-introspective: The person denies the softer side of self; that is, emotions in general and feelings such as tenderness and passivity. He or she also denies processes like defensiveness and conflict with self (Luft, 1984).

ward a goal, group maintenance roles focus on the personal relations among members of a team. Just as task roles are helpful in aiding a team to achieve its goals, maintenance roles are helpful in aiding a team to work together. These behaviors help the team maintain itself so that members will contribute ideas and will be willing to continue collaborating toward progress on the team's task. Both kinds of roles are needed, and each complements the other. For example, a newcomer to a meeting can determine how well a team maintains itself by observing how people interact as they are accomplishing the team task. He or she might observe that as one person speaks, that person receives the undivided attention of the team, whereas when another person speaks, people yawn or talk among themselves. He or she may notice how the team welcomes a late arrival, whether people's questions are listened to or are ignored, or whether the team takes the client's wishes and desires into consideration. Although it looks as if the team is working on the task areas, members are concurrently accumulating data on "What kind of team is this? Will I be accepted? What's the philosophical bond of the other members?"

Team members may assume many different roles in team maintenance. To return to the example of the team dealing with transition from the hospital to the community, the *encourager* may ask for additional opinions. The *supporter* may agree with suggestions of others and offer recommendations. The *harmonizer* may attempt to mediate differences among members or points of view, or to relieve tension with a joke. These roles help a team to maintain itself in order that work on its task can proceed without becoming immobilized by inappropriate social behaviors.

In addition to positive task maintenance roles, members may assume roles that create conflict and decrease team cohesiveness. These behaviors may meet individual needs that are irrelevant to the team task and that are not conducive to helping the team work as a unit. To return to the hospital-to-community case study, an *aggressor* may question (with relatively veiled sarcasm) the competence and veracity of another member. This member may then assume the role of the *blocker* and may raise objections to every suggestion. The *self-confessor* may then use this confusion to express personal problems and gain sympathy through catharsis by going off task and discussing his or her problems at home. The *recognition-seeker* may respond with his or her personal advice and may describe in glowing detail how it was successful in his or her own life. The *dominator* may then try to get the team back on task with an assortment of strategies, such as interrupting, flattery, or asserting superior status.

By this time, both the task and the maintenance of the team are forgotten, as individuals begin to act only to satisfy their personal needs. If this type of behavior is not controlled by the leader, then tardiness, absenteeism, and ultimately group dissolution may result. To summarize, while interdisciplinary team process can be valuable, it is often plagued by dysfunctions, which must be controlled by the team leader. These dysfunctions can be overcome if members are trained to recognize these behaviors, if consumers are empowered to participate as equal members, and if leaders take the time to develop group leadership skills.

Conclusions

Concern with change and improved delivery of services has been central to the mental health field since its inception. The trend toward interdisciplinary team process is being driven by the increasing scope of mental health service orientation and the realization that many mental health problems can no longer be addressed by viewing the individual as solitary and passive. No longer is the primary concern just the remediation of deficits, but also the development of assets and support networks. This chapter has defined some of the major issues related to the adoption of interdisciplinary team process. It has examined the parameters of interdisciplinary planning, as defined by the agency service model and the way professionals and lay persons interact as part of a team. It has discussed how the individual is viewed in the treatment process and how individual resources and supports can be utilized in rehabilitation. Finally, it has presented an overview of how teams are established and how group process, leadership, and group dysfunctions can affect outcomes for the individual. Clearly, consumers, parents, families, and direct care personnel appear to be the most disenfranchised from the present mental health planning process, despite the fact that they are the individuals most responsible for the person with a psychiatric disability. It is therefore hoped that the adoption of interdisciplinary team process will provide the vehicle for involving these individuals, not only to enhance the roles of individuals using mental health services, but also to improve outcomes by bringing their unique resources and supports to bear in solving problems and improving their quality of life.

References

Abelson, M. A., & Woodman, R. W. (1983). Review of research on team effectiveness: Implications for teams in schools. *School Psychology Review, 12,* 125–136.

Anthony, W. A. (1979). *The principles of psychiatric rehabilitation.* Baltimore: University Park Press.

Anthony, W., Cohen, M., & Farkas, M. (1990). *Psychiatric rehabilitation,* Boston: Center for Psychiatric Rehabilitation.

Anthony, W. & Blanch, A. K. (1988). *Supported employment for persons who are psychiatri-*

cally disabled: An historical and conceptual perspective (Contract #G008435005). Washington, DC: National Institute on Disability and Rehabilitation Research.

Bailey, D. B., Helsel-DeWert, M., Thiel, J. E., & Ware, W. B. (1983). Measuring individual participation on the interdisciplinary team. *American Journal on Mental Health, 88*, 247–254.

Bales, R. (1950). *Interaction process analysis.* Reading, MA: Addison-Wesley.

Bales, R. (1970). *Personality and interpersonal behavior.* New York: Holt, Rinehart and Winston.

Bass, B. M., & Leavitt, H. J. 1963. Some experiments in planning and operating. *Management Science, 9*, 574–585.

Benne, K. D., & Sheats, P. (1948). Functional roles of group members. *Journal of Social Issues, 2*, 42–47.

Borenzweig, H. (1974). Social work and psychoanalytic theory: A historical analysis. In P. E. Weinberger (Ed.), *Perspectives on social welfare.* New York: Macmillan.

Burns, B. J., Burke, J. D., & Kessler, L. G. (1981). Promoting health–mental health coordination: Federal efforts. In A. Broskowski, E. Marks, & S. H. Budman (Eds.), *Linking health and mental health.* Beverly Hills, CA: Sage Publications.

Campbell, P. H. (1987). The integrated programming team: An approach for coordinating professionals of various disciplines in programs for students with severe and multiple handicaps. *Journal of the Association for Persons with Severe Handicaps, 12*(2), 107–116.

Chamberlin, J. (1984). Speaking for ourselves. An overview of the ex-psychiatric inmates movement. *Psychosocial Rehabilitation Journal, 8*(2), 56–63.

Chamberlin, J. (1989). Ex-patient groups and psychiatric rehabilitation. In M. D. Farkas & W. A. Anthony (Eds.) *Psychiatric rehabilitation programs: Putting theory into practice*, (pp. 207–225). Baltimore: Johns Hopkins University Press.

Chase, Wright, & Ragade. (1981). Decision-making in an interdisciplinary team. *Behavioral Science, 26*, 206–215.

Cooper, M. R., & Wood, M. T. (1974). Effects of member participation and commitment in group decision-making on influence, satisfaction, and decision riskiness. *Journal of Applied Psychology, 59*, 127–134.

Craig, T. J. H., Peer, S. M., & Ross, M. D. (1989). Psychiatric rehabilitation in a state hospital transitional residence: The Cottage Program at Greystone Park Psychiatric Hospital, Greystone Park, New Jersey. In M. D. Farkas & W. A. Anthony (Eds.), *Psychiatric rehabilitation programs: Putting theory into practice* (pp. 57–69). Baltimore: Johns Hopkins University Press.

Danley, K., & Anthony, W. (1987). The choose–get–keep model. *American Rehabilitation, 13*(4), 6–9.

Dowell, D. A., & Ciarlo, J. A. (1983). Overview of the community mental health center's program from an evaluation perspective. *Community Mental Health Journal, 19*, 95–128

Ewalt, P. L., & Honeyfield, R. M., (1981). Needs of persons in long-term care. *Social Work, 26*(3), 223–231.

Fairweather, G. W. (1980). *The Fairweather Lodge: A twenty-five year retrospective.* San Francisco: Jossey-Bass.

Feather, N. T. (1982). *Expectation and actions: Expectancy values models in psychology.* Hillsdale, NJ: Erlbaum.

Fiorelli, J. S. (1988). Power in work groups: Team member's perspectives. *Human Relations, 41*(1), 1–12.

Flynn, C. ,& Harbin, G. (1987). Evaluating interagency coordination efforts using a multidimensional, interaction, developmental paradigm. *Remedial and Special Education, 8*(3). 35–44.

Gerace, L. (1988). Schizophrenia and the family: Nursing implications. *Archives of Psychiatric Nursing, 2*(3), 141–145.

Gilliam, J. E., & Coleman, M. L. (1981). Who influences IEP committee decisions? *Exceptional Children, 47*, 642–644.

Goering, P. N., Huddart, C., Wasylenki, D. A., & Ballantyne, R. (1989). The use of rehabilitation case management to develop necessary supports: Community rehabilitation services, Toronto, Ontario. In M. D. Farkas & W. A. Anthony (Eds.), *Psychiatric rehabilitation programs: Putting theory into practice* (pp. 197–207). Baltimore: Johns Hopkins University Press.

Gowdy. E., & Rapp, C. (1989). Managerial behavior: The common denominators of effective community-based programs. *Psychosocial Rehabilitation Journal, 13*(2), 33–49.

Grusky, O., & Tierney, K. (1989). Evaluating the effectiveness of county-wide mental health care systems. *Community Mental Health Journal, 25*, 3–19.

Hefferin, E. A., & Katz, A. H. (1971). Issues and orientations in the evaluation of rehabilitation programs. *Rehabilitation Literature, 32*, 66–73.

Kelly, J. G. (1966). Ecological constraints on mental health services. *American Psychologist, 21*, 535–539.

Lefley, H. P. (1988). Training professionals to work with families of chronic patients. *Community Mental Health Journal, 24*(4), 338–354.

Levine, M. & Perkins, D. (1987). *Principles of community psychology.* New York: Oxford University Press.

Luft, J. (Ed.). (1984). *Group Processes.* Mountain View, CA: Mayfield Publishing.

Lyon, S. L., & Lyon G. (1980). Team functioning and staff development: A role release approach to providing integrated educational services for severely handicapped students. *Journal of the Association for the Severely Handicapped, 5*(3) 250–263.

Marshall, C. (1989). Skill teaching as training in rehabilitation counselor education. *Rehabilitation Education, 3*, 19–26.

Minkoff, K. (1987). Resistance of mental health professionals to working with the chronic mentally ill. In A.T. Meyerson (Ed.), *Barriers to treating the chronic mentally ill.* (New Directions for Mental Health Services, No. 33, pp. 3–20). San Francisco: Jossey-Bass.

Mowbray, C. T., & Freddolino, P. (1986). Consulting to implement nontraditional community programs for the long-term mentally disabled. *Administration in Mental Health, 14*, 122–134.

Moxley, D. P. (1988). Exploring the validity of social network indicators for use in psychosocial rehabilitation. *Psychosocial Rehabilitation Journal, 11*(4), 4–10.

Mulder, M, & Wilke, H. (1970). Participation and power equalization. *Organizational Behavior and Human Performance, 5*, 430–448.

Nemec, N. B. & Furlong-Norman, K. (1989). Supports for psychiatrically disabled persons. In M. D. Farkas & W. A.. Anthony (Eds.), *Psychiatric rehabilitation programs: Putting theory into practice* (pp. 192–197). Baltimore: Johns Hopkins University Press.

Pierce, J., & Blanch, A. K. (1989). A statewide psychosocial rehabilitation system: Vermont. In M. D. Farkas & W. Anthony (Eds.), *Psychiatric rehabilitation programs: Putting theory into practice* (pp. 170–179). Baltimore: Johns Hopkins University Press.

Pluckman, M. (1972). Professional territoriality. *Nursing Forum, 11*, 300–310.

Rieken, H. W., & Homans, G. C. (1954). Psychological aspects of social structure. *Handbook of Social Psychology* (Vol. 2, pp. 786–832. Reading, MA: Addison-Wesley.

Roberts, C. S. (1988). Conflicting professional values in social work and medicine. *Health and Social Work, 14*(3), 211–218.

Sadler, J. Z. & Hulgus, Y. (1990). Knowing, valuing, acting: Clues to revising the biopsychosocial model. *Comprehensive Psychiatry, 31*(3), 185–195.

Sands, R. G., Stafford, J., & McClelland, M. (1990). I beg to differ: Conflict in the interdisciplinary team. *Social Work in Health Care, 14*(3), 55–72.

Sarbin, T. R. (1970). A role theory perspective for community psychology: The structure of social identity. In D. Adelson & B. Kalis (Eds.), *Community psychology and mental health: Perspective and challenges.* Scranton, PA: Chandler.

Stern R., & Minkoff, K. (1979). Paradoxes in programming for chronic patients in a community clinic. *Hospital and Community Psychiatry, 30*, 613–617.

Stroul, B. A. (1989). Community support systems for persons with long-term mental illness: A conceptual framework. *Psychosocial Rehabilitation Journal, 12*(3), 9–26.

Thibaut, J. W., & Kelley, H. H. (1959). *The social psychology of groups.* New York: Wiley.

Tischler, G. L., Henisz, J., Myers, J. K., & Garrison, V. (1972). The impact of catchmenting. *Administration in Mental Health,* 22–29.

Tuckman, B. W., & Jensen, M. A. C. (1977). States in small group development revisited. *Group and Organizational Studies, 2*, 419–42.

Turner, J., & Ten-Hoor, W. J. (1978). The NIMH community support program: Pilot approach to a needed social reform. *Schizophrenia Bulletin, 4*, 319–349.

Vroom, V. H. (1969). Industrial social psychology. In E. Lindsey & E. Aronson (Eds.), *The handbook of social psychology,* (Vol. 5, 2nd ed.). Reading, MA: Addison-Wesley.

Wallace, G. (1976). Interdisciplinary efforts in learning disabilities: Issues and recommendations. *Journal of Learning Disabilities, 9*, 59–65.

Weinberger, J., & Greenwald, M. (1982). Training and curricula in psychiatric rehabilitation: A survey of core accredited programs. *Rehabilitation Counseling Bulletin,* May, 287–290.

Wolfensberger, W. (1972). *Normalization.* Toronto, Canada: National Institute on Mental Retardation.

Yoshida, R. K,. Fenton, K. S., Maxwell, J. P., & Kaufman, M. J. (1978). Group decision-making in the planning team process: Myth or reality? *The Journal of School Psychology, 16*, 234–244.

SECTION II
SUPPORTS AND REHABILITATION FOR COMMUNITY LIFE

Chapter 6

Comprehensive Models of Psychosocial Rehabilitation*

JUDITH A. COOK
SARA J. HOFFSCHMIDT

Psychosocial rehabilitation (PSR) is a community-based model of mental health and rehabilitation service delivery for persons with severe and persistent mental illness. Though it was developed more than 4 decades ago, this approach has timely relevance to current treatment and community-living objectives of mental health consumers and professionals alike. At the same time, this multicomponent and widely varied model presents challenges to administrators, researchers, and policymakers seeking a better understanding of PSR. In this chapter we present a selective overview of PSR programming, touching on the model's history, its general principles, its client and staff populations, and the nature of its services addressing vocational, residential, social, crisis, case management, educational, and medical needs. Also presented is a brief review of PSR research and of information on funding and administrative issues, as well as PSR approaches for special populations, such as young adults, those living in rural communities, older persons, homeless individuals, ethnically diverse populations, and consumers with substance use disorders.

History of the PSR Movement

After World War II, several pioneer community-based psychosocial agencies emerged, calling themselves "halfway houses." These included the Rutland Corners in Massachusetts, the Montpelier and Burlington Rehabilitation Houses in Vermont, Portals House in Los Angeles, Fellowship Club in San Francisco, Manning House in Dallas, and Saints and Sinners Club in Phoenix (Tanaka, 1983). During the 1950s and 1960s, the first hallmark PSR agencies came into being in the United States, among them Fountain House, Horizon House, Center Club, Hill House, Thresholds, Portals, Fellowship House, and Prospect House. These agencies were formed with the mission of improving the lives of people with mental illness, many of whom were newly deinstitutionalized, due to breakthroughs in psychopharmacology and the birth

*The content of this chapter was developed under a grant from the National Institute on Disability and Rehabilitation Research, Department of Education cooperative agreement number H133B00011, and the National Institute of Mental Health, Systems Development and Community Support Branch. The content of this chapter does not necessarily reflect the views of the Institute and does not imply endorsement by the U.S. government.

of the community mental health movement. Fountain House in New York City is considered the birthplace of many of the essential elements of the psychosocial rehabilitation model (Beard, Propst, & Malamud, 1982).

General Goals, Organization, and Principles of Psychosocial Rehabilitation Programs

A central goal of PSR is prevention of unnecessary rehospitalization; accordingly, an emphasis is placed on developing both the strategies to manage symptomatology and the skills that will enable individuals to lead a productive life in the community. Another basic element of psychosocial programs is that they are organized as programs to which persons "belong" and in which clients are referred to as "members." Members have opportunities for managing the program and for being involved in maintenance, programming, service delivery, evaluation, and administrative tasks.

Tanaka (1983) suggests the following general definition for a PSR program:

> A goal-oriented program for the mentally ill which provides coping experiences toward improved living in the community. The program emphasizes common sense and practical needs and usually includes services of vocational, residential, socialization, education, personal adjustment, and the prevention of unnecessary hospitalization. The psychosocial rehabilitation setting is purposefully informal to reduce the psychological distance between staff and member and consciously engages the member as an active participant in program planning, development, policy making, implementation, and evaluation. (p. 7)

Principles of Psychosocial Rehabilitation

A number of authors have explored the principles of PSR. Although emphases are different in various conceptualizations, most include the following: (a) client choice, (b) situational assessment; (c) comprehensive rehabilitation service planning; (d) a biopsychosocial approach; (e) an emphasis on strengths and wellness; (f) empowerment of consumers; (g) family involvement and psychoeducation; (h) community-based services, integrated settings, and natural supports; (i) ongoing services; (j) evaluation of services and of member outcomes; and (k) staff commitment and involvement.

Client Choice: The key to PSR is the active involvement of members in the decision to seek rehabilitation, the development of the rehabilitation plan, implementation of the plan, and ongoing evaluation of the plan. This principle recognizes how a member's sense of hopelessness may delay or hinder help-seeking and interprets the decision to enter rehabilitation as an acknowledgment of hopefulness (Farrell, 1986). It involves consumers in identifying their strengths as well as weaknesses and promotes their active participation in every step toward full implementation of the rehabilitation plan. Because success means growth and change, ongoing evaluation of the plan allows constructive feedback for modifications and enhancements to better meet members' needs.

Situational Assessment: Situational assessment involves conducting rehabilitation assessments through observation of persons performing targeted tasks in actual or simulated environments (Anthony & Jansen, 1984). Assessment techniques that are rejected with this approach are those selected on the basis of convenience, admiration for "high-tech" methods of evaluation as ends-in-themselves, or because they are less labor intensive. Research supports the predictive validity of vocational situational assessments (Bond & Friedmeyer, 1987; Cook, Jonikas, & Solomon, 1992). Using situational assessment, vocational evaluation might include a chance to work on a community job placement for real pay; residential assessment could involve a series of overnight stays at an agency residence; and educational assessment might include a chance to attend several lectures at a local community college.

Comprehensive Rehabilitation Service Plan: A plan is necessary to help members reach their desired goals. This plan typically involves a set of rehabilitation goals and coordinated services designed to address these goal areas. The plan outlines changes in the client that involve the acquisition of skills (Anthony, Cohen, & Cohen, 1984). Rehabil-itation plans also detail changes in clients' environments that will be necessary in order to reach stated goals (Anthony & Liberman, 1986). PSR incorporates the help of families, friends, employers, neighbors, and other role partners in consumers' lives (Black, 1987).

Continual evaluation of the client's progress involves asking the question, "Is rehabilitation occurring?" by focusing on whether changes are evident in clients' skill levels or their supportive networks. While change is emphasized, services designed to help *maintain* acquired skills and outcomes also are part of rehabilitation (Cook, Jonikas, & Solomon, 1992). The service plan is behavioral, reflecting the here-and-now focus of PSR (Dincin, 1975). The plan also includes specific dates and measures of service completion, as well as designation of the persons responsible for service delivery.

Biopsychosocial Approach: Psychiatric rehabilitation requires a holistic approach because of the nature of mental illness (Dincin, 1990). As a disability, mental illness affects the entire person, including intrapsychic functioning, social interaction, independent living skills, vocational skills, physical health, and spiritual well-being. Psychosocial models typically addresses many if not all of these areas in goal setting and service delivery.

Emphasis on Strengths and Wellness: While the mental health and rehabilitation fields tend to focus on symptoms, deficits, and deviancies, PSR builds on members' strengths, talents, and skills (Cnaan, Blankertz, Messinger, & Gardner, 1989; 1990). Such a focus increases the chances that the rehabilitation plan will be built on members' abilities as well as disabilities (Cnaan,

Blankertz, Messinger, & Gardner, 1988). Another reason to build on skills is that doing so enhances confidence and promotes a more positive self-image than exclusive reliance on a deficit model. Still another reason is to promote a sense of hope among members who have long histories of failure and discouragement.

Empowerment of Consumers: The belief in empowerment pervades the PSR philosophy (Beard, Propst, & Malamud, 1982). Empowerment is implied in the PSR emphasis on building on strengths; it is evident in the focus on acquiring new skills; it is present in the provision of new organizational responsibilities for members. Whether supervising their peers' work on prevocational crews or on community job placements, running "Members' Councils," engaging in training of mental health professionals, lobbying policymakers, or providing feedback in program evaluation, the members' involvement is stressed by PSR programs.

Family Involvement and Psychoeducation: The importance of family involvement in PSR stems from the fact that large proportions of inpatients return to live with families after release. Statistics indicate that 40 to 70% of persons return to families following discharge (Goldman, 1982; Lamb & Oliphant, 1978). Research has shown that relatives often feel inappropriately excluded from decisions about mental health and rehabilitation goals and plans (Hatfield, Fierstein, & Johnson, 1982; Spaniol, Jung, Zipple, & Fitzgerald, 1987). PSR services often include family support groups that offer services based on psychoeducational models (Anderson, Hogarty, & Reiss, 1980). Such models typically provide some combination of basic information about mental illness (etiology, causes, medication information), coping and behavioral management strategies for living with a mentally ill relative, emotional support, and assistance with understanding social service systems such as mental health and disability systems (Cook, Hoffschmidt, Cohler, & Pickett, 1992).

Community-Based Services, Integrated Settings, and Natural Supports: PSR focuses on the community as a locus for training and support. A fundamental principle of PSR is that the closer the services are to the real world, the more effective they will be. One reason for this is the difficulty with transfer of training from one setting to another. A second reason for basing services in the community is because many younger members prefer the community setting as one that is less stigmatizing (Cook, Solomon, & Mock, 1989). The community also is necessary for integration; without integration, the benefits of normalization cannot be realized. Integration also provides the chance for role modeling among members of PSR programs. A new vocational concept that has long been incorporated into PSR programming is the use of "natural supports" (Cook & Razzano, in press). This involves using part of an individual's already existing environment to provide long-term supports. Use of non-handicapped coworkers to provide job training and coaching, and use of consumer case managers are two examples of this approach.

Ongoing Services: PSR programs typically acknowledge that the rehabilitation process can be lengthy, especially given the reoccurring nature of mental illness and the need for ongoing support for certain goals. Making a long-term commitment to work with members and then developing services to honor that commitment is a hallmark of the PSR approach (Gardner, 1985). The notion of lifelong membership in the PSR program embodies this commitment and its corollary development of new, long-term, ongoing service delivery models (Cook, Jonikas & Solomon, 1992).

Evaluation of Services and of Member Outcomes: PSR is attuned to the issue of member evaluation of services; articles appearing as early as 1977 discuss how PSR agencies can implement program evaluations (Witheridge, Streicker, & MacInnes, 1977). Some programs have developed member-run program evaluation components, including Fountain House, Thresholds, Hill House, and The Club. Client satisfaction surveys also are used to assess consumer satisfaction and suggestions for program improvement. Outcomes are measured and followed over time, to assess members' progress toward community living, their level of satisfaction with services, and their suggestions for program improvements.

Staff Commitment and Involvement: There is widespread recognition that PSR staff must possess particular values, attitudes, and kinds of expertise that set them apart from other mental health and rehabilitation professionals. First, staff avoid the tendency to establish staff–client relationships that include rigid boundaries and large amounts of role distance (Tanaka, 1983). Rather than approaching clients from a so-called neutral position, the emphasis is on *advocacy* on behalf of clients. Through member involvement in goal setting and decision-making, staff demystify the rehabilitation process for members (Anthony, Cohen, & Farkas, 1982).

Who Receives Psychosocial Rehabilitation?

The variation in populations served by PSR is great, both from program to program, and within programs. Many programs will accept virtually anyone with psychiatric problems, while other agencies limit their members to exclude persons with a history of violent or extreme behavior, or a substance abuse problem that the agency feels unequipped to manage. The people who join different programs also may vary, depending on the emphasis of the program. For example, Thresholds serves a very disabled population, as the incoming membership averages seven prior hospitalizations, most have diagnoses of schizophrenia, and more than 93% are unemployed upon admission. Nonetheless, the population at Thresholds may be somewhat higher functioning than those at other agencies, because of Thresholds' emphasis on vocational goals; in other words, some clients unable to pursue vocational goals may find a program such as Thresholds too stressful and demanding (Bond, Dincin, Setze, & Witheridge, 1984; Cook & Razzano, in press).

Stroul (1986) reports that the average age of clients being served by PSR agencies tends to be low, averaging in the mid-20s through 30s. This younger population has necessitated certain changes in programming (Bachrach, 1982). For example, younger members are more prone to substance abuse problems, so the linkage relationship with the substance abuse treatment system becomes very important (Pepper & Ryglewicz, 1982). Young adults often require enhanced educational components in their rehabilitation plans (Cook, Wessell & Dincin, 1987), and may be more resistant to participating in programs with older, lower functioning clients (Cnaan, Blankertz, Messinger & Gardner, 1988).

Comprehensive Services of Psychosocial Rehabilitation

While not every PSR program provides all of the following services, many provide assistance in most of these areas. The hallmark of PSR is the coordination of each member's rehabilitation plan so that it is individualized and comprehensive.

Social Skills and Recreation

One of the most important and beneficial services of PSR is social skills training and an agenda of recreation and leisure time activities (Weinberg & Marlow, 1983). Often, social skills development is arrested at the first appearance of mental illness. From then on, isolation, loneliness, and limited opportunities for social interaction can continue throughout a member's life. Consistent with the PSR philosophy of normalization, many programs have extended hours into the evenings and weekends in order to provide members with opportunities for social interaction. Recreation hours often are held during times when other people would be engaging in such

activities, such as evenings, weekends, and holidays. The informal learning that can occur during interaction in interest groups and outings is invaluable and makes the members' assimilation into the community as complete and comfortable as possible (Cook, Pickett, & Jonikas, 1989). Another valuable aspect of recreation time is that it gives individuals an opportunity to develop the much needed support systems and self-esteem that are often instrumental in preventing rehospitalization (Black, 1987). Employed members can use planned recreational hours as a means of receiving support and of maintaining connection to the program, while staff are able to monitor members' progress (Beard et al., 1982; Stroul, 1986). Therapeutic camping programs and outward bound experiences also can promote growth and greater sense of efficacy (Peretti & Dincin, 1971).

PSR agencies also may provide more formal social skills and problem solving training in groups. The learning and enhancement of social interaction and problem solving skills helps the individual in multiple ways, such as negotiating relations with coworkers in order to maintain employment, living independently, developing a social network, and learning to utilize community resources. The development of skills to deal with new situations in a variety of settings (generalization) directly affects overall adaptation to the community. Some agencies have concentrated on using social skills training principles in applied areas, such as employment; one example is a set of on-the-job curricula, developed at Thresholds, to help members learn social skills, stress management, and symptom control at work.

Crisis Service and Outreach Component

Outreach work and crisis services are provided by PSR agencies as a means of following up on program dropouts, showing people that they are missed and cared for, and supporting rehospitalized members. Community outreach is used for maintaining a link with clients in crisis or with those who fall through the cracks of service delivery (Turkat & Buzzell, 1982). The "Reach-Out" Programs at Fountain House are one example of such a service, in which staff or members work with a member in crisis or one who has stopped attending the program (Beard, Propst, & Malamud, 1982). Some PSR crisis services (Witheridge, 1988) are modeled on the assertive outreach model developed in Madison, Wisconsin (Stein & Test, 1980; Stein, Test, & Marx, 1975). Phone calls, home visits, negotiation of complaints and concerns, and linkage to needed services are part of this type of crisis outreach in PSR programs (Fraser, 1987).

Case Management Component

PSR case management almost eludes definition, as the practice of case management differs greatly from agency to agency and program to program. Despite its great number of variations, case management is one of the central components of PSR (Dincin, 1975). The case manager, together with the client, is responsible for the coordination of services delivered under the rehabilitation plan.

The resources that the case manager coordinates may be inside or outside the PSR agency, including residential services, medication management, medical services, funding sources, vocational rehabilitation, and educational services. Within the agency, the case manager works with the member to create a daily schedule of vocational training or employment, education, social skills and therapeutic groups, and medication management. Finally, the case manager and the member typically engage in individual supportive therapy, as part of the process of identifying those factors that will help to ensure the member's stability and success, and avoidance of unnecessary rehospitalizations. The use of case management methods for *rehabilitation* and not solely for clinical care is a major characteristic of PSR (Farrell, 1986).

Much of PSR case management involves "linkage services" (Fraser, 1987). Links with other organizations can be formal or informal, and they are essential for ensuring that all of a client's needs are met. For example, Fellowship House in Miami has established relationships with community agencies and has made an agreement with several medical practitioners and dentists to volunteer their services for physical health care. Likewise, Beach House in Virginia Beach has an in-house vocational coordinator who works with outside vocational service agencies to broker vocational services for Beach House's members (Stroul, 1986).

Residential and Independent Living Component

Housing is often one of the most immediate needs of members, especially if they are newly discharged from hospitals, waiting for public funding, or on a very limited budget. Assistance in arranging housing also is required, given public attitudes of rejection and stigma regarding having persons with psychiatric disabilities as neighbors or tenants (Solomon & Davis, 1984). The goal of promoting independent living skills in the community is reflected by the residential services that many PSR agencies offer. Some programs have a wide array of residential options, designed to meet the varying needs and abilities of their members. Residential services may range from highly supervised to unsupervised, may be agency owned and managed or commercially available residences, and may be either transitional or permanent (Jonikas & Cook, 1990).

The initial setting for residential services is often the group home. In most group homes, 24 hour staff supervise and support members, and an emphasis is placed on learning and redeveloping independent living skills, such as cooking, cleaning, and personal care. Smaller, familylike environments are preferable to larger facilities, which may be more similar to institutionalization, and may carry stigma while preventing community adjustment (Dincin, Selleck, & Carter, 1980). In most programs, a member will start out in a group home, and after adequate living skills are acquired and a time limit is reached, the member progresses to a less supervised setting.

Many PSR agencies offer housing in *supervised apartments*. Here, members have an opportunity to live alone or share an apartment with others, and they receive support from a staff member who may live within the same apartment complex or may use a home visiting model. Supervised apartments help to further develop independent living skills, and members living together learn to cooperate with minimal staff intervention. Depending on the needs of an individual, a long-term supervised apartment may be desirable. If members desire greater independence, they may take advantage of *scattered site or satellite apartments*, which staff do not directly supervise. Instead, the agency may own the housing or have an agreement with a landlord, and it may hold leases and guarantee payment for the members (Stroul, 1986). In *supported housing* approaches, the residence is owned by a landlord or by the member (i.e., "normal" housing), and supports are offered to help the member remain as long as he or she desires (Ridgeway & Zipple, 1990).

Although some services have time limits on many of their housing options, in order to promote growth and progression, other programs view the security of *stable, permanent housing* as being more important. For example, Fountain House and Thresholds lease apartments to members on a permanent basis, where they have the same opportunities for developing independent living skills as in transitional housing. However, members have no time limit, and they may develop independence at an individualized pace.

An additional residential service that a PSR program may provide is *crisis housing*. Crisis housing may be preferable to hospitalization and is often necessary as an intermediate shelter before a member can be placed in program housing. As with all residential services, an effort is made to make housing fit with the rest of a member's needs while taking into account community location, the member's available financial resources, and the type of staffing required for support (Witheridge, 1990).

Educational Component

One type of education available in PSR is the skills training that is so integral to achieving independent living. For example, many psychosocial agencies offer courses ranging from cooking, diet planning, budgeting, and domestic chores, to medication, identification of symptoms, means of using community resources, negotiation of benefits, and use of public transportation. Members may never have had the opportunity to learn and use community living skills, which may make a large difference in an individual's overall adjustment to the community (Stroul, 1986).

Evidence indicates that members of PSR programs perform significantly below age-appropriate levels in mathematics and reading skills (Cook, Wessell, & Dincin, 1987). Accordingly, education in the psychosocial setting may also include more formal education such as courses applied toward the completion of a high school diploma or General Education Diploma (G.E.D.), or remedial classes in basic math and reading. Thresholds has an educational program that enables members to take remedial courses in mathematics or reading, and it is accredited to award a high school diploma or the G.E.D. (Cook, Solomon, & Mock, 1989). Another innovative program at Thresholds is the "Community Scholar Program," which offers college preparatory courses and helps members find postsecondary educational opportunities and negotiate the application process (Cook, Jonikas, & Solomon, 1992). The Community Scholar Program also offers ongoing support to members once they become students in the community. The opportunity for continuing education is particularly important for PSR members because education often has been interrupted due to hospitalization and psychological difficulties. Education can improve self-esteem through a sense of accomplishment and can provide the skills training necessary to move beyond entry-level employment.

Medical Component

Due to the revolution in psychopharmacology, the majority of individuals receiving PSR services are prescribed some type of psychotropic medication. To respond to members' needs for sensitively and consistently monitored medication, many PSR agencies establish consulting arrangements with psychiatrists so that members can receive their services in-house (Dincin, 1975). The presence of medical staff can greatly improve the chances of preventing relapse, as the need for medication adjustments can be carefully monitored (Cohen, Dincin, & Amdur, 1975). As others have pointed out (Liberman & Rueger, 1984), a large amount of evidence from clinically controlled studies indicates the superiority of coordinated medication and psychosocial services over either method alone, for preventing relapse and increasing social functioning (Dincin & Witheridge, 1982; Heinrichs & Carpenter, 1982; Keith & Mathews, 1982; Mosher & Keith, 1979).

In addition, medication groups and information sessions can be used to educate members about psychotropic drugs and ways in which they can be a positive and helpful aspect of treatment (Cohen & Amdur, 1981). Evaluations of this approach at Thresholds indicate that education significantly improves members' knowledge of drugs and attitudes toward taking medications at posttest, although retention at follow-up is questionable (Streicker, Amdur, & Dincin, 1986).

In addition to medication management, many programs deliver services to promote the general physical health of their members. This is done in recognition that physical ailments are additional stressors in the life of a member, and that many members have not been able to receive adequate medical care. Some PSR programs have established the maintenance of physical health as one of their primary rehabilitation goals. Agencies such as Fellowship House, Thresholds, and The Club offer smoking-cessation groups and aerobics, along with free medical, dental, ophthalmological, and podiatric screenings. Education about contraception (Dincin & Wise, 1979) and sexually transmitted diseases, including human immunodeficiency virus (HIV) risk reduction, are other examples of this type of programming.

Another type of education provided by PSR programs is family psychoeducational services. This is done in recognition that family members of PSR clients typically are experiencing high levels of emotional distress and family burden, as they attempt to help their relative cope with psychiatric disability (Cook, 1988; Cook & Pickett, 1987). Psychoeducational approaches provide basic information about mental illness, medications, how to support the family member with mental illness, and how to avoid having the family focus exclusively on the disability (Dincin, Selleck, & Streicker, 1978).

Vocational Component

Availability of in-house vocational rehabilitation services is another hallmark of the PSR approach. Central to the PSR philosophy is the universality of the need for productive, meaningful work. This incorporates the philosophy that, with the right opportunities and supports, most if not all persons with mental illness can successfully participate in vocational rehabilitation (Cook & Razzano, in press).

Pioneered by Fountain House, the transitional employment (TE) model of vocational rehabilitation is commonly used by PSR programs. In this approach, clients hold a series of time-limited placements, during which they acquire job skills, a work history, and increasing confidence necessary to assume independent commercial employment. Supported employment approaches have been added to TE programming in many locations (Cook, Jonikas, & Solomon, 1992; Forman, 1988). Supported employment services may include career awareness and exploration, prevocational training, on-the-job training, vocational assessment and evaluation, assistance with job finding, job development and placement, ongoing vocational support, and education and advocacy with employers and coworkers (Cook, 1992).

One of the most common opportunities within psychosocial rehabilitation agencies is for prevocational training. Prevocational training usually occurs on a variety of work crews within the agency, and tasks that are essential for running the program are performed. For example, many agencies have a *clerical crew*, where sorting, filing, and other secretarial skills are learned; a *maintenance crew*, where members are trained in janitorial skills and repairs; and a *kitchen crew*, where members learn food preparation by preparing meals for those who attend the program. Prevocational experiences are important both for the development and relearning of skills and for boosting confidence, self-esteem, and an awareness of one's capabilities (Turkat & Buzzell, 1982).

When a member is prepared for a community-based work experience, he or she may proceed to a TE placement. TE typically consists of a time-limited, entry level job in a commercial work setting that the agency has obtained for its members. Members may work in a group with a job coach who is a paid staff member providing job skills training, supervision, and support; members also may work on their own, supervised directly by the firm's own managerial personnel (Roussel & Cook, 1987). Individuals with TE placements usually earn at least minimum wage. Members enter these jobs with an understanding that the placements are temporary and that they will hold one or more positions before finding their own jobs. The fact that members must do work that meets industry standards is emphasized, and programs prefer not to subsidize the employers. Staff typically perform the job first, to assess its requirements in a process referred to as "task analysis." After a member is selected to fill the job, staff have access to the workplace in order to provide further support and assistance if needed. In general, transitional employment is an opportunity for members to test their work readiness, acquire a work history and job references, and build their confidence as employees (Beard et al., 1982).

Past Research on Psychosocial Rehabilitation

In a 1987 study, Dion and Anthony found that rehabilitation interventions had a positive effect on outcomes, including recidivism, time in the community, employment and productivity, skill development, and client satisfaction. These positive results also were documented in a 1984 review of PSR research at Thresholds (Bond, Dincin, Setze, & Witheridge, 1984). Thresholds programming was found to reduce hospital utilization and to increase both independent living and academic achievement. In addition, length of time in the program was positively related to higher rates of employment after termination, and to significant increases in members' levels of residential independence. Finally, participation in Thresholds programming resulted in a net reduction in the average cost of client treatment (Bond, Dincin, Setze, & Witheridge, 1984).

Fellowship House in Miami also has conducted a series of studies, in which decreases of 88% to 92% were found in the number of days that members were hospitalized in the year following program involvement, as compared to the year before membership in the program. At Fountain House, it was found that, compared with control subjects, members spent twice as long in the community before rehospitalization and were hospitalized an average of 40% fewer days (Beard, Propst, & Malamud, 1982).

How Psychosocial Rehabilitation Is Funded

The sources from which PSR agencies derive their funding are as diverse as the agencies themselves (Mohelsky, 1988). Most programs base their sliding fee scale on a member's ability to pay and then subsidize the difference between the fees and the program costs with state and local funding and with private donations. For example, Thresholds obtains funding from the State of Illinois's Department of Rehabilitation Services, with which it contracts to provide vocational rehabilitation, and it also receives money from the state's department of mental health and from corporations, foundations, and private donations. In addition, federal grants fund parts of Thresholds programming, such as services to youth, vocational placements in local theaters, and the availability of staff support at the workplace (Cook & Razzano, in press). Fellowship House has a unique system whereby professional training is provided to individuals and organizations interested in PSR, which accrues revenue and encourages the dissemination of psychosocial principles (Stroul, 1986).

Often, creativity is the rule for finding adequate funding. For example, Independence Center in St. Louis, Missouri, has developed programming that is so diverse that the center is able to obtain funding as a day program, as partial hospitalization, as a place for vocational training and evaluation, and as a psychosocial program (Harvey & Meltzer, 1983). Independence Center also has developed a strong liaison with St. Louis University, resulting in contracts with state funding sources for mental health services, contracts with the state vocational rehabilitation department for training and evaluation, and a contract with the Veterans Administration (Stroul, 1986).

Implementing the Psychosocial Rehabilitation Model

The diversity among PSR programs can be attributed in part to the fact that the earlier programs developed simultaneously and somewhat experimentally, in the absence of an explicitly defined model. Although any new program will develop in ways that will make it distinctive from other programs, there are now several training and dissemination facilities to help the initial implementation of

the psychosocial model. For example, since 1976, Fountain House in New York City has offered a training program to mental health centers and agencies across the country. Other training centers include the Thresholds National Research and Training Center on Rehabilitation and Mental Illness in Chicago, Illinois; Independence Center in St. Louis, Missouri; and Matrix Research Institute in Philadelphia, Pennsylvania. Increasingly, PSR agencies are recognizing their responsibility to train mental health and rehabilitation professionals working outside the PSR model.

In 1975, the International Association of Psychosocial Rehabilitation Services (IAPSRS) was established. Its functions include development and dissemination of the PSR model through conferences, a journal, a newsletter, and various other publications, as well as involvement in policy issues related to PSR. IAPSRS has a membership of 400 agencies and 900 individuals and reports that nearly 1000 agencies in the United States provide at least two of the essential psychosocial services in a recently compiled directory of programs (Hughes, personal communication, 1991).

Tailoring the Model for Special Populations

Rural Programming

Given the genesis of many PSR programs in urban settings, agencies have been faced with the need to adapt the model to accommodate persons in rural areas (Pressing, Peterson, Barnes, & Riley, 1983). For example, in 1985, Thresholds opened a branch in a rural area of Illinois (Kankakee), in order to provide services to a community in which a state hospital had recently closed (Fraser, 1987). Staff found that they needed to be quite innovative in order to make the PSR model work in a rural environment. One obstacle that Thresholds–Kankakee faced was the scarcity of services in the area. Because a range of services for different types of people at different levels of functioning did not exist, the program model had to be altered to fit individuals with a wide range of needs.

Another rural issue is that of linkage. Initially, Thresholds–Kankakee was viewed suspiciously by other providers. Aggressive outreach efforts eventually improved relations between the agency and the local hospital, psychiatrists, and mental health centers, and the advantages of a small, cooperative system began to emerge. Another obstacle is the distance that separates people in rural areas and the lack of an adequate transportation system. Thresholds–Kankakee worked out an agreement with the Illinois Department of Rehabilitation Services for partial reimbursement of the costs for transporting members via vans to the agency. The travel required in rural communities exacerbates many of the difficulties that already affect people with mental illness: Medication and therapy appointments can be difficult or impossible to get to, resulting in hospitalization; social networks are limited due to the lack of transportation to a common meeting place; jobs or education may be available but inconveniently located; and clients' desires for residential independence may conflict with their needs for transportation assistance from their families. Finally, case management and community outreach must be more active and tenacious to compensate for the distance and isolation of rural areas (Pressing et al., 1983).

Elderly Individuals with Mental Illness

Another special population that is growing and requires adaptation of the PSR model consists of elderly persons with severe mental illness. The elderly mentally ill population includes people who have aged throughout the era of deinstitutionalization, as well as people whose illnesses have developed during their later years. Elderly persons with mental illness often are isolated from mainstream service delivery, and their potential for rehabilitation and improvement is all too often ignored (Bernstein & Rose, 1991). In reality, all that is necessary is an adjustment of psychosocial goals to the needs of the elderly, which may mean a greater medical emphasis and less of a vocational emphasis.

In 1980, the State of Florida sponsored a project called the "Geriatric Residential Treatment System" (GRTS), in order to provide community-based PSR and treatment for elderly people with mental illness (Bernstein & Rose, 1991). Services were provided through a residential system and included client advocacy, guidance, support, and living skills training. Services began in a professional group home, with the stay averaging about 150 days, and the emphasis during this phase was on assessment of psychological and physical needs, and on the progressive challenge of more and more independent living skills. The next phase involved an intermediate group home which was a less structured environment, where support focused on attainment of greater residential independence. The stay in the intermediate group home averaged 1 1/2 years before members progressed to a third home, the satellite home. Progression was primarily based on evidence of stability and self-maintenance, and a level of independence and living skills closely approximating fuller independent living. After an average of 1 year in the satellite home, individuals progressed to community residences.

Over a 7-year period, 92.5% of the GRTS program residents remained stable and productive in the community, without need for hospitalization. In addition, 201 of 425 original residents were discharged from the residential continuum, 41.6% being placed in less restrictive settings. The GRTS program shows that PSR can benefit an elderly population, and that program replications emphasizing the special needs of elderly people with mental illness are greatly needed (Bernstein & Rose, 1991).

In addition to Florida, several other states have ongoing projects aimed at improving services to elderly persons with mental illness. Projects such as Iowa's Outreach Demonstration Project, New York's Project Rescue, Wisconsin's Mobile Outreach to Seniors, Colorado's Elderly Empowerment Program, and Washington's Community Home Health

Care Project have a major outreach component, to respond to the fact that many elderly people with mental illness are living in non-mental health oriented settings, such as shelters, boarding homes, nursing homes, and other isolated settings (Community Support Network News [CSNN], 1987).

Homeless Persons with Mental Illness

As they do with elderly persons with psychiatric disabilities, PSR agencies address homeless persons with mental illness via assertive community outreach. Although there are disagreements among researchers in defining both homelessness and mental illness, estimates show that from one fifth to one third of homeless individuals have a history of at least one hospitalization for psychiatric reasons (Bassuk & Lamb, 1986).

Community-outreach service providers are concerned with quality of life and prevention of unnecessary hospitalization and with the notion that services should be provided to those in greatest need (Witheridge, 1990). In addition, assertive outreach workers provide services in settings where the individual is living and encountering problems, in order to most effectively teach coping methods. The assertive outreach worker is an advocate as well and helps the individual learn how to negotiate various systems for treatment, housing, and benefits. The intent of the outreach worker's efforts is to reduce daily stress and create a preventive or anticipatory approach to problems so that crisis is avoided (Engstrom, Brooks, Jonikas, Cook, & Witheridge, 1991).

One of the first responsibilities of staff providing services to homeless persons who have mental illness is that of identifying who is a potential client in need of help. The outreach worker must know where to find target clients, such as shelters, bus terminals, airports, and on the street, and how to engage and then assess the needs of the homeless client. Many of these needs are immediate, such as shelter, food, or clothing. In addition to some of the more general outreach worker

functions, an outreach worker to persons who are homeless needs to be well-informed about issues relating to physical health problems that may have been exacerbated by homelessness. Finally, an outreach worker to homeless persons with mental illness needs to have long-term goals for the client and to know public entitlement policies and procedures thoroughly, as a means of establishing financial security and more permanent housing for the client. Although many of the outreach strategies for homeless persons are similar to those for domiciled clients, the homeless mentally ill population presents some of the greatest challenges and problems to service providers (Engstrom et al., 1991).

Members with Substance Abuse Disorders

Few studies have adequately addressed the problems facing persons with alcohol and other substance abuse problems concurrent with mental illness, or dual diagnoses, despite the fact that estimates of a co-occurring substance abuse problem in persons with mental illness range from 25–35% to 50–75% (Havassy, 1989). Young adults with mental illness are at especially high risk for coexisting chemical dependency (Bergman & Harris, 1985). The need to address dual diagnoses in PSR program members is critical, as substance abuse can produce myriad complications in combination with severe mental illness (Straussman, 1985). Substance abuse is often underdiagnosed in persons with mental illness and can cause misdiagnosis of a client's psychiatric disorder. In addition, dually diagnosed clients have poorer prognoses than clients who do not abuse substances and have higher rates of psychiatric hospitalization (Havassy, 1989).

In order to identify dual diagnoses, service providers need to obtain meticulous case histories of clients and must grapple with the issue of drug testing for members with a positive history of substance abuse. In terms of treatment, service providers must understand the interplay between a client's substance abuse problem and her or his mental illness and must integrate these issues into the overall treatment plan. Four general phases are part of treatment for the dually diagnosed client. First, the member needs to be engaged, most often by showing the connection to getting something the individual wants, such as symptom relief, food or shelter, avoidance of legal problems, or vocational progress. Second, the persuasion phase involves convincing the member that abstinence is best, and that negative symptoms and problems in functioning are related to the drug abuse. Third, during the primary treatment phase, the member engages in group therapies, often with a 12-step program, such as Alcoholics Anonymous, but specifically geared toward dual diagnosis. Fourth, in the final relapse prevention phase, both member and service provider try to deal with relapses in a productive way, and work to prevent them from happening (Osher, 1989).

Horizon House in Philadelphia and the Harbinger Program in Grand Rapids, Michigan, are two PSR programs that have designed special service programs for dually diagnosed members who are homeless (*CSNN*, 1989). The Harbinger House model adds specialists in mental illness and substance abuse to assertive outreach teams. Members receive detoxification, intensive individual support, and vocational services as part of their rehabilitation plan. Horizon House has developed a residential continuum of group home, board and care, and independent apartments where individualized "tenancy" contracts and case management services provide a range of substance abuse treatment and residential services, along with physical, social, and vocational rehabilitation.

Cultural Sensitivity to Needs of Minority Populations

Leona Bachrach (1989) proposes that one of several principles underlying programming for persons with mental illness is that "model programs are responsive to the distinctiveness of local cultures" (p. 234). Although few studies have addressed ethnic minority and cross-cultural issues in PSR, there is little question that these issues are of central importance in providing rehabilitation. Some research suggests that although ethnic minority members perform as well as their nonminority counterparts on agency-sponsored job placements, such minority members do not fare as well once they progress to the level of independent employment (Cook & Roussel, 1987).

One reason for these findings may be that ethnic minority families do not always perceive the same needs for their mentally ill relatives, and may not recognize the need for social programming or independent living, due to different cultural expectations and options. For example, inner-city Black families have been shown to value and preserve networks within the community which may provide a healthy and beneficial interdependence for a family member with mental illness, in contrast to the White mainstream culture's value of independence (Lefley, 1985). Perceived needs also are influenced by cultural views and definitions of mental illness. In some Latin American cultures, mental illness is described simply as bad nerves or "nervios," and both psychological and medical treatments are avoided; in some Asian cultures, mental illness is considered so shameful that treatment outside the family or community is not sought.

Other cultural minority issues in providing rehabilitation necessitate an understanding of the combined influences of poverty and urbanicity along with ethnic minority status (Cook, 1990). The presence of a family member with a severe mental illness may be less distressing than needs created by poverty, gang violence, or risk of homelessness. Clients may be poorly educated, due to inadequate public schooling, may have difficulty finding decent housing in areas with little low cost housing, and may have greater difficulty finding jobs in economically depressed areas. The relationships among economics, race, and culture also may influence the expectations of service providers, who may assume the deficiency or inadequacy of the ethnic minority client's experience.

Many rehabilitation agencies have addressed ethnic minority and cultural issues by promoting the use of bilingual and ethnically diverse staff and by offering problem solving and support groups that deal with minority issues, pride, self-esteem, and discrimination, among other topics. In general, PSR agencies should be prepared to review cultural assumptions and then modify or innovate, with the goal of better meeting the needs of the clients in that particular community (Cook, Jonikas, & Solomon, 1992).

Conclusions and a Look to the Future: Consumer Service Delivery and Expansion of the Model to Other Populations

As PSR looks to the future, the consumer empowerment movement continues to develop and change the ways in which PSR is provided (Leete, 1988). Agencies across the country are rising to the challenge of increasing members' involvement in all aspects of service delivery (Smith & Ford, 1986). True to its egalitarian principles, the field of PSR now has consumer run agencies, consumers who provide outreach and case management, and grants that train consumers to provide services. The National Mental Health Consumers' Association (NMHCA) was established in 1985 to protect and advocate for consumer rights, to promote consumer run alternatives in programming, to fight stigma and economic discrimination, and to improve the accountability of the mental health system to consumers. In 1988, the National Institute of Mental Health funded nine consumer operated service demonstration projects in California, Colorado, Indiana, Maine, Missouri, New Hampshire, New York, Ohio, and Wisconsin, in order to explore the effectiveness and encourage the development of consumer oriented programs. Project SHARE in Philadelphia has created several successful consumer designed and operated initiatives, including the National Mental Health Consumer Self-Help Clearinghouse, which promotes and assists the development of consumer run

projects across the country via written and audiovisual materials, consultations, and training events (CSNN, 1988). Other organizations that are "of, by, and for" people with psychiatric disabilities are founded on a belief that the consumer has a unique wisdom and insight into the mental health system, along with knowledge of mental illness and a desire to provide support and leadership to others experiencing mental illness (Moxley & Freddolino, 1990).

Other new directions include a growing impetus to serve persons with disabilities in addition to mental illness. A program to provide PSR services, including case management, housing, and job placements, to persons with mental illness and hearing impairment has been developed at Thresholds in Chicago (Graham, 1991). In addition, developmental and learning disabilities, visual impairment, and other physical disabilities that accompany severe mental illness necessitate refinement and adaptation of PSR technology.

In conclusion, by the end of the twentieth century, the fields of mental health and rehabilitation are at a crossroads. Deinstitutionalization has created the need for community living and treatment models for providing services formerly offered in institutional settings. The enduring nature of these changes will stem from legislation such as the recently enacted Americans with Disabilities Act (ADA), the reauthorization of the Handicapped Act Amendments of 1983, and the Individuals with Disabilities Education Act (IDEA) legislation mandating a transition-to-work plan for all teenage youth (including those with psychiatric disabilities) in special education. With large numbers of mental health consumers living, learning, and working in the community, the final decade of the twentieth century has the potential to be one of growth and expansion for PSR programs. At the same time, reductions in mental health funding and encroachment by other disciplines willing to imitate the form but not the content of PSR approaches are challenging PSR agencies across the country (Gardner, 1985). As PSR programs address the needs of their members, they are faced with imperatives for even greater consumer involvement and setting more ambitious goals, as members' aspirations rise. Recent legislation will provide further impetus for advocacy on behalf of and in partnership with members. While the ability of PSR to meet these challenges remains to be seen, the movement that started less than a half-century ago already has made dramatic changes in the realization of community living for persons with mental illness.

Acknowledgments

The authors wish to thank Dr. Lisa Razzano of the Thresholds National Research and Training Center for her critical contributions to the preparation of this manuscript.

References

Anderson, C., Hogarty, G., & Reiss, D. (1980). Family treatment of adult schizophrenic patients: A psycho-educational approach. *Schizophrenia Bulletin, 6,* 490–505.

Anthony, W. A., Cohen, M., & Cohen, B. (1984). Psychiatric rehabilitation. In J. Talbott (Ed.), *The chronic mental patient: Five years later.* New York: Grune & Stratton.

Anthony, W. A., Cohen, M., & Farkas, M. (1982). A psychiatric rehabilitation treatment program: Can I recognize one if I see one? *Community Mental Health Journal, 18*(2), 83–97.

Anthony, W. A., & Jansen, M. A. (1984). Predicting the vocational capacity of the chronically mentally ill. *American Psychologist, 39*(5), 537–544.

Anthony, W. A., & Liberman, R. P. (1986). The practice of psychiatric rehabilitation: Historical, conceptual, and research base. *Schizophrenia Bulletin, 12*(4), 542–553.

Bachrach, L. L. (1982). Young chronic patients: An analytical review of the literature. *Hospital and Community Psychiatry, 33,*(3), 189–197.

Bachrach, L. L. (1989). The chronic patient: The legacy of model programs. *Hospital and Community Psychiatry, 40,* 234–235.

Bassuk, E. L., & Lamb, R. H. (1986). Homelessness and the implementation of deinstitutionalization. In E. Bassuk (Ed.), *The mental health needs of homeless persons.* San Francisco, CA: Jossey-Bass.

Beard, J. H., Propst, R. N., & Malamud, T. J. (1982). The Fountain House model of psychiatric rehabilitation. *Psychosocial Rehabilitation Journal, 5,* 47–53.

Bergman, H. C., & Harris, M. (1985). Substance abuse among young adult chronic patients. *Psychosocial Rehabilitation Journal, 9*(1), 44–48.

Bernstein, M. A., & Rose, D. (1991). Psychosocial programming for the elderly who are mentally ill. *Psychosocial Rehabilitation Journal, 14,* 3–13.

Black, B. J. (1987). Reflections on the *social* in *psychosocial. Psychosocial Rehabilitation Journal, 10*(3), 4–9.

Bond, G. R., Dincin, J., Setze, P. J., & Witheridge, T. F. (1984). The effectiveness of psychiatric rehabilitation: A summary of research at Thresholds. *Psychosocial Rehabilitation Journal, 7,* 6–22.

Bond, G. R., & Friedmeyer, M. H. (1987). Predictive validity of situational assessment at a psychiatric rehabilitation center. *Rehabilitation Psychology, 32,* 99–111.

Cnaan, R. A., Blankertz, L., Messinger, K. W., & Gardner, J. R. (1988). Psychosocial rehabilitation: Towards a definition. *Psychosocial Rehabilitation Journal, 11,* 61–77.

Cnaan, R. A., Blankertz, L., Messinger, K. W., & Gardner, J. R. (1989). Psychosocial rehabilitation: Towards a theoretical base. *Psychosocial Rehabilitation Journal, 12,* 33–55.

Cnaan, R. A., Blankertz, L., Messinger, K. W., & Gardner, J. R. (1990). Experts' assessment of psychosocial rehabilitation principles. *Psychosocial Rehabilitation Journal, 13,* 59–73.

Cohen, M., & Amdur, M. (1981). Medication groups for psychiatric patients. *American Journal of Nursing, 81,* 259–265.

Cohen, M. A., Dincin, J., & Amdur, M. (1975). *Questions patients ask about psychiatric medication: A joint project of the Thresholds and Northwestern Memorial Hospital's Institute of Psychiatry.* Chicago, IL: Thresholds and Northwestern University.

Community Support Network News (CSNN) (1987). Services to the elderly with psychiatric disabilities. *CSNN, 3*(3), 1–13.

Community Support Network News (CSNN) (1988). Consumer/ex-patients initiatives. *CSNN, 5*(2), 1–13.

Community Support Network News (CSNN) (1989). Initiatives for young adults with mental illness & substance abuse problems. *CSNN, 5*(4), 3–7.

Cook, J. A. (1988). Who "mothers" the chronically mentally ill? *Family Relations, 37,* 42–49.

Cook, J. A. (1990). *Minority issues in psychosocial rehabilitation: A re-examination.* Chicago: Thresholds Research Institute.

Cook, J. A. (1992). Job ending among youth and adults with severe mental illness. *Journal of Mental Health Administration,19*(2), 158–169.

Cook, J. A., Hoffschmidt, S., Cohler, B., & Pickett, S. (1992). Marital satisfaction among parents of the severely mentally ill living in the community. *American Journal of Orthopsychiatry, 62*, 552–563.

Cook, J. A., Jonikas, J. A., & Solomon, M. L. (in press). Models of vocational rehabilitation for youth and adults with severe mental illness. *American Rehabilitation.*

Cook, J. A., & Pickett, S. A. (1987). Feelings of burden and criticalness among parents residing with chronically mentally ill offspring. *Journal of Applied Social Sciences, 12*(1), 79–107.

Cook, J. A., Pickett, S. A., & Jonikas, J. A. (1989). *The community exploration program: Vocational laboratory experiences for psychiatrically disabled youth.* Chicago, IL: Thresholds Research Institute.

Cook, J. A., & Razzano, L. (in press). Natural vocational supports for persons with severe mental illness: Thresholds supported competitive employment program. In L. Stein (Ed.), *Innovations in mental health services.* San Francisco, CA: Jossey-Bass.

Cook, J. A., & Roussel, A. E. (1987, April). *Who works and what works? Effects of race, class, age, and gender on employment among the psychiatrically disabled.* Paper presented to the annual meeting of the American Sociological Association, Chicago, IL.

Cook, J. A., Solomon, M. L., & Mock, L. (1989). What happens after the first job placement: Vocational transitioning among severely emotionally disturbed and behavior disordered adolescents. *Programming for Adolescents with Behavior Disorders, 4*, 71–93.

Cook, J. A., Wessell, M., & Dincin, J. (1987). Predicting educational achievement levels of the severely mentally ill: Implications for psychosocial program administrators. *Psychosocial Rehabilitation Journal, 10*, 23–37.

Dincin, J. (1975). Psychiatric rehabilitation. *Schizophrenia Bulletin, 1*, 131–148.

Dincin, J., Selleck, V, & Streicker, S. (1978). Restructuring parental attitudes—working with parents of the adult mentally ill. *Schizophrenia Bulletin, 4*, 597–608.

Dincin, J., & Wise, S. (1979). Sexual attitude reassessment for psychiatric patients. *Rehabilitation Literature, 40*, 222–231.

Dincin, J., Selleck, V., & Carter, S. (1980). Implementing the rehabilitation approach in a community residential setting. *Rehabilitation Counseling Bulletin, 24*, 72–83.

Dincin, J., & Witheridge, T.F. (1982). Psychiatric rehabilitation as a deterrent to recidivism. *Hospital and Community Psychiatry, 33*, 645–650.

Dincin, J. (1990). Speaking out. *Psychosocial Rehabilitation Journal, 14*(2), 83–85.

Dion, G. L., & Anthony, W. A. (1987). Research in psychiatric rehabilitation: A review of experimental and quasi-experimental studies. *Rehabilitation Counseling Bulletin, 30*, 177–203.

Engstrom, K., Brooks, E. B., Jonikas, J. A., Cook, J. A., & Witheridge, T. F. (1991). *Creating community linkages: A guide to assertive outreach for homeless persons with severe mental illness.* Chicago, IL: Thresholds National Research and Training Center.

Farrell, D. (1986). Thresholds: A delivery system. In C. Smith (Ed.), *Proceedings of the Schizophrenia Conference* (p. 73–80). Edmonton, Canada: Alberta Hospital, Edmonton, Alberta, Canada.

Forman, J. D. (1988). Sheltered work in a non-sheltered setting. *Psychosocial Rehabilitation Journal, 9*(3), 13–18.

Fraser, V. V. (1987). Adapting a psychosocial rehabilitation agency to a rural community. *Psychosocial Rehabilitation Journal, 11*, 67–71.

Gardner, J. R. (1985). Scanning the environment: Psychosocial rehabilitation at the crossroad. *Psychosocial Rehabilitation Journal, 8*(3), 4–7.

Goldman, H. (1982). Mental illness and family burden: A public health perspective. *Hospital and Community Psychiatry, 33*, 557–560.

Graham, K. K. (1991). Comprehensive mental health services for deaf people with major mental illness: Thresholds Bridge Program for the Hearing Impaired. *Hospital and Community Psychiatry, 42*, 1057–1058.

Harvey, R. B., & Meltzer, T. (1983). Funding a new psychiatric rehabilitation center. *Psychosocial Rehabilitation Journal, 6*(1), 7–14.

Hatfield, A. B., Fierstein, R., & Johnson, D. (1982). Meeting the needs of families of the psychiatrically disabled. *Psychosocial Rehabilitation Journal, 6*(1), 27–40.

Havassy, B. (1989). *Co-occurrence of severe mental and substance abuse disorders: Current knowledge and implications for new research* (Report prepared for the National Institute of Mental Health, National Plan of Research to Improve Services for People with Severe Mental Disorders). San Francisco, CA: University of California, San Francisco.

Heinrichs, D. W., & Carpenter, W. T. (1982). The psychotherapy of the schizophrenic disorders. In L. Grinspoon (Ed.), *Psychiatry: 1982 annual review* (pp. 154–166), Washington, DC: American Psychiatric Association.

Jonikas, J. A., & Cook, J. A. (1990). *Helping persons with mental illness live in the community: Two residential models that promote neighborhood integration.* Chicago, IL: Thresholds Research Institute.

Keith, S. J., & Mathews, J. M. (1982). Group, family, and milieu therapies and psychosocial rehabilitation in the treatment of the schizophrenic disorders. In L. Grinspoon (Ed.), *Psychiatry: 1982 annual review* (pp. 166–177), Washington, DC.: American Psychiatric Association.

Lamb, R., & Oliphant, E. (1978). Schizophrenia through the eyes of families. *Hospital and Community Psychiatry, 29*, 803–806.

Leete, E. (1988). A consumer perspective on psychosocial treatment. *Psychosocial Rehabilitation Journal, 12*, 45–52.

Lefley, H. (1985). Culture and mental illness: The family role. In A. B. Hatfield & H. P. Lefley (Eds.), *Families of the mentally ill: Coping and adaptation* (pp. 30–59). New York: Guilford Press.

Liberman, R. P., & Rueger, D. B. (1984). Drug–psychosocial treatment interactions: Comprehensive rehabilitation for chronic schizophrenics. *Psychosocial Rehabilitation Journal, 7*(3), 3–30.

Mohelsky, H. (1988). Psychosocial rehabilitation and our economy. *Psychosocial Rehabilitation Journal, 12*(1), 55–60.

Mosher, L. R., & Keith, S. J. (1979). Research on the psychosocial treatment of schizophrenia: A summary report. *American Journal of Psychiatry, 136*, 623–631.

Moxley, D. P., & Freddolino, P. P. (1990). A model of advocacy for promoting client self-determination in psychosocial rehabilitation. *Psychosocial Rehabilitation Bulletin, 14*(2), 69–82,

Osher, F. (1989). The dually diagnosed: Patient characteristics and treatment strategies. *Community Support Network News, 5*(4), 1, 10–11.

Pepper, B., & Ryglewicz, H., (Eds.). (1982). *The young adult chronic patient.* San Francisco, CA: Jossey-Bass.

Peretti, P., & Dincin, J. (1971). Rehabilitation through camp participation for former mental patients. *Journal of Applied Rehabilitation Counseling, 2*, 27–31.

Pressing, K. O., Peterson, C. L., Barnes, J. K., & Riley, B. D. (1983). Growing wings: A psychosocial rehabilitation program for chronically mentally ill patients in a rural setting. *Psychosocial Rehabilitation Journal, 6*(4), 13–24.

Ridgeway, P., & Zipple, A. M. (1990). The paradigm shift in residential services: From the linear continuum to supported housing approaches. *Psychosocial Rehabilitation Journal, 13*(4), 11–32.

Roussel, A. E., & Cook, J. A. (1987). The role of work in psychiatric rehabilitation: A therapeutic alternative to competitive employment. *Sociological Practice, 6*, 149–168.

Smith, M. K., & Ford, J. (1986). Client involvement: Practical advice for professionals. *Psychosocial Rehabilitation Journal, 9*(3), 25–34.

Solomon, P., & Davis, J. M. (1984). Community attitudes toward residential facilities for psychiatric patients. *Psychosocial Rehabilitation Bulletin, 8*(2), 38–41.

Spaniol, L., Jung, H., Zipple, A., & Fitzgerald, S. (1987). Families as a resource in the rehabilitation of the severely psychiatrically disabled. In A. B. Hatfield & H. P. Lefley (Eds.), *Families of the mentally ill: Coping and adaptation.* New York: Guilford Press.

Stein, L. I., & Test, M. A. (1980). Alternative to mental hospital treatment. *Archives of General Psychiatry, 37*, 392–397.

Stein, L.I., Test, M.A., & Marx, A.J. (1975). Alternative to the hospital: A controlled study. *American Journal of Psychiatry, 132*, 517–522.

Straussman, J. (1985). Dealing with double disabilities: Alcohol use in the club. *Psychosocial Rehabilitation Journal, 8*(3), 8–14.

Streicker, S. K., Amdur, M., & Dincin, J. (1986). Educating patients about psychiatric medications: Failure to enhance compliance. *Psychosocial Rehabilitation Journal, 9*, 15–28.

Stroul, B. (1986). *Models of community support services: Approaches to helping persons with long-term mental illness.* Boston, MA: Center for Psychiatric Rehabilitation.

Tanaka, H. T. (1983). Psychosocial rehabilitation: Future trends and directions. *Psychosocial Rehabilitation Journal, 6*, 7–12.

Turkat, D., & Buzzell, V. (1982). Psychosocial rehabilitation: A process evaluation. *Hospital and Community Psychiatry, 33*, 848–850.

Weinberg, R. B., & Marlow, H. A., Jr. (1983). Recognizing the social in psychosocial: The importance of social network interventions. *Psychosocial Rehabilitation Bulletin, 6*(4), 25–34.

Witheridge, T. F. (1988). Scattered-site crisis services at Thresholds. *Community Support Network News, 4*, 5–6.

Witheridge, T. F. (1990). Assertive community treatment as a supported housing approach. *Psychosocial Rehabilitation Journal, 13*, 69–75.

Witheridge, T. F., Streicker, S. K., & MacInnes, W. D. (1977). Establishing a research program at a psychosocial rehabilitation agency. *Psychosocial Rehabilitation Journal, 1*, 13–20.

Chapter 7

Supports and Rehabilitation for Housing and Community Living

PAUL J. CARLING

This chapter focuses on the housing and community living needs of people with psychiatric disabilities. It describes how the field's approach to meeting these needs is changing, and how consumers are affected by the nation's affordable housing crisis. A variety of community "program models," and research on their effectiveness is described, along with some critical problems associated with using residential treatment facilities as housing. *Supported housing*, a new approach based on principles of consumer choice and community integration, is described. Finally, a description of how to work with individuals to achieve their housing and support goals is presented.

Background and Scope of the Problem

Since the late 1950s, we have significantly reduced public hospital use and have expanded community services (Kiesler, 1982). The critical need for stable housing linked to supports, however, has only emerged in the 1980s as a major policy dilemma (Carling & Ridgway, 1987). A majority of the 1.7 to 2.4 million Americans with long-term mental illness—based on diagnosis, disability, and duration of disorder (Goldman, Gatozzi, & Taube, 1981)—live in inadequate housing,

lack needed supports, or are homeless (U.S. Department of Health and Human Services [U.S. DHHS], 1980, 1983). The problem is complex: Without active rehabilitation, many individuals lack the skills and supports needed for successful community living. In addition, the recurring nature of long-term psychiatric disabilities may result in people losing housing as they experience repeated hospitalizations (Budson, 1981; Chafetz & Goldfinger, 1984). Housing discrimination based on stigma is a day-to-day reality. Landlords refuse to rent to these individuals, cutting off access to available rental housing (Aviram & Segal, 1973; Hogan, 1985a, 1985b; Segal, Baumohl, & Moyles, 1980). Moreover, many people with psychiatric disabilities are poor, with average reported annual incomes from $3,000 to $7,000 and unemployment rates as high as 85% (Anthony & Dion, 1986).

Failure to focus on people's permanent housing needs has had multiple effects. Many individuals remain in psychiatric hospitals because of the lack of housing (U.S. DHHS, 1980). Others cycle through emergency rooms and general hospitals in costly and often inappropriate stays (Chafetz & Goldfinger, 1984; Geller, 1982). Many others have been moved to custodial nursing and boarding homes. Most of these settings lack active rehabilitation or treatment, contribute to declines in functioning, and are often exploitative (Carling, 1981; Kohen & Paul, 1976; Segal & Aviram, 1978; U.S. Senate Special Committee on Aging, 1976). The lack of permanent housing and support options also results in substantial burden on families (Hatfield, Fierstein, & Johnson, 1982; Wasow, 1982), who serve as case managers and landlords with little or no community support. Of those who find independent housing in the community, many do so in very low income neighborhoods, where substandard housing and high crime rates are typical. Oversaturation of these neighborhoods by people with disabilities often leads to community backlash (Coulton, Holland, & Fitch, 1984; Ridgway, 1987). An increasing number are homeless. Finally, people with psychiatric disabilities compete for housing with other low income groups. Because of societal stigma against mental illness, other groups are generally viewed as more suitable tenants.

The Affordable Housing Crisis

Two factors reduce access to housing for *all* people with limited incomes: a decade-long decline in affordable housing stock and the rising cost of housing in relation to income. This combination puts home ownership out of reach of many middle income Americans and puts decent housing out of reach of most of those at or below the poverty level. In addition, with a cut of nearly 80% in federally assisted housing for low-income and special needs groups since 1981, there has been a dramatic increase in homelessness (Low Income Housing Information Service, 1988).

Because disabilities can be economically catastrophic, people with disabilities are disproportionately represented in the demographic group that is called "very poor," or well below the poverty level. Most people who are disabled by a mental illness and are served by the public mental health system receive Supplemental Security Income (SSI) as their primary source of income. In comparing SSI income and affordability of housing in every U.S. county, McCabe, Edgar, King, Mancuso, and Emery (1991) found that *there is not a single county* where people with SSI can afford to rent either an efficiency/ studio or a one-bedroom apartment. This finding, along with results of studies of consumer perceptions of the housing problem (Ridgway, 1988), show that income may be the major barrier to housing, rather than the psychiatric disability itself. It is an especially vexing barrier, given the results of consumer-preference studies indicating that most consumers prefer their own apartment in housing that is integrated (i.e., not developed specifically for people with a label or disability). This is a particularly difficult problem in urban areas, where much of the affordable housing stock (e.g., welfare hotels, boarding homes, and other marginal settings) have been lost to *gentrification* (replacing low income housing with high priced housing). These trends promote segregated, group solutions to urban homelessness, in spite of consumers' preferences.

Financing Issues

The low income of tenants with psychiatric disabilities and the cutback in government funding of housing present major dilemmas for financing housing for this group. Nonetheless, a number of creative approaches to the financing of housing have surfaced in the mid-1980s (Randolph, Laux, & Carling, 1987). These strategies are used for three purposes: to offer access to existing housing, to preserve existing housing, and to develop new affordable housing. To offer *access* to housing, mental health systems are creating rent subsidy programs at the state level, in connection with, or as an alternative to, the federal housing subsidy program (Section 8), as well as contingency funds to help with furnishings, utility hookups, other start-up costs, and emergency housing payments. To *preserve* existing affordable housing, mental health systems are creating limited pools of capital dollars to be used to purchase and renovate such housing, usually in coalition with other low income advocacy groups. To *develop* housing, mental health systems are using a variety of approaches: (a) targeting capital (formerly used for facilities) for development of integrated housing in partnership with others, (b) purchasing distressed properties, (c) creating capital funds that can internally subsidize the cost of housing so that it remains perpetually affordable, or (d) mixing public and private funds, such as in limited equity ventures or through the use of tax credits. One other creative example is the use of back payments from an SSI lawsuit to develop housing (Rubinstein & James, 1990).

Residential Program Models

The mental health field's response to people who need both housing and treatment is undergoing significant change. Historically, mental health agencies have viewed housing as a social welfare problem and defined their role exclusively in terms of treatment. Public housing agencies, in turn, contended that mentally ill consumers need specialized residential programs and viewed the housing needs of mentally ill persons as a mental health responsibility (Carling & Ridgway, 1987). Thus, housing needs are often ignored. When mental health systems have responded to housing needs, they have typically combined treatment needs and living needs in a residential service. Practically speaking, this means that consumers were offered therapeutic facilities, not housing. Transitional halfway houses proliferated in the 1960s. In the 1970s, the concept of a residential continuum emerged and included a variety of models, such as quarterway houses and halfway houses (Budson, 1981), three-quarterway houses (Campbell, 1981), family foster care (Carling, 1984), crisis alternative models (Stein & Test, 1985; Test, 1981), Fairweather Lodges (Fairweather, 1980), apartment programs (Carling, 1978; Goldmeier, Shore, & Mannino, 1977), boarding homes

(Kohen & Paul, 1976), nursing homes (Carling, 1981), and shelters for homeless persons (Baxter & Hopper, 1984). These programs have typically been segregated, professionally staffed, and congregate in nature (Carling & Ridgway, 1987). Described next are the typical residential program models that a researcher, professional, consumer, or family member might encounter in communities.

Types of Residences

Halfway Houses and Group Homes

These settings generally fall into two categories: transitional residences or long-term group homes, based on how long people stay there. How long people stay may depend on what other housing or supports are available.

Long-term Group Homes: In long-term group homes, the goal is long-term housing and support. Typically, there are awake on-site shift staff members on a 24-hour basis. Variations include asleep on-site, or on-call off-site staff members, depending on perceived intensity of needed services. These programs try to improve skills and quality of life and seek to allow for the possibility of movement to another situation, but with little active expectation that this should happen.

Transitional Residences: These arose due to increased expectations for community success, and the growing awareness of normalization and integration. Also, housing people in long-term group homes implies both long-term funding and long-term responsibility for housing by mental health agencies. Transitional residences typically have active programming, and an expectation that people will use the environment, the group culture, and the skills training (provided by staff members) to set goals and to move toward more independent living. Typical activities offered by staff members may include assistance with goal setting, teaching living skills, helping people organize to move on, and providing assistance to help clients become more comfortable using community resources, seeking employment, and getting settled in a new home.

Group homes are often hampered by (a) the lack of skilled or trained staff members; (b) a lack of clarity about the specific interventions the staff should be providing, apart from the milieu; (c) the inherent problems in providing services and in responding to rapid individual changes within a group environment that has a formal program structure; (d) the lack of community housing options to allow people to move out of these settings when *they* want to, rather than when a bed is available; and (e) the difficulty of combining the role of landlord, therapist, and agent of social control. These are difficulties that many consumers articulate in their rejection of such programs (Ridgway, 1988).

Quarterway Houses, and Other Hospital-Based Programs

Typically located on hospital grounds and intended to ease the transition of patients from an inpatient ward, these programs are staffed by hospital employees. They often offer the opportunity for cooking, some privacy, and the practice of some skills, albeit ones that are more relevant to group or hospital living than to living in one's own housing. While these settings offer more freedom to patients, they often have difficulties with combining ward or inpatient roles with community support roles for staff. In addition, hospital administrative structures often make it difficult for people to have the personal freedom to actually control significant aspects of the setting, or to move easily from this setting into the community and back.

Family Foster Care

Family foster care involves arranging for an individual to live with a surrogate family, which provides basic shelter, meals, and some level of support. Families who offer this option may or may not be trained but are sup-ported by public funds. Family foster care (and board and care) predominated in the early days of deinstitutionalization, as extensions of hospital programs. The use of this model has declined in general (Carling, 1984), but many persons still reside in foster homes, often with few supports or opportunities for integration. Better linkages with these sites by community support staff are critical. Two separate uses of family care have emerged since the mid-1970s: as a crisis alternative to hospitals, and as a source of community support during the transition out of a hospital. As a crisis setting, the Southwest Denver Model, replicated widely and described in Carling (1984), used trained families, with strong backup from a community mental health center, to provide emergency services to people who otherwise would have been admitted to a state hospital. A notable example of the transitional option, also replicated widely, is called the "Short Term Bed (STB) Program" in Northeast Kingdom, Vermont (also described in Carling, 1984), which provides a caring home on a short term basis for individuals who are leaving a hospital, and who are trying to establish roots in a particular community. Meanwhile, community support workers provide help to find housing and work, and to build or reestablish a social network.

Crisis Alternative Residences

This option is increasingly popular in systems that are focused on downsizing state hospitals, because the literature makes it clear that people in crisis can be better served in community-based environments, including their own homes, than in institutions. A variety of options (Stroul, 1988), include group settings, the use of a few beds in a group home, crisis apartments, foster care (described previously), short inpatient stays with creative staffing or administrative structures, and consumer operated "safe houses." These options are all more restrictive than home-based crisis services, which are also expanding throughout the country.

Group Crisis Residences: In this major historical alternative to hospitalization, these settings approximate the functions of a hospital emergency room and provide intensive social support. Round-the-clock staff members have varying professional backgrounds and provide access to psychiatric care and medication, although some of these settings (e.g., Chamberlin, 1978) emphasize the need to have an opportunity to work through such crises without medication. Advantages include the collection of specifically skilled staff in one place and the development of a highly specialized set of interventions. Disadvantages include the concentrated collection of a number of individuals with mental illness who are in crisis, which can create a chaotic and over-stimulating environment, and can limit the program's ability to support individuals in maintaining as many areas of functioning as possible through the crisis; difficulties in addressing persons in an individualized fashion; and difficulties in having clients retain maximal control over their options and choices through a crisis.

Crisis Apartment Options: Some mental health systems, such as in Maine (Wygal, 1988), fund apartment options for crises. Apartments are left empty until a crisis occurs, at which time staff members are brought in to provide support for an individual who cannot stay at home. The first line of support is by homemaker services, which help the person to continue daily functions such as cooking, cleaning, and self-care. Medical and community support services are immediately available, as well. This program has been successful in diverting significant numbers of individuals away from admission to the state hospital. However, it may present more administrative complexities for agencies, as they try to have staff members immediately available for crisis response. As such, these settings can best be developed as part of an overall outreach-oriented crisis-response system, in which these apartments are simply viewed as another resource to the crisis team.

Inpatient Options: While this chapter does not focus on inpatient services, there have been a number of creative uses of staffing relationships with local inpatient settings, where case managers support individuals during brief hospitalizations, or in which hospitals allow an individual to be "guested" (i.e., not admitted), in order to reduce dependence on the hospital setting as an immediate response to crisis, or to shorten the inpatient stay itself.

Safe Houses: These settings are few in number but a subject of increasing interest nationally. They are operated by consumers and may or may not have formal connections with the mental health system. One such example is described by Chamberlin (1978). They place a high value on choice, including the choice to not receive medication during a crisis and to avoid involuntary commitment. Their major intervention is intensive personal and social support. They tend to serve individuals who have little interest in, or active aversion to, traditional mental health services, and they are typically described by consumer leaders as being important but unavailable elements of a community support system (Ridgway, 1988).

Home-Based Crisis Services: These services, the least restrictive method of resolving most crises, are typically based in outreach crisis teams. A promising home-based service that is replacing the crisis residential approach is the Home Intervention Team in Washington County, Vermont (Curtis, 1990), which moves an entire complement of staff members, including psychiatrists and psychiatric nurses, into an individual's home, with the client's consent, for as long as crisis assistance is needed. This program has had great success in hospital diversion and is only used when all other alternatives have been exhausted and involuntary commitment is imminent.

Fairweather Lodges

Begun as a transitional intervention to assist long stay patients to plan their own community reentry, the program has been modified through replication. Central elements (Fairweather, 1980) are a planned process in which an inpatient group decides how to acquire a house and create a community business. Staff members serve as planning consultants and then provide off-site support to the group after they select a house and move in together. There is a strong emphasis on group problem solving and on mutual support. The original model incorporated some specific constraints, which have become unworkable in more recent times, such as an expectation that no community member could decide on marriage and still remain in the lodge. Similarly, early replications focused on same-gender houses. More recent replications have seen many clients use this option as a transitional experience, to assist them in initial community reentry. Lodges have been very popular in areas such as Michigan, Texas, and Oklahoma but have not been widely replicated in other areas.

Transitional Apartment Programs

A rapidly growing part of mental health systems since the late 1970s (Carling, 1978), these programs evolved from the halfway house model. They typically involve off-site staff members assisting people who are living in apartments to become more rooted in the community and to increase their independent living skills. In some cases, agencies rent or own entire apartment buildings, which has the disadvantage of segregation and congregation, or an agency may simply rent a few units in one or more buildings. In some cases, a separate apartment will be rented for staff members, so that immediate support can be available, although the trend seems more and more to rely on outreach case management and crisis staff for this purpose. In early programs, the agency held the lease and required tenants to remain active in the program and take medications, as a condition of staying in the housing. Similarly, early programs stressed time limits, after which tenants would have to find a long-term housing situation. More re-

cent trends have been to have the tenant hold a standard lease, to promote an entirely voluntary relationship with service staff, and to eliminate any time limits, so that tenants can stay as long as they wish in their own housing.

Boarding Homes

These settings were also used as a predominant response to deinstitutionalization in many states. Typically, they involve either small or very large settings into which hospital patients were placed, and in which the individual's SSI check, often supplemented by state funds, was used to provide for basic necessities and supervision and support. Federal and state investigations of these settings have revealed widespread abuse of people's rights, a lack of attention to basic cleanliness and safety, and even physical danger to residents. As a result, mental health systems are deemphasizing the use of these settings in the 1990s. Nonetheless, large numbers of individuals continue to reside in these settings, and service providers face difficult choices in addressing their needs. Some mental health systems have tried to make these settings a formal part of their array of residential options, which may involve targeting significant (and usually scarce) funds to this option, in order to upgrade the environments and the services they offer, an approach that may limit the ability to similarly target such funding for less restrictive housing options. A more common approach has been to increase access by regulatory and service agencies to such settings, and to provide strong outreach and community support to residents, so that they can be encouraged to plan for their eventual return to a less segregated and more independent option. A few such settings, often the smallest ones, appear to offer a caring environment for individuals who have limited options.

Nursing Homes

As with boarding homes, nursing homes have been a major, and typically inappropriate by-product of deinstitutionalization (Carling, 1981; U.S. Senate Special Committee on Aging, 1976). There are few mental health services, and virtually no psychiatric services in most of these settings, and thus they should not be viewed as a mental health treatment environment. However, there have been a number of creative nursing home linkage projects in which mental health agencies offer community support services to nursing home residents.

Homeless Shelters

These settings have mushroomed in response to the growing problem of homelessness and have, in effect, become a major industry in the United States, which is expected to provide indefinite residence for many homeless people. Problems with shelters have been dramatically portrayed in the literature (Kozol, 1988) and are frequently rejected for reasons of personal safety by people with psychiatric disabilities (Ridgway, 1988). On the other hand, a number of creative linkages with shelters have been undertaken by mental health programs, including low-profile services that focus on engagement and responding to basic needs before offering any mental health services. Specialized shelters have been developed for people with psychiatric disabilities, and these have often been linked to emerging projects, offering transitional housing for the homeless or even linked to permanent housing.

Shelters present a major challenge to mental health staff members, in that a set of housing and support options needs to be organized on an immediate basis for an individual who not only is in crisis, but also may have had many negative experiences in the past with the mental health system, or may have simply become so rootless as to have enormous difficulty in staying within a particular housing setting. Nonetheless, the specific skills involved in working with individuals who are homeless are becoming a priority for many mental health agencies, and many creative examples of interventions that are both respectful and effective are beginning to emerge.

Evaluation of Residential Program Models

A recent national survey of more than 2500 community residential programs in all states serving adults with psychiatric disabilities (Randolph, Sanford, Simoneau, Ridgway, & Carling, 1988) found that, despite broad development of residential programs in the 1980s, only a small number of agencies provide these services in most states. Few agencies offer more than one option, and most programs were large congregate settings. The newer supervised apartment and supportive housing approaches use larger numbers of households, each of which serves a small number of people, an approach that is more consistent with normalization principles (Taylor, Racino, Knoll, & Lutfiyya, 1987). Intermediate care facilities, nursing homes, and shelters had few formal ties with mental health services. Transitional housing also was not as common as expected. Most programs provided long-term housing. Surprisingly, residential services are *not* intensive in their provision of mental health services: they are staffed by paraprofessionals who have received little mental health training, and they do not provide specific or frequent interventions with residents. Follow-up services were informal and inconsistent. Residents were primarily young adults with major mental disorders, but these programs served *twice* as many persons who were functional as they did those who were gravely disabled. This finding raises serious concerns about whether such expensive resources should be serving so many persons who are functioning well.

Our knowledge about what works in residential programs is hampered by both methodological and conceptual problems. In six major reviews covering several hundred alternatives to hospitalization, only a handful of studies met basic criteria of experimental design (Braun et al., 1981; Carpenter, 1978;

Dellario & Anthony, 1981; Kiesler, 1982; Test & Stein, 1978). Taken as a whole, however, these studies indicate that community-based treatment is virtually always as effective as, or more effective than, hospital-based treatment in helping people with psychiatric disabilities to achieve employment outcomes, to gain reentry into the community, and to appropriately reduce their use of medication and outpatient services. Apparently, any of a wide range of community services can assist in achieving some measure of community integration.

With regard to residential programs, Cometa, Morrison, and Ziskoven (1979), reviewing a total of 109 studies, concluded that evidence of the effectiveness of transitional halfway houses in reducing recidivism, improving economic self-sufficiency, and improving community adjustment was "highly suspect" (p. 25). Transitional residential programs may, in fact, be preferable to institutional care, but according to this review, they fall short of helping people to achieve community integration. An extensive study of sheltered care environments conducted by Segal and Aviram (1978), and an analysis of the deinstitutionalization literature by Tabor (1980), indicate that characteristics of the *community* are more important than characteristics of *residents* in predicting the degree to which people actually participate in community life, while specific characteristics of the *facility* were the least important factor. These studies suggest that outcome research should be reframed to include a focus on where people live and how they spend their time, rather than focusing solely on the interventions or facilities that professionals provide.

In summary, there have been relatively few rigorous evaluations of specific residential programs, and virtually no attempts to examine professionals' success in helping people to get and keep normal housing. The lack of information on program effectiveness is a critical deficit, which can result in grossly inefficient use of resources and, most important, in seriously curtailed opportunities for people with psychiatric disabilities.

Foundations for a New Approach: Supported Housing

Two recent reviews of the outcome research literature on psychiatric disabilities (Anthony & Blanch, 1989; Wilson, in press) summarize findings that provide a framework for ways to provide people with decent housing and to provide ongoing support. These reviews conclude that (1) a psychiatric disability is not necessarily a lifelong degenerative process; (2) most people with psychiatric disabilities can maintain homes, jobs, friends, and families; (3) mental health services must be highly flexible in order to be responsive to individual needs, and correspondingly, people with the highest level of disability seem to have the most individually distinctive needs; (4) people *can* make positive choices about the kind and intensity of supports they receive; (5) given choice, most people do not define themselves principally as "chronic mental patients"—instead, they value independence and productivity more than any other treatment outcomes.

Despite the growth of residential services and the emergence of new models, residential programs do not, *per se*, meet housing needs. In fact, serious questions have been raised about failing to distinguish between residential treatment and housing, or even the assumption that people need to participate in such programs prior to independent living (Racino, 1991; Taylor et al., 1987). The growing acceptance of a rehabilitation approach (Anthony & Blanch, 1989; Blanch, Carling, & Ridgway, 1988), demystifies the acquisition of housing by defining it as a process of building critical skills and supports to "choose," "get," and "keep" the housing one desires.

A range of research and training activities undertaken by the Center for Community Change (CCC) at the University of Vermont, partly in collaboration with Boston University's Center for Psychiatric Rehabilitation, has revealed significant dissatisfaction among consumers, their families, and service providers with the traditional approach of using residential programs to address both housing and support needs. A number of these critical emerging issues are presented next, as a series of myths. These myths arise from the use of outdated assumptions about people with psychiatric disabilities as primarily either patients or service recipients, particularly as these assumptions relate to their housing and support needs.

Common Myths About Housing and Support

Myth 1. Most People Need a Residential Continuum: A residential continuum (Pepper, 1985) assumes that people should pass through a series of settings developmentally, as they move toward independent living (see Myth 3). This developmental view is positive, but it confuses *where* people live with how they happen to be functioning, and with the supports they need at a given time. It promotes the trauma of multiple moves and requires that people live in programs to get needed supports. As such, it promotes chronic dislocation and delays real integration (i.e., having a real home, work, and a social network). A *continuum* implies that people have to spend large amounts of time preparing for community living. In contrast, a rehabilitation approach suggests that people learn skills by practicing them directly where they are needed. Finally, and most important, the continuum approach is inconsistent with what most consumers want. It is not a tenable *housing* option anyway because most systems offer residential programs to only 2% to 5% of their clients (Randolph, Sanford, Simoneau, Ridgway, & Carling, 1988).

Myth 2. Most People Need Transitional Housing: While there is a clear need for emergency shelter, and respite and crisis options, transitional housing programs, such as those for people who are homeless, also confuse the need for a home with the need for supports. While consumer preference studies suggest that a small proportion of people want transitional housing to be available, we should avoid assuming that people in a particular situation (e.g., homeless or hospitalized) routinely need this option. In fact, developing transitional housing often takes attention away from permanent housing and decentralized supports, which can make transitional programs obsolete. We all experience transitions, and we need support and stability (not moving) to use them as an opportunity for growth.

Myth 3. The Goal Is "Independent Living" and People Should Prepare for this Goal Through Skills Training in Group Homes: Most programs espouse independent living as a goal, sometimes as some mythical state in which people need no support from professionals and are left to fend for themselves in isolated apartments with little to occupy their time. In fact, all of us are *interdependent*; the goal of rehabilitation programs is to help individuals to develop homes, work, and social networks that will support growing self-reliance. The focus, therefore, should be on community integration and support, not independence. The skills training that goes on in most residential programs is ephemeral, rarely individualized, and relevant only to living in relatively large groups. Training in these settings presents significant learning-transfer problems to the real living environment.

Myth 4. Professionals (or Families) Know Best What Consumers Need—Besides, Consumers Cannot Choose or Articulate Their Needs: Until recently, the debate about what people need has been among *professionals*. More recently, families have begun to attempt to define needs, and only very recently, we have begun to hear broadly from consumers. Although the rhetoric of mental health systems is now that services must be consumer driven, few systems or programs use any systematic way to gather information from consumers about their needs and experiences in order to plan or evaluate programs, although this information should determine the services we put into place. Fortunately, there is a growing body of information about what kinds of housing and supports consumers want (discussed in the subsequent subsection, "Consumer Perspectives"). The perspective of families can be used to define families' needs. Professionals have vital information about their experiences in meeting these needs, as well. Therefore, we should avoid abstract discussions about whether people need group homes. Instead, such discussions are more useful as a conversation with consumers and their families, focused on the basic question, "How can we help you?"

Myth 5. Focusing on Housing and Supports Instead of Residential Programs Is Not Practical: This myth holds that all of these ideas about choice, integrated housing, and flexible support are fine, but they are not practical, especially in urban (or rural) areas, or with homeless (or seriously mentally disabled) persons. There *are* enormous barriers to integrated housing in urban areas, such as poverty and the lack of affordable housing. In spite of this, there are as many innovative housing and support initiatives in large cities as there are in rural areas and small cities. Just as Torrey and Wolf (1988) found that the quality of mental health systems had little relationship with comparative funding, whether mental health agencies make progress on housing and supports seems to be a function of a clear mission, access to information about what consumers want, skills related to political organization, housing expertise, and knowledge of state-of-the-art community support strategies (Livingston & Srebnik, 1991).

Myth 6. The Large Numbers of Individuals Who Continue to Live with Families Are a Low Priority for Housing and Supports: Most people are discharged from hospitals to family homes, yet traditional housing and support strategies have virtually ignored that reality. Instead, systems focus on people who are in housing crisis. This places unconscionable demands on families and accounts for the fact that housing is a top priority of most family groups. Unfortunately, because of the myths and confusion in the mental health field,

families often focus on residential program development, not housing. Families need broad and reliable supports for members who are still living at home, helping the individual to achieve his or her own goals for housing, work, and social connections; to separate from the family; and to establish a system of long-term supports.

In order to overcome these myths, Randolph, Zipple, Rowan, Ridgway, Curtis, and Carling (1988) recommended several directions for the field: (1) discarding the continuum concept and promoting supports to all individuals wherever they live, (2) deemphasizing transitional residences and congregate programs, (3) using a rehabilitation approach to housing and supports, and (4) using consumers' preferences and choices to develop housing.

Consumer Perspectives

Preferences for Housing and Support

A growing body of information describes what kinds of housing and supports consumers actually want. In a 1990 national summary of more than 43 consumer preference studies focused on housing and supports, Tanzman (1990) concluded that people with psychiatric disabilities want the same kinds of housing that all other citizens want. In a countywide needs assessment in Washington state, Daniels and Carling (1986) found that professionals and their clients held almost opposite views about housing and support needs. Professionals favored transitional, highly staffed residential programs for most consumers, while their clients wanted normal housing with flexible supports. Most consumers preferred to live with one other person, rather than alone or in a larger group.

In 1990, the first statewide study was undertaken in Vermont, regarding consumers' preferences for housing and supports among people who were homeless, in the state hospital, or receiving community services (reported in Tanzman, 1990). The results showed that persons preferred their own apartment or house rather than either mental health facilities or programs, single room occupancy hotels (SROs), their family home, or community care (boarding) homes. The major barrier consumers saw to achieving this preference was a lack of adequate income. Most people wanted to move to find a better place, have more space, freedom, and autonomy. People in SROs were the least satisfied of all, including those in the state hospital or those who were homeless. The most preferred housing characteristics were freedom and autonomy, permanence, security, and privacy. Only one tenth of the respondents reported needing live-in staff; most people preferred that staff members be available by telephone, or in person if necessary, on a 24-hour basis.

As contrasted with traditional placement approaches, most consumers preferred *not* to live with other consumers; they felt that it was difficult to live with other people's problems as well as their own. Instead, they wanted to live with a friend or a romantic partner. A small number of consumers wanted to live in a group, but *not* in a program. This study shows that consumers, whether homeless, in a state hospital, or in community programs, can clearly articulate their needs for both housing and supports.

The findings from this study have been replicated in 43 studies across the country since then. Tanzman (1990) concluded that in spite of the use of a wide variety of research methods, study samples, professional versus consumer interviewers, and geographical differences in these studies, the overwhelming majority of people with a psychiatric disability prefer regular integrated housing, housemates that are not other consumers, and supports that are available but not live-in.

Consumer Policy Perspectives

Ridgway (1988) reports on a national housing policy forum of consumer leaders, who described their experiences with homelessness and residential programs; these leaders concluded that (a) systems should develop the housing options that most people prefer—independent or shared apartments with support services; (b) housing should be decent and permanent, and should be developed in neighborhoods that are safe and near shopping, services, and transportation; (c) services should be voluntary and should focus on developing skills, such as handling stress, dealing with landlords, managing money, and seeking support; (d) increased disability benefits and special funds should be created to help people move into and keep housing (e.g., loan funds for security deposits, rent subsidies) and to increase people's employment opportunities; (e) case management should be improved (with lower caseloads and higher pay), and new staff roles developed, similar to the personal care attendant model; (f) staff members need training to help people choose, acquire, and keep housing, and to listen to consumers; (g) consumers should be hired and trained as service providers in outreach, case management, skills teaching, and program management roles; (h) more self-help options are needed (including user-run housing), as is greater consumer input into decision-making, through housing forums, using ex-patients to collect information, and always involving consumers in the planning and developing of housing; (i) education efforts are needed to reduce stigma within the community and to inform public officials about consumers' concerns; (j) more regulation of board-and-care homes is needed, as is legislation ensuring further affordable housing; and (k) consumers should work with coalitions to keep public awareness at a high level.

The learnings from the community support and rehabilitation literature in mental health, from other fields, and from consumers themselves suggest that the key ingredients of community integration are a focus on consumer goals and preferences, an individualized and flexible rehabilitation process, and a strong emphasis on normal housing, work, and social networks (Blanch, Carling & Ridgway, 1988; Carling, Randolph, Blanch, & Ridgway, 1987). In the field of mental health, this approach has been termed *supported housing* (National Institute of Mental Health [NIMH], 1987). As planners and advocates focus beyond residential programs to providing broad support in all housing settings, mental health policies are being reformulated. The National Association of State Mental Health Program Directors (NASMHPD, 1987) approved the following policy statement that sharpens their focus even more clearly and endorses the concept of supported housing.

> All people with long-term mental illness should be given the option to live in decent, stable, affordable and safe housing, in settings that maximize their integration into community activities and their ability to function independently. Housing options should not require time limits for moving to another housing option. People should not be required to change living situations or lose housing options when their service needs change, and should not lose their place of residence if they are hospitalized. People should be given the opportunity to actively participate in the selection of their housing arrangements from among those living environments available to the general public. . . . Necessary supports, including case management, on-site crisis intervention, and rehabilitation services should be available at appropriate levels and for as long as needed by persons with psychiatric disabilities, regardless of their choices of living arrangements. Services should be flexible, individualized and provided with attention to personal dignity. Advocacy, community education and resource development should be continuous. (pp. 1–2)

It has been suggested that the field of mental health is in the midst of a paradigm shift with regard to people with the most severe disabilities (Blanch, Carling, & Ridgway, 1988; Carling, 1989; Ridgway & Zipple, 1990), from an era of institutional and facility-based thinking, to a transitional period in which people were seen principally as service recipients needing a comprehensive community support system (Turner & TenHoor, 1979), to a world view in which people are seen principally as citizens with a potential for, and a right to, full community participation and integration (Carling, 1987; Racino, 1991; Wilson, in press).

In an excellent summary of the essential features that distinguish supported housing from the traditional mental health approaches that have been used for meeting housing and support needs, Ridgway and Zipple (1990) concur that the field is undergoing a paradigm shift toward homes, not residential treatment settings; choices, not placement; normal roles, not client roles; client control, not staff control; physical and social integration, not segregated/congregate grouping by disability; *in vivo* learning in permanent settings, not preparatory learning in transitional settings; individualized, flexible services and supports, not standardized levels of service; most facilitative, not least restrictive environments; and long-term supports/interdependence, not independence.

Supported housing, then, is organized around three central principles: (1) consumers choose their own living situations; (2) consumers live in normal, stable housing, not in mental health programs; and (3) consumers have the services and supports required to maximize their opportunities for success over time. Two recent reviews of the characteristics of local supported housing programs (Blanch, Carling & Ridgway, 1988) and state-level innovations (Carling & Wilson, 1988) provide information on the specifics of this approach.

Implementing Supported Housing

Steps to Develop Housing and Support

The following section describes how to begin implementing the supported housing approach. It is most helpful to initiate a planning process that will involve key constituencies, clarify the goals and intended outcomes of the proposed effort, gather basic information on current and needed housing and supports, consider changes that have to be made in current agency or system operations, and develop a political strategy to achieve the intended goals.

Step 1. Involve Key Groups: All of the key constituencies who will be most affected by these efforts should be involved from the beginning. These include consumers, family members, staff members, managers, and policymakers in mental health, and experts in housing access, finance, and development.

Step 2. Clarify Mission and Intended Outcomes:
The planners should take time to develop a clear mission and set of intended outcomes for this effort. Key sticking points typically involve disputes about choice, integrated housing, and how to arrange services and supports. The NASMHPD Mission Statement (NASMHPD, 1987) is often a useful tool for planning groups to use as a point of departure.

Step 3. Gather Critical Information:
Four basic types of information are needed in order to develop a meaningful housing and supports plan: information on housing need, housing availability, service needs, and services availability. The easiest way to establish housing needs is to conduct a *consumer preference survey* (see Tanzman, 1990), which uses consumer interviewers to ask other consumers questions about where they have lived, their current living situation, where they would like to live, and the services and supports they would find helpful. To assess the housing stock of a community, local government has basic data on the location, affordability, and condition of housing, and on any critical gaps in housing. The consumer preference study can also form the basis for describing how useful current services are (when supplemented with information from families and key staff) and for defining the kinds of services and supports that are needed in order to help people to be successful in their own homes, as well as to redefine the role of current residential programs. Specific changes in the types of services that may be most needed (e.g., converting a day treatment program to a continuous treatment case management team) and in the types of funding needed (e.g., redirecting program funds to establish a rent subsidy program) can form recommendations for restructuring the service system so that it is more consistent with the mission. Not all of these changes can be accomplished immediately or without difficulty. Therefore, it is also critical to establish clear initial priorities for housing and support initiatives.

Step 4. Develop Housing Strategies:
Housing strategies generally fall into three categories: access, preservation, and development. Unless there is a serious shortage of affordable housing, it is best to concentrate initial efforts on accessing existing housing through developing support services, building relationships with landlords, and creating housing contingency and/or subsidy funds (Curtis, 1990). Becoming involved in local housing coalitions is also an effective way to preserve affordable housing, which otherwise might be lost due to gentrification or other pressures. Development of housing is a complex and time-consuming effort but is an important part of the overall strategy. It should be primarily the responsibility of the housing community itself. A variety of innovative financing strategies are now emerging, including the creation of housing development corporations, mental health based development funds, mixing public and private resources, and using distressed properties. These financing approaches are also making home ownership possible for some consumers.

Step 5. Develop a Political Strategy:
Change efforts rarely proceed without resistance. To avoid this, involve people from the outset, package your plan with skill, and present your plan thoughtfully. Focus on the potential of people to become more self-sufficient and less reliant on public services. A partnership of consumers, families, and mental health and housing professionals can make this vision of helping people get what they want a reality.

Overview of a Rehabilitation Approach to Housing and Support

This section of the chapter summarizes key issues in a rehabilitation approach to housing and supports. The reader who wishes a more in-depth treatment of this topic is referred to Carling and Ridgway (1987), who describe the conceptual basis for this approach, specific roles and responsibilities of staff, and a variety of actual program examples. A rehabilitation approach includes goal planning, assessment of skills and resources, skills teaching, resource development, and ongoing support, all based on the aspirations and self-defined needs of the consumer.

Individual Goal Planning—The Core of a Rehabilitation Approach: In a rehabilitation approach, all interventions are goal driven (Anthony & Blanch, 1989). Individual consumers' preferences and experiences form the basis for designing a plan, assessing needs, and providing services. Many consumers may need assistance to relearn skills related to what they like and dislike, what has worked or helped in the past, and so forth. The plan should begin with a long-term goal and then break down the goal into a series of short term activities. Practitioners and other planners should avoid a common tendency to limit the consumers' choices because their goals are considered unrealistic or because of a concern that they may fail. In fact, no one makes consistently good choices, and much learning comes from apparent failures. There are extensive materials on implementing rehabilitation goal planning available from the Center on Psychiatric Rehabilitation at Boston University, and through the extensive writings of Anthony and colleagues (Anthony, Cohen, & Farkas, 1990).

Assessment of Skills and Resources: What specific skills and resources will be necessary to achieve the person's goal? Functional assessments are only useful if they relate to a specific person's goal and a specific environment. People succeed or fail generally on the basis of a relatively few make-it-or-break-it skills in specific settings. Too often, we try to assess all possible living skills or environmental demands, and limit a person's choices until he or she has mastered all of these. A better approach is *in vivo* training in the environment a person wants to be in. What resources will an individual need? There are human resources (neighbors, coworkers, friends, mental health staff, and so forth), as well as financial resources for gaining access to and maintaining housing.

Development of a Support Plan: Planners should figure out what supports a person will need before and during the moving in process, not after a crisis develops. They should provide intensive support, if desired, during the actual process of moving in, anticipate what kinds of supports must be increased and decreased over time, and create a specific crisis plan in advance.

Special Issues

Moving In: There are myriad details involved in moving, including deposit and rent, utility hookups, furnishings, introduction to neighbors, figuring out transportation to work and services, identifying community resources for shopping and recreation, and so forth. It is helpful to involve friends, relatives, and others in the move itself, creating a network of support during this period.

Ongoing Support and Monitoring of Needs: Planners should establish a regular pattern of contact, through which tenant and professional can monitor changing needs and can arrange for changes in supports. This pattern may also indicate times when an individual may not want to be involved with professionals and should involve great respect for the person's desires, a continuing offer of assistance, and communication to the individual about the natural and sometimes negative consequences of behavior related to medications, maintaining one's apartment, and so forth.

The Importance of Role Models: Positive role models can be very helpful for individuals who have limited experience with community living. Encourage participation in self-help groups, consumer operated services, and drop-in centers. Increase hiring of former consumers as service providers, and encourage a variety of ways to increase the consumer's voice in a service agency's operations, such as on the board of directors, in training, and in all planning, program development, and evaluation activities. This high level of visibility increases consumers' expectations of themselves and instills a sense of hope that pervades the agency's operations and programs.

Individuals Who Are Homeless: With regard to housing needs, people who are homeless are a very diverse group whose needs for housing, in general, differ little from those of the overall group of people with psychiatric disabilities or—in fact—from the general population of homeless individuals. What is distinct about their needs is typically a near absence of significant material resources, as well as very restricted or nonexistent social support networks. Further, for a small group of individuals who are either long-term users of shelters, or for those who have been transient for some time, professionals face real challenges in helping people to take root in many housing situations. People need an extended process of engagement and many opportunities to try out a variety of living situations, with an overall goal of increasing the time that an individual stays in any one place. There has been an increase recently in transitional housing programs, in which people, at their own pace, can readjust to community living, and such settings undoubtedly help some individuals in that process. For others, there will continue to be a sense of fierce independence which results in avoiding anything that looks like a program, and in those cases, individualized, persevering staff support will continue to be the best alternative. Finally, it should be noted that ready access to material resources, such as emergency housing funds, is critical to the success of responding to the needs of persons who are homeless.

Parents with Children: Until recently, there has been almost no research, and little programmatic attention to the specific needs of single parents and the special needs of women (who are more likely to be single parents) in mental health systems. With regard to housing, it is critically important that systems plan for the housing needs of people with children. In fact, the Ohio Mental Health Housing Task Force (1986) found that more than one third of the housing that was needed statewide for people with psychiatric disabilities must accommodate children. The implications of this need include working with landlords to accommodate this need and fighting discrimination in housing that restricts tenancy by those with children.

People with Both Psychiatric Disabilities and Substance Abuse Problems: There is a burgeoning literature on the needs of people with both psychiatric disabilities and substance abuse problems. With regard to housing, substance abuse poses challenging problems for the tenant, as well as for the relationship with the landlord and the service agency. Many individuals with these dual problems fail to receive needed support services, may be disruptive in their housing, and are particularly vulnerable to eviction. The role of the service agency, however, is not to provide special housing or to impose special lease conditions on these individuals, but rather to work to overcome these behaviors, and to support people through the natural consequences that can arise from them.

Racial and Cultural Issues: Finally, it should be noted that there are a number of issues in cultural diversity that are relevant to housing. Persons involved in housing programs need to be aware of differing cultural traditions with regard to preferred living arrangements, the relative emphasis on extended families, and the cultural/racial/ethnic appropriateness of services that are offered to the various clients. Two important steps to becoming responsive include affirmative hiring of a diverse staff and training of all staff members regarding issues of diversity and cultural relevance.

Advantages and Limitations of the Supported Housing Approach

The supported housing approach, while an exciting response to some of the limitations of traditional approaches, brings with it a wealth of difficulties and challenges, largely because it represents a far more ideal way of thinking about people and their needs than is reflected in current attitudinal, programmatic, and funding realities. By advocating major change throughout a system, it also flies in the face of many vested interests, both professional and economic.

Systems that take on a supported housing approach can easily become overwhelmed with such goals as basing housing on consumers' preferences, especially because staff members are typically acting in crisis mode, with little time to ask *anyone* else's views. Listening to consumers, whether in a process of formulating new goals with an individual, or planning a new statewide approach to housing, takes time, more time than is required for the implementation of current approaches. Furthermore, they may not like much of what they hear from consumers, and most of the resources and tools they have with which to create housing are only useful for facility-based approaches. Similarly, services are rarely organized to support people wherever they wish to live.

With regard to housing, both systems and local agencies have significant real estate holdings in their facilities. Often, they do not have management- or the practice-level staff who have skills in housing access, preservation, financing, and development, nor do they have the relationships with housing systems that they need. Systems face resistance from local agencies and professional groups in moving quickly toward a consumer-driven approach. Implementing supported housing also takes resources that are often unavailable, at least in the form in which they are needed, in mental health systems. Rent subsidies, pools of capital that can be accessed quickly to make opportunistic deals, and flexible funds for furnishings for consumers—all of these represent bureaucratic nightmares in some systems. In these cases, trying to implement supported housing often makes it crystal clear to a system that the major barriers clients face are, in fact, the characteristics of the system itself. In spite of these formidable barriers to change, however, it seems clear that most states are moving in this direction, albeit at very different paces, and with differing strategies.

For all of these reasons, though, it is also clear, that while policy change in this area can proceed relatively rapidly, implementing a supported housing approach is essentially a long-term proposition for a mental health system. After changing policies, the actual planning practices, the financing structures, the relationships and expectations with service providers and with other government agencies (such as those governing housing), the management information systems, and the staff roles all need to change. It is likely that, in most systems, residential facilities and group living settings will continue to be used, even as other systems begin decongregating them. In this way, supported housing is no different from any other change in mental health: implementation is always widely variable. The difference with supported housing, however, is its ripple effect on other aspects of the system. Once a system begins to take consumer choice and voice seriously, for example, it is exceedingly difficult to return to making decisions on more traditional bases.

Summary and Conclusions: Future Challenges in Housing and Community Living Support

In summary, the field of mental health has begun to make significant progress in reconceptualizing its roles and responsibilities for housing and supports. New knowledge about what consumers actually want and about the needs of families, new policies and funding mechanisms through which agencies and systems can respond to these needs, and new program approaches are all emerging. As the field continues to experience major change, it is both significant and promising that this change is resulting in an increased focus on the basic need for a home and in a deepening commitment to pursue a variety of strategies that will assist people to have their own homes, with the supports they want, in spite of their psychiatric label.

The field of mental health also has a great deal to learn from other groups who require special supports in their housing: people with low incomes, elders, and those who are homeless with developmental disabilities, including mental retardation. A 1987 comprehensive review of the research related to housing and community integration for all disability groups (Carling, Randolph, Blanch, & Ridgway, 1987) concluded that (a) housing needs are similar for each of these groups, although support needs are more varied; (b) supports appear to be the critical factor in whether people can remain in a housing situation of their own choice; (c) housing problems are less closely related to disability than they are to economic and social factors, such as poverty, affordable housing trends, and discrimination; (d) strong differences of opinion often exist between professionals and consumers about specific needs for housing and supports, regardless of which disability group is involved; (e) choices and control over one's environment are critical necessities regardless of special need, and consumers wish both to be centrally involved in planning their own housing and supports and to have the opportunity to manage their own services; (f) because of the lack of in-home supports and services, elders and people with disabilities are plagued by transience, dislocation, and the risk of institutionalization; and (g) the model of a residential continuum is increasingly beset by conceptual and practical problems. This review concluded that the broader disability community is increasingly emphasizing normal housing and the need to avoid the transformation of housing into service settings. Thus, community integration approaches avoid congregation and segregation and instead focus on building relationships between disabled and nondisabled individuals.

As public policy shifts away from residential facilities and toward integrated housing and supports, additional research is needed about where and how consumers prefer to live, successful strategies for facilitating meaningful client choices and for developing housing and supports, documentation of the costs and benefits of housing and support initiatives, identification of clinical interventions best suited to normal housing, and an elaboration of the role of peer support in community success. Carling, Randolph, Blanch, and Ridgway (1987) concluded that the key unresearched questions are "Where do people with mental illness live?" "Where do they want to live?" and "How can we help them succeed there?" (p. 23).

Answering these questions requires a shift from professionally defined to consumer defined research. With regard to housing, it is important to understand the impact of choice versus placement on success, and the contribution to success of particular types of neighborhoods. Broad dispersion of housing versus physical proximity may have an impact on the capacity of consumers to support each other, and for staff to be available and readily accessible to provide requested assistance. Practitioners need to understand the positive value of a consumer or ex-patient community, while assisting people to become part of the larger community. In order to better understand how to facilitate integration, it would be helpful to study the impact of different types of living arrangements, including size, number of residents, location and make-up of the housing, its appearance, and its stability, on relevant integration outcomes, such as number and type of relationships and activities involving people without disabilities. Through expanded research on consumer choice, housing, and supports, it is possible to build the critical knowledge base necessary to achieve community integration for people with psychiatric disabilities.

Finally, because access to affordable housing has become a national crisis, the public's support for increased federal and state spending and taxation for housing is at an all time high (National Housing Institute, 1988). Thus, even as federal housing programs are being cut, the U.S. Congress has passed new housing legislation. The National Affordable Housing Act and the Fair Housing Amendments Act are intended to further promote housing integration, including for people with a psychiatric disability. The Americans with Disabilities Act (ADA) is a landmark piece of legislation that specifically promotes the goal of full community integration for people with psychiatric disabilities. These trends will continue to shape not only mental health's response to housing needs, but also that of our larger society, as it responds to a broader need for full community inclusion.

References

Anthony, W. A., & Blanch, A. (1989). Research on community support services: What have we learned? *Psychosocial Rehabilitation Journal*, *12*(3), 55–81.

Anthony, W. A., Cohen, M., & Farkas, M. (1990). *Psychiatric rehabilitation*. Boston: Boston University, Center for Psychiatric Rehabilitation.

Anthony, W. A., & Dion, G. (1986). *A review of psychiatric rehabilitation research*. Washington, DC: National Rehabilitation Information Center.

Aviram, U., & Segal, S.P.(1973). Exclusion of the mentally ill: Reflection on an old problem in a new context. *Archives of General Psychiatry, 29*, 126–131.

Baxter, E., & Hopper, K. (1984). Troubled in the streets: The mentally disabled homeless poor. In J. A. Talbott (Ed.), *The chronic mental patient: Five years later* (pp. 49–62). New York: Grune & Stratton.

Blanch, A. K., Carling, P.J., & Ridgway, P. (1988). Normal housing with specialized support: A psychiatric rehabilitation approach to living in the community. *Rehabilitation Psychology*, *4*(32), 47–55.

Braun, P., Kochansky, G., Shapiro, R., Greenberg, S., Gudeman, J., Johnson, S., & Shore, M. F. (1981). Overview: Deinstitutionalization of psychiatric patients—A critical review of outcome studies. *American Journal of Psychiatry*, *138*, 736–749.

Budson, R. D. (Ed.). (1981). *New directions for mental health services: Issues in community residential care*. San Francisco: Jossey-Bass.

Campbell, M. (1981). The three-quarterway house: A step beyond the halfway house toward independent living. *Hospital and Community Psychiatry*, *32*, 500–501.

Carling, P. J. (1978). Residential services in a

psychosocial rehabilitation context: The Horizon House model. In J. Goldmeier (Ed.). *New directions in mental health care: Cooperative apartments*, (pp. 52–64). Adelphi, MD: National Institute of Mental Health.

Carling, P. J. (1981). Nursing homes and chronic mental patients: A second opinion. *Schizophrenia Bulletin*, *7*, 574–579.

Carling, P. J. (1984). *Developing family foster care programs in mental health: A resource guide*. Rockville, MD: National Institute of Mental Health.

Carling, P. J. (1987, October). *The community support movement: Transforming our future*. Keynote presentation at the Eighth National CSP Learning Community Conference, Burlington, VT.

Carling, P. J. (1989). Access to housing: Cornerstone of the American dream. *Journal of Rehabilitation*, *55*(3), 6–8.

Carling, P. J. (1990). Supported housing: An evaluation agenda. *Psychosocial Rehabilitation Journal*, *13*(4), 95–104.

Carling, P. J., Randolph, F. L., Blanch, A. K., & Ridgway, P. (1987). *Rehabilitation research review: Housing and community integration for people with psychiatric disabilities* (National Rehabilitation Information Center Review). Washington, DC: D:ATA Institute.

Carling, P. J., & Ridgway, P. (1987). Overview of a psychiatric rehabilitation approach to housing. In W. A. Anthony & M. Farkas, *Psychiatric rehabilitation: Turning theory into practice* (pp. 28–80). Baltimore: Johns Hopkins University Press.

Carling, P. J., & Wilson, S. F. (1988). *Strategies for state mental health directors in implementing supported housing* (Report of the Denver Meeting on Implementation of Supported Housing). Burlington, VT: University of Vermont, Center for Community Change through Housing and Support.

Carpenter, M. D. (1978). Residential placement for the chronic psychiatric patient: A review and evaluation of the literature. *Schizophrenia Bulletin*, *4*, 384–398.

Chamberlin, J. (1978). *On our own: Patient controlled alternatives to the mental health system*. New York: Hawthorne Books.

Chafetz, L., & Goldfinger, S. M. (1984). Residential instability in a psychiatric emergency setting. *Psychiatric Quarterly*, *56*, 20–34.

Cometa, M. S., Morrison, J. K., & Ziskoven, M. 1979). Halfway to where? A critique of research on psychiatric halfway houses. *Journal of Community Psychology*, *7*, 23–27.

Coulton, C. L., Holland, T. P., & Fitch, V. (1984). Person–environment congruence and psychiatric patient outcome in community care homes. *Administration in Mental Health*, *12*, 71–88.

Curtis, L. C. (Ed.). (1990). *Accessing community housing development activities.* Burlington VT: University of Vermont, Center for Community Change through Housing and Support.

Daniels, L. V., & Carling, P. J. (1986). *Community residential rehabilitation services for psychiatrically disabled persons in Kitsap County.* Boston: Boston University, Center for Psychiatric Rehabilitation.

Dellario, D., & Anthony, W. (1981). On the relative effectiveness of institutional and alternative placements of the psychiatrically disabled. *Journal of Social Issues, 37,* 21–33.

Fairweather, G. (1980). The Fairweather Lodge: A twenty-five year retrospective. In G. Fairweather (Ed.), *New directions for mental health services,* (Vol. 7) San Francisco: Jossey-Bass.

Geller, M. P. (1982). The "revolving door": A trap or a life style? *Hospital and Community Psychiatry, 33,* 388–389.

Goldman, H. H., Gatozzi, A. A., & Taube, C. A. (1981). Defining and counting the chronically mentally ill. *Hospital and Community Psychiatry, 32,* 21–27.

Goldmeier, J., Shore, M. F., & Mannino, F. V. (1977). Cooperative apartments: New programs in community mental health. *Health and Social Work, 2,* 119–140.

Hatfield, A. B., Fierstein, R., & Johnson, D. (1982). Meeting the needs of families of the psychiatrically disabled. *Psychosocial Rehabilitation Journal, 6*(1), 27–40.

Hogan, R. (1985a). *Gaining community support for group homes.* Unpublished manuscript. Lafayette, IN: Purdue University.

Hogan, R. (1985b). *Not in my town: Local government opposition to group homes.* Unpublished manuscript. Lafayette, IN: Purdue University.

Kiesler, C. A. (1982). Mental hospitals and alternative care: Noninstitutionalization as potential public policy for mental patients. *American Psychologist, 37,* 349–360.

Kohen, W., & Paul, G. L. (1976). Current trends and recommended changes in extended care placement of mental patients: The Illinois system as a case in point. *Schizophrenia Bulletin, 2,* 575–594.

Kozol, J. (1988). *Rachel and her children: Homeless families in America.* New York: Crown Publishers.

Livingston, J., & Srebnik, D. (1991). States' strategies for promoting supported housing for persons with psychiatric disabilities. *Hospital and Community Psychiatry, 42*(11), 1116–1119.

Low Income Housing Information Service (Washington, DC).(1988). *Low Income Housing Bulletin, 1*(2), :LIHIS

McCabe, S. S., Edgar, E. R., King, D. A., Mancuso, L., & Emery, B. (1991). *Holes in the housing safety net . . . Why SSI is not enough: A national comparison study of supplemental security in-come & HUD fair market rents.* Burlington, VT: University of Vermont, Center for Community Change through Housing and Support.

National Association of State Mental Health Program Directors (1987). *Position statement on housing and support for people with long-term mental illness.* Alexandria, VA: Author.

National Housing Institute (1988) *A status report on the American dream.* Princeton, NJ: RL Associates.

National Institute of Mental Health (1987). *Guidelines for meeting the housing needs of people with psychiatric disabilities.* Rockville, MD: Author.

Ohio Mental Health Housing Task Force (1986). *Final report.* Columbus: Ohio Department of Mental Health.

Pepper, B. (1985). Where and how should young adult chronic patients live? The concept of a residential continuum. *Tie Lines, 2,* 1–6.

Racino, J. A. (1991). Living in the community: Independence, support and transition. In F. R. Rusch, L. DeStafano, J. Chadsey-Rusch, L. A. Phelps, & E. Suzaminski (Eds.), *Transition from school to work for youth and adults with disabilities.* Sycamore, IL: Sycamore Publishing Company.

Randolph, F. L., Laux, R., & Carling, P. J. (1987). *In search of housing: Creative approaches to housing for people with psychiatric disabilities* (Monograph Series on Housing and Mental Health). Boston: Boston University, Center for Psychiatric Rehabilitation.

Randolph, F. L. Ridgway, P., & Carling, P. J. (1991). Residential programs for persons with severe mental illness: A nationwide survey of state-affiliated agencies. *Hospital and Community Psychiatry, 42*(11), 1111–1115.

Randolph, F. L., Sanford, C., Simoneau, D., Ridgway, P., & Carling, P. J. (1988). *The state of practice in community residential programs: A national survey* (Monograph Series on Housing and Rehabilitation in Mental Health). Boston: Boston University, Center for Psychiatric Rehabilitation.

Randolph, F., Zipple, A., Rowan, C. A., Ridgway, P., Curtis, L., & Carling, P. J. (1988). *Exemplary residential programs: A national survey* (Monograph Series on Housing and Rehabilitation in Mental Health). Boston: Boston University, Center for Psychiatric Rehabilitation.

Ridgway, P. (1987). *Avoiding zoning battles.* Washington, DC: Intergovernmental Health Policy Project.

Ridgway, P. (Ed.). (1988). *Coming home: Ex-patients view options and needs* (Proceedings of a National Consumer Housing Forum). Burlington, VT: University of Vermont, Center for Community Change through Housing and Support.

Ridgway, P., & Zipple, A. M. (1990). The paradigm shift in residential services: From the linear continuum to supported housing approaches. *Psychosocial Rehabilitation Journal, 13*(4), 11–31.

Rubenstein, L., & James, L. B. (1990). New funding strategy for housing for people with mental disabilities. In A. T. Meyerson & P. Solomon (Eds.), *New developments in psychiatric rehabilitation: Vol. 45, New directions for mental health services.* San Francisco: Jossey-Bass.

Segal, S. P., & Aviram, U. (1978). *The mentally ill in community-based sheltered care: A study of community care and social integration.* New York: Wiley.

Segal, S. P., Baumohl, J., & Moyles, E. W. (1980). Neighborhood types and community reaction to the mentally ill: A paradox of intensity. *Journal of Health and Social Behavior, 21,* 345–359.

Stein, L. I., & Test, M. A. (1985). *The training in community living model: A decade of experience.* In H. R. Lamb (Ed.), *New directions for mental health services,*(Vol. 26). San Francisco: Jossey-Bass.

Stroul, B. (1988). *Crisis residential services in a community support system.* Rockville, MD: National Institute of Mental Health.

Tabor, M. A. (1980). *The social context of helping: A review of the literature on alternative care for the physically and mentally handicapped.* Rockville, MD: National Institute of Mental Health.

Tanzman, B. H. (1990). *Researching the preferences of people with psychiatric disabilities for housing and supports: A practical guide* (Monograph Series on Housing and Rehabilitation in Mental Health). Burlington, VT: University of Vermont, Center for Community Change through Housing and Support.

Taylor, S. J., Racino, J., Knoll, J., & Lutfiyya, Z. (1987). *The nonrestrictive environment: A resource manual on community integration for people with the most severe disabilities.* New York: Human Policy Press.

Test, M. (1981). Effective community treatment of the chronically mentally ill: What is necessary? *Journal of Social Issues, 37,* 71–86.

Test, M., & Stein, L. (1978). Community treatment of the chronic patient: Research overview. *Schizophrenia Bulletin, 4,* 350–364.

Torrey, E. F., & Wolfe, S. M. (1988). *Care of the seriously mentally ill: A rating of state programs.* Washington, DC: Public Citizen Health Research Group.

Turner, J., & TenHoor, W. (1979). The NIMH community support program: Pilot approach to a needed social reform. *Schizophrenia Bulletin, 4,* 319–344.

U.S. Department of Health and Human Services, Steering Committee on the Chronically Mentally Ill. (1980). *Toward a National Plan for the "Chronically Mentally Ill."* (Report to the Secretary by the DHHS Steering Committee on the Chronically Mentally Ill). Rockville, MD: Public Health Service.

U.S. Department of Health and Human Services (1983). *Report to Congress on shelter and basic living needs of chronically mentally ill individuals.* Washington, DC: Author.

United States Senate, Special Committee on Aging, Sub-Committee on Long-Term Care (1976). *Supporting paper no. 7: The role of nursing homes in caring for discharged mental patients (and the birth of a for-profit boarding home industry).* Washington, DC: U.S. Government Printing Office.

Wasow, M. (1982). *Coping with schizophrenia: A survival manual for parents, relatives, and friends.* Palo Alto: Science and Behavior Books.

Wilson, S. F. (in press). Community support and integration: New directions for client outcome research. In S. Rose (Ed.), *Case management: An overview and assessment.* White Plains, NY: Longman.

Wygal, S. F. (1988). *Crisis services in Maine's community support system.* Augusta, ME: Department of Mental Health and Mental Retardation, Office of Community Support Systems.

Chapter 8

Supports and Rehabilitation for Employment

THOMAS J. SIMMONS
VIRGINIA SELLECK
ROBERT B. STEELE
FRANK SEPETAUC

In 1943, the U.S. Congress passed legislation (P.L. 78-113) that enabled persons with mental illness to participate in services provided by the Office of Vocational Rehabilitation (OVR). Prior to the 1943 legislation, the focus of OVR services was almost exclusively for persons with physical disabilities (Neff, 1988). Altering service eligibility brought about a variety of service changes and provided an impetus for deinstitutionalization and for reducing the populations being served in overcrowded segregated programs for persons with mental illness (Neff, 1988). Prior to the 1943 act, eligible populations for rehabilitation services were only those persons who were attempting to regain access to employment after the acquisition of a disability. After the passage of this legislation, eligible populations for services also included persons who had never been able to gain access to employment (Kiernan & Payne, 1982). The next significant changes in the delivery of vocational rehabilitation (VR) services occurred in 1965 and in 1973, with the passage of legislation (P.L. 89-933 and P.L.93-112, respectively). These acts prompted a greater emphasis on service delivery for persons with more severe physical and psychiatric disabilities.

In practice and in theory, though, the VR model developed a different perspective with respect to the delivery of services than was present in the traditional medical/curative model (Strauss & Carpenter, 1974; Strauss, Hafez, Lieberman, & Harding, 1985). With a rehabilitation orientation, services sought to improve the functional capacity of an individual through training or compensation, in order to develop and maintain independent employment (Strauss, Harding, Silverman, Eichler, & Lieberman, 1988). The VR approach did not assume that the person would ever be cured or recover. An additional barrier to the provision of successful VR services to persons with mental illness was VR's emphasis on closures, which required consistent performance of the worker for 3 months after placement. Consequently, services for persons with mental illness, based on VR legislation, did not develop quickly, nor were they effective in achieving the stated goal of facilitating the ability to work. Further, VR was not a significant service option in the early efforts to provide employment services for persons with severe mental disabilities.

Services that evolved for persons with severe and persistent mental illness were provided through a variety of alternative service models. In the 1950s and 1960s, vocational programs were primarily provided in segregated environments, which were institutional in nature (Black, 1988; Neff, 1988).

During the 1970s and early 1980s community mental health centers (CMHCs) tended to provide services to persons with mild impairments and overlooked or did not feel responsible for persons with severe and persistent mental illness (Bond, 1991a). Also, during this time frame, psychosocial rehabilitation (PSR) programs that were based on the physical rehabilitation model (Anthony, Cohen, & Danley, 1988) began to evolve. Implementation of PSR in the vocational domain was achieved largely through transitional employment (TE) programs. Only since the middle 1980s have services for persons with psychiatric disabilities emphasized strategies of community integration and consumer empowerment in providing vocational alternatives. Program models such as supported employment, job club, and assertive community treatment offer some aspect of a more normalized consumer-directed emphasis, with significant supports or assistance being provided by professional staff members.

Developing and implementing vocational services for persons with severe and persistent mental illness is a puzzle with many pieces. This chapter provides a description of those pieces and of the ways in which those pieces may fit together. What follows is an overview and description of trends and models that have promise for VR and career development for persons with severe psychiatric disabilities. Consumer factors are discussed, relative to their importance and diversity in the placement process. A description of coordination of service supports is also included, to apprise the practitioner of the impact of factors outside the workplace. Finally, community and employer awareness is addressed, with an emphasis on describing methods of overcoming obstacles and of improving the overall vocational process for persons with severe and persistent mental illness.

Program Models

The development of programs in a variety of settings has provided a wide array of methods and strategies to provide career services and to assist persons with severe and persistent mental illness to obtain and maintain employment. Bond, (1991b), Bond and McDonel (1991), and Rogers, Sciarappa, and Anthony (1991) reviewed numerous models and described implementation issues and benefits to persons with severe and persistent mental illness. This section provides an overview of these models and finishes with more detailed definitions of best practice methods of providing vocational and career services to persons with severe mental illness.

Model Typologies

Bond (1991a) delineated a typology of vocational programs for persons with severe psychiatric disabilities. Hospital programs, sheltered workshops, vocational counseling, job clubs, assertive community treatment (ACT), TE, and supported employment (SE) were described by Bond, with clarification of the essential aspects of implementing each model.

The hospital program has historically emphasized work that was performed within the hospital or for short periods of time in the community while in residence in a hospital (Barbee, Berry, & Micek, 1969). In many cases, the objectives of these early hospital programs were concerned with assisting the person to develop self-esteem, to keep the patient active, and to achieve therapeutic outcomes, with employment being only a secondary concern. Consequently, in most cases, the results of these services were not completely satisfactory in the attainment of employment (Bond & Boyer, 1988). In fact, Davies (1972) indicated that most hospital programs did not provide demands and pressures that were equivalent to those experienced in normal employment situations.

Sheltered workshop programs have been

extensively used as a vocational alternative for persons with severe and persistent mental illness (Cohen, 1976; Gray, 1980; Roomey, 1984). In the sheltered workshop model, unskilled work is used as a medium to develop employment related skills (e.g., personal–social skills) which are necessary in most jobs. Work and training are performed in a segregated setting, and the participant is generally paid below minimum wage. Sheltered workshop programs are utilized both as a final placement and as a temporary way station for providing transitional services for later competitive placement. There appear to be significant problems with this model, relative to its ability to effectively deliver remunerative services and to place people in competitive jobs (GreenLeigh Associates, 1975; Whitehead, 1977).

Bond and Boyer (1988) delineated a subcategory of the sheltered workshop program, which could be described as the "client employing business" (p. 244). In client employing programs, separate services are developed, which are designed to meet the needs of the participants. However, these programs are generally self-sufficient entities that are operated by the participants. The client employing business includes small businesses such as greenhouses, bakeries, yardwork crews, janitorial services, and warehouse work. The small business is formed through a nonprofit corporation, which is generally affiliated with a rehabilitation agency. Once the business initiates operation, leadership is required, along with all of the usual entrepreneurial activities that other small businesses command. While the client employing business does show promise, the operation of the business and the need for a tremendous amount of business sense and entrepreneurial leadership would seem to limit the likelihood of this model being able to meet the needs of a large portion of persons who have severe and persistent mental illness (Bond, 1991a).

Job clubs have been suggested as an effective means for providing employment related services to persons who have severe and persistent mental illness (Azrin & Philip, 1979). The job club approach was originally developed by Azrin and Besalel (1979). The approach used in job club is a systematic application of behavioral technology to the rehabilitation field. In particular, the job club includes a wide variety of tried-and-true methods; however, Azrin and colleagues indicated that the methods were standardized and consistent and provided within an intensive framework.

The job club approach utilizes group techniques, which include 32 strategies that the participant is expected to use in pursuing a job. These strategies range from contacting friends and relatives for job leads to developing interviewing skills and maintaining progress charts. The premise of the club approach is that activity and persistence result in employment. Consequently, the job club emphasizes continuing effort in the form of making possible employment contacts and following up leads, which will afford the participant a greater chance of acquiring employment. Limitations of the job club approach are that (a) the approach only deals with one aspect of the employment process—getting the job—and not with maintaining the job; (b) there is a great deal of pressure placed on participants, which—for some participants—may be detrimental; (c) the predominant method of finding a job is through the participant's own job seeking—this may be problematic if the participant has significant problems with self-esteem or has personal characteristics that initially may be problematic; (d) employment retention rates have not been demonstrated to be long term (Bond, 1991).

Assertive case management, otherwise termed *training in community living* (TCL), is another method of delivering vocational services to persons with severe mental illness. This method of service delivery is based on the assumption that the participant needs specific and concrete assistance in everyday employment tasks (Stein & Test, 1980). This model does not assume transfer of training; rather, the model expects that each aspect of the job—from finding the job, to getting the participant to the place of work, to performing the vocational tasks, and to arranging for social interactions during and after work—are required training targets. TCL staff develop their own vocational options in which a network of vocational alternatives are offered through a variety of job sites. Bond et al. (1988) indicated that the major drawback to the TCL program is the brokering of services rather than offering the services directly to the participant. Bond et al. (1988) also indicated that it is still not clear as to whether the participants are able to maintain their level of success after the intensive case management has ceased.

TE, a fifth model, was an outgrowth of PSR, which emphasizes the holistic involvement of providing services that would include social, residential, leisure, and vocational aspects of program development. The TE model, more specifically, focuses on the development of general work skills by placing participants in temporary entry level jobs with staff supervision in order to evaluate *employability skills* (those skills that relate to getting and maintaining a job) and to provide the participant with an experience that is successful and breaks the pattern of repeated failures (Bond et al., 1988).

TE programs consist of both small work crews and individual placements in settings where a variety of types of work are performed (e.g., from manual labor to office work). While participants can be either paid or not, the emphasis within the work setting is on the development of skills related to attendance, punctuality, proper dress, interacting with coworkers, work tolerance and so forth. Work hours are varied, based on the individual needs of the participant. The emphasis of the work pattern is on increasing to the maximum possible the amount of hours and days worked. Certain problems—such as the participant's ability to adapt to change, the lack of *flow* (movement into competitive employment), a participant's possible learned dependency on staff members, and an emphasis on entry level jobs—do appear to limit the benefits that TE might provide a participant.

SE is another program/model that has been shown to provide vocational benefits to persons with severe and persistent mental illness. SE had its beginnings with agencies providing services to persons with mental retardation and developmental disabilities and focused on the place-and-train model (Bond et al., 1988). Madeline Will (1984) first proposed SE in a position paper in which she defined a conceptual model of bridges from school to work for persons with disabilities. Within this framework, SE was proposed as a mechanism for attaining long-term employment. Federal law (P.L. 99-506) defines SE as,

> competitive work in integrated settings (a) for individuals with severe handicaps for whom competitive employment has not traditionally occurred, or (b) for individuals for whom competitive employment has been interrupted or intermittent as a result of a severe disability and who, because of their handicap, need ongoing support services to perform work. Supported employment is further defined by the refinement of its components (i.e., competitive work, integrated settings, severe handicaps, and ongoing support services) in the final regulations. (*Federal Register*, May 12, 1988, p. 16982.)

The primary emphasis, consequently, is on finding a job for a participant in the community for a minimum of 20 hours per week, in an integrated setting, providing long-term or ongoing assistance, and earning wages commensurate with their production abilities. Implementation of SE for persons with severe and persistent mental illness has focused on what Anthony (1990) has called the "Choose–Get–Keep" approach. This particular approach emphasizes the aspect of greater involvement of the participant in the selection, acquisition, and maintenance of the employment. During the *choose* phase, job or career interests and the employment goal are selected through a collaborative effort of the professional staff and the participant. The *get* phase stresses job-search activities, job-seeking skills, and the development of individualized training needs, which allow for the participant to become employed in his or her chosen job. The final phase of *keeping* the job involves the delineation of skill deficits, individual supports, environmental modifications, and service coordination needs, in order to maintain the individual on the job. Bond (1991b) reported that, based on his analysis of the literature, SE was expensive, it required 2 to 3 years to start up and maintain an effective SE program, and much more research was needed to determine program consistency and effectiveness.

Evaluation of Program Models

Results of studies of the aforementioned vocational models have been mixed or negative, especially for those service models based on the earlier more segregated programs, in developing and maintaining employment (Anthony, Cohen and Danley, 1988; Bond, 1991b). Bond and McDonel (1991) found that persons with severe psychiatric disabilities have employment rates ranging from 0% to 20%. Anthony, Cohen, and Danley (1988), in their review of outcome data for persons with severe and persistent mental illness, provided information on predictive factors related to vocational capacity. Anthony et al.'s (1988; p. 62) analysis revealed five major findings:

1. Measures of psychiatric symptoms do not predict vocational outcomes.
2. The psychiatric diagnosis does not predict vocational rehabilitation outcomes.
3. Measures of psychiatric symptoms do not correlate with the psychiatrically disabled person's skills.
4. Measures of skills do predict vocational rehabilitation outcomes.
5. Training in critical vocational skills improves vocational rehabilitation outcomes.

Bond and McDonel, 1991, on the other hand, indicate that "no well organized information base" on effectiveness of vocational services for persons with severe and persistent mental illness was in existence prior to 1986. Further, studies since 1986 provide few firm data from which to predict success for persons participating in the psychiatric VR process (Bond et al., 1988). Bond et al. (1988), in his review of 24 controlled studies of persons with severe mental illness, found that there were no differences in employment rates when comparing experimental with control groups. However, Bond et al. (1988) did find that, when ongoing support was provided to consumers with severe mental illness, higher rates of *paid* employment were achieved.

Consistent with the Bond et al. (1988) findings on supports, MacDonald-Wilson, Revell, Nguyen, and Peterson (1990) found that persons with severe psychiatric disabilities earned $4.39 per hour on average and were employed 40.3% of the time in their first or subsequent job placement 18 months after first placement. Another recent longitudinal study of vocational outcomes for persons with severe psychiatric disabilities participating in PSR was reported by Rogers, Anthony, Toole, and Brown (1991). Rogers et al. (1991) indicated that 40.9% of the sample with a *vocational goal* were employed after 12 months.

Do the aforementioned programs benefit persons with severe and persistent mental illness in their attempts to achieve employment? As can be seen by the data, the answer to this question is different, based on the perspective one takes on employment outcomes. As was stated previously herein, Bond and Boyer (1988) concluded that, when looking at controlled studies, none of the aforementioned models were effective in providing long-term employment outcomes for persons with severe mental health problems. Bond's major criticism was that many models addressed the issue of getting a person employed; however, either the amount of time that the person with a disability stayed employed was not addressed, or the data indicated no lasting effects beyond a few weeks or months. Bond and his colleagues suggest that vocational programs that include a strong component of client involvement along with ongoing supports would seem to be of great benefit to persons with psychiatric disabilities. Conclusions from the foregoing data and analysis would indicate that more research is required on service delivery strategies to determine what works and for whom.

Sample Approaches to Program Design and Implementation

One method that would appear to meet the foregoing criteria of consumer involvement and ongoing supports is the combination of SE and job club approaches (Azrin & Besalel, 1979). The job club approach, as described previously herein, not only emphasizes the training of usual job seeking skills (JSS), but also includes the participant's involvement in the development of job leads and acquisition of employment in the context of a support group (Azrin & Philip, 1979). The primary differences between the job club and traditional JSS programs are that the job club requires consumers to "contact friends, prepare résumés, identify employment skills, schedule job seeking efforts, dress appropriately each day of training, and actively seek a job" under the direct supervision of the counselor or group leader (Azrin & Philip, 1979). Additionally, job club participants are required to participate in ongoing group counseling and support activities. Primary to the focus of the job club approach is the "intensive nature" of its procedures (Azrin & Philip, 1980). Azrin and Philip (1980) reported that job finding success was related to the number of sessions the participant attended and the number of interviews obtained.

SE, as reported earlier, emphasizes job matching and a place-and-train orientation, along with providing *long-term supports* (Wehman & Moon, 1988). As we have seen from the preceding review, a major criticism that has been aimed at vocational services for persons with severe mental illness has been the lack of ongoing supports, among others. Consequently, the addition of SE to a job club program could deliver a strong up-front consumer participation, along with continued supports that could maintain employment.

While there have been no published studies indicating successful implementation of the aforementioned combination programs, Simmons (1985) provided pilot data that lend some support to the combined job club and SE approach. Simmons's (1985) job club/SE approach was implemented through a combination of behavioral contracting, systematic supervision, group process techniques, career counseling, and a strong emphasis on job development and placement. The program was implemented in 4-hour shifts over a 10-day period (5 days per week over 2 weeks), with ongoing 1 day a week contacts for 6 months or until the participant acquired a job. Each participant and staff member was required to develop and commit to the fulfillment of an individualized behavioral contract, which spelled out what both parties were expected to perform. This contract listed such things as participation in classroom activities, numbers of employer contacts, medication utilization, development of a résumé, and so forth, as well as the services the staff members were to provide (résumé typing, classroom instruction, and support). Each day, this contract was reviewed and was modified, if necessary.

The classroom training consisted of much the same activities as Azrin and Philip (1979) describe. The participants were placed in a job club with persons having other types of disabilities and provided assistance in career exploration, résumé development, methods of developing jobs, and group discussion. All participants were encouraged and expected to performs tasks independently and to be open for staff criticism and input from other participants. All participants were required to perform tasks outside of the classroom. These outside activities ranged from making employer contacts to performing some paperwork (acquiring the name and address of a former employer or possibly developing job leads). The participants with psychiatric disabilities were expected, like the other participants, to participate in all meetings and to maintain contact and participate in weekly follow-up group sessions until they found a job.

The SE program evolved around the developments within the job club and was implemented as described previously, in relation to the place-and-train paradigm. Each participant was referred into an SE program and was evaluated based on information obtained from the job club, and a placement profile was developed. The participant and the staff person were both responsible for job development activities. On-site training was provided, as needed, along with ongoing follow-up counseling, which was provided by case managers.

Simmons (1985) reported that of 8 persons who were diagnosed as having psychiatric disabilities and who had participated in a combined job club/SE program, 7 completed the job club program and moved into SE services, 5 obtained competitive jobs, and 4 of the 5 who acquired jobs maintained those jobs for a minimum of 4 months.

Consumer Factors Related to Employment

Various aspects of the individual must be considered when implementing a vocational/employment program for persons with severe and persistent mental illness. In all cases, individual differences require serious attention and must be thoroughly considered. As can be seen from a variety of perspectives, each individual is different and must be afforded an appropriate match between service provision and the wants and needs of the individual. The aspects of the consumer that the authors feel are most important and deserve significant attention with respect to effort in coordinating are the assessment of individual characteristics and the stages of the consumer's career path. As is true for people *without* mental illness, stresses in home life, financial setbacks, physical illness, and other occurrences can have repercussions in the person's job.

Assessment

Botterbusch (1991) and Prieve and DePoint (1988) indicate that even though persons with severe mental illness are not a homogeneous group diagnostically, they do share certain characteristics: their mental health is tenuous, they tend to have acute anxiety and poor interpersonal skills, and many are on psy-

chotropic medication. In addition, many are veterans and homeless, with little vocational history or work experience they can recall or rely on. The provision of rehabilitation services to people with severe and persistent mental illness requires both an understanding of psychiatric disabilities and of VR, and then letting go of traditional approaches and beliefs (Russert & Frey, 1991). Traditional views of vocational assessment rely on the administration of standardized instruments to predict future performance. In many instances, occupational traits are measured before the person is selected for consideration for job placement. Areas assessed may include attitudes, values, interests and abilities, aptitudes, and an overall assessment of the work personality.

For individuals with limited work experiences and persistent mental illness, vocational evaluation usually results in one or more of the following outcomes: (a) few or no real job matches found for the individual; (b) the recommendation that the person evaluated is not ready for community employment; (c) the suggestion that the individual should be placed in a sheltered workshop to acquire skills needed for future placement; and (d) the conclusion that in general, people with severe disabilities are essentially unemployable (Menchetti & Vdvari-Solner, 1990).

The true complexity of the rehabilitation process can be lost if viewed through the instrument instead of the individual. Wesolek and McFarlane (1991) describe evaluators and rehabilitation specialists as concerned about "lack of consistent predictability and overall accuracy of assessment information." Still, vocational evaluation remains a vital process that connects the person with the type of vocational service provided. With the recent trends toward community employment and development of training sites through supported employment programming, traditional methods are being replaced with functional and behavioral assessments.

Behavioral assessment shares certain assumptions with functional assessments. Halpern and Fuhrer (1984) state that "functional assessment is the measurement of purposeful behavior in interaction with the environment, which is interpreted according to the assessment's intended use" (p. 3). Behavioral assumptions are that behaviors may have multidimensional causes and that the environment and the person interact to cause behavior. Both attempt to match the person with the environment. A functional assessment system identifies a specific current or future environment, assesses functional skill in relationship to the requirements for success in the environment, involves the client in the assessment, does not use symptomatology as a global measure of functionality, and is repeated over time (Dellario, Goldfield, Farkas, & Cohen, 1984).

Traditional and restrictive views of the purpose and potential of career counseling are slowly changing in the face of growing evidence that career development and human development are connected (Herr, 1989). Brown (1985) recommends a form of career counseling defined as "the process of helping an individual select, prepare for, enter, and function effectively in an occupation as a viable option and intervention with clients that have rather severe emotional problems" (p. 199). Zunker (1986) views career counseling as a seven stage process including experience identification, interest identification, skill identification, value and needs identification, education/training planning, occupational planning, and finally a lifelong learning plan. For persons with severe mental illness, a career counseling process is important in terms of gaining a self-understanding in relation to assessment information, experience, and immediate and long range planning—that is, helping to shape a career path.

The Program for Assertive Community Treatment (PACT) vocational model as described by Russert and Frey (1991) combines the principles of behavioral and functional analysis with career support and unifies them into a vocational philosophy and working program model. PACT clients are employed at rates of 40% to 50%, and 80% are engaged in active vocational interventions. One important factor in the PACT model is that assessment is a vital part of each segment of the continuum of services. This goes beyond the assess-train-place model and offers another dimension, in that the goals of assessment have become a dynamic and ongoing part of the rehabilitation process, instead of a singular component of service delivery. This also brings individualization into the concept of continuum of services and may assist in longer retention and contribute to quality in placement and flexibility in service delivery and long-term support, which is critical in community support services.

Career Path Stages

Vocational rehabilitation programs must be acceptable to the consumers who use them. This means that they must be responsive to the age and developmental level of the consumer. It is unwise to assume that all consumers will accept traditional entry level jobs simply because these are the most plentiful for job developers. Further, the way in which the VR program is presented and the rationale given to consumers about why certain steps are suggested makes a big difference in how consumers feel about such programs.

Anthony et al. (1988) has described a very sensitive approach in which the consumer is treated as an individual, and planning of service intervention and skill teaching are developed accordingly. However, for the purposes of the program planning, it is useful to recognize that there will be some similarities among consumers, and it is not necessary to reinvent the wheel with each individual. The following discussion seeks to delineate the similarities of support needs and to provide a description of how programs might ensure their responsiveness to the different characteristics (vocationally speaking) of consumers.

The vocational maturity of the consumer is affected by several factors—most notably, the age at which disability occurred and, consequently, interrupted the individual's vocational development. The current age of the consumer is also important, to ensure the age appropriateness of VR techniques. Developing an individualized program to meet the maturational needs of the consumer is challenging and—if not appropriately included in the VR program's design—could result in services being broadly designed but ineffective. Consequently, programs have often been in the position of offering the same VR services to all clients, when with slight alterations, these services can be matched appropriately to the age and maturity level of the consumer.

When thinking about vocational development, it may be helpful to broadly characterize three stages: early, middle, and late. The authors offer these stages not to suggest a rigid categorization of consumers, but rather as a checkpoint to ensure that programs have strategies in place to respond to appropriate needs of service recipients.

Early Stage

The individual in this stage may have experienced his or her first bouts of illness in early or late adolescence, may still be in the throes of vocational exploration, and may not be much farther along than rather idealized notions of what specific occupations entail, as well as the necessary skills to perform them. Often, people at this stage have not yet or have just recently completed high school.

If persons are still adolescents or in their early 20s, denial of the illness may be a prominent feature both for them and/or their family members. Grief for the lost potential of the individual is particularly painful at this point. In addition, normal issues of adolescence or early adulthood such as substance abuse and medication compliance, are critical. On the other hand, years may have passed, and an individual might be into his or her 30s but still be in the early stage of vocational development. In particular, when choosing a strategy, its acceptability to the consumer is critical. For example, it may be age appropriate for an adolescent or young adult (early 20s) to use a series of trial employment positions in fast-

food establishments, while the same intervention may feel demeaning to a 35-year-old.

Strategies for the Early Stage

1. Field trips to businesses and factories or guest speakers at the VR program may provide the consumer with valuable career exploration experiences. Thresholds in Chicago successfully utilized a visiting chef's program, which had successful restaurateurs visit and prepare a meal with the adolescent members. This provided role modeling, a chance to ask questions about this career path, and the opportunity to actively perform cooking tasks.

2. Vocational exploration groups may be utilized to provide support and assistance to the individual in exploring career choice. These groups may use a variety of exercises and standardized materials to help people crystalize their interests and get a better idea about the world of work.

3. Job tryouts similar to TE in the classic sense as practiced by Fountain House in New York (and elsewhere) are an excellent vehicle for person with severe and persistent mental illness to try out a series of short-term jobs.

Middle Stage

A large group of people experience their first hospitalization in early adulthood. They may have been in college or trade school, or even employed and well on the way to developing a vocational path. Here again, the sadness for the lost career is present and may even be more acute because significant progress was made toward the desired end. People may try repeatedly to resume where they left off, and for some people, this is successful. For others, there may be repeated failures, and the attempt to go back may almost take on an obsessive quality. (One individual we know who came from a family of jewelers had more than 10 different jewelry sales jobs before coming to grips with the fact that his symptoms of anxiety and paranoid ideation were a very poor mix with the high stress, performance driven world of jewelry sales. He has managed now to work behind the scenes for a gold buyer, for whom he does weighing and casting).

Persons with severe and persistent mental illness in this middle stage have to reconcile their perception of their abilities with their present work skills. Generally, this discrepant perception does not require traditional psychotherapy but the ability to encourage consumers and to be sensitive to the feelings of loss, disappointment, and discouragement that people in this middle phase usually experience. It is ironic and not altogether helpful that the staff workers who are employed in agencies working with this group are often at the beginnings of their own careers. Consumers occasionally express the belief that these workers "don't know how I feel" and, indeed, the staff members probably do not; good training in active listening and members' empathy are critical if staff members are to be effective. The Thresholds National Research and Training Center has a *Job Coach Training Manual* in preparation, which elaborates on these issues. Other consumers can be particularly helpful to each other in this area—sharing feelings and experiences can be both comforting and instructive. Staff members can be helpful by facilitating such interactions in groups or in one-to-one situations.

Strategies for the Middle Stage

1. Look for residual skills and ability. People may wish to remain in the same job family, so it is useful to explore the training needs for related occupations (i.e., the person who made it partway through medical school may choose to be a physical therapist or a medical technician; the teacher may wish to be a library aide; the computer programmer/analyst might go for data entry).
2. Address self-esteem issues. This is an area where family feelings are important, and an involved family can be supportive to vocational reassessment. Further,

the family and significant others can assist the individual in participating fully in the rehabilitation process. There is some evidence that involved families help people to stay in rehabilitation programs (Selleck, 1987). The staff person can assure the consumer that this process is not unusual for anyone to go through.
3. It has been our experience that for some people, the atmosphere is more important than the task. For example, doing janitorial work at a McDonald's or factory may not be palatable, but doing the same tasks at a theater or museum is. (A programmatic example is the Theater Arts Project at Thresholds, where jobs are found in theaters, both for groups and individuals. The work tasks are clerical and janitorial, but the atmosphere is distinctive.)
4. Address the importance of hobbies or avocations. Some people will never be able to attain the kind of career satisfaction they had envisioned or possibly experienced in the past. It is also true and sometimes helpful to impart the notion that vast numbers of people in this culture who are employed in routine or unpleasant jobs find great personal satisfaction in activities *outside* of work. Sports, clubs, volunteers, and so forth, are all areas that should be encouraged.

Late Stage

This stage may include people in the following circumstances:

- People who have had a disability caused by mental illness for a long time, and people who receive social security income
- People who are older and may have been living in highly structured board and care homes, intermediate care facilities, or nursing homes
- Older people who are now interested in VR

People in these situations often bring some special concerns to the rehabilitation process, particularly with regard to income security. Many of them lived through the years when social security attempted to reduce the rolls of people receiving benefits, and they went through the frightening experience of having their incomes withdrawn. Most also recall the difficulties they had in acquiring disability benefits in the first place, and they are quite concerned about the risk to their security if they try to work and then lose their entitlements.

These older adults are also more likely to lack parental and other family support. The strength of this group, however, is that they are often much more knowledgeable about their own illness and have come to grips with their symptoms and medical needs.

Strategies for the Late Stage

1. Scrupulous attention must be paid to state and federal regulations about income and benefits. Staff members must have these facts and must be able to reassure consumers about how to maintain benefits or how to predict when they will terminate. Consumers themselves are often in a position to consult with one another and to participate in visits to social security officers.
2. Because of the financial issues, some people in this phase prefer the piece rate, sheltered work option because their government income is not threatened.
3. Age appropriateness of job and surroundings is important. Visits to potential job sites will be useful, to look for a good match.

Nonvocational Issues

A wide variety of nonvocational issues have great impact on the vocational functioning of people with serious mental illness, in addition to those that affect all persons—with or without mental illness, such as stresses in home life, financial setbacks, physical illness, and other occurrences. Some specific issues may be especially stressful, such as the following: medications, financial assistance, substance abuse, case management, residential services, and personal psychological factors.

Medication Issues

It is critical for a VR practitioner to be well informed about medication issues in general, and about the specific circumstances of the consumers they assist. Changes in medication can be quite upsetting both physiologically and psychologically. Increased lethargy, dry mouth, blurred vision, constipation, akathisia, and other so-called minor side effects can have a devastating effect on an individual's efficiency and attitude at work. This is one area, in particular, where reasonable accommodations (as mandated by the Americans with Disabilities Act [ADA]) can be particularly useful if the consumer is comfortable in alerting the employer to the situation. Accommodations such as more breaks, permission to have water at the work station, and flex time could make periods of medication adjustment smoother for both employer and employee. Some consumers are especially sensitive about having privacy to take their medication. This can be a subject for discussion with the employer. If the consumer is unwilling to share this information, he or she may wish to consult the psychiatrist about the schedule of dosage to see whether changes can be made to reduce or eliminate mid-day administration.

Another serious concern that must be faced by consumers who do *not* share their medical situation with the employer is the risk they face if they are injured or become ill in a way that keeps them from alerting emergency medical professionals to their medication regimens. In some companies, it is possible for the human resources department to be aware of these matters *without* sharing them with line supervisors. It is the responsibility of the rehabilitation practitioner to bring these issues to the attention of consumers and to discuss the options.

In addressing the preceding issues about medications, various aspects of the treatment milieu must be addressed in order that an effective overall plan can be developed. First, there must be a tight communication loop between the treating psychiatrist, the treatment team, and the employer, to ensure that all issues that relate to generating a response to a possible problem are detailed. It is not uncommon for an individual to exhibit different behavior in different settings or to have other side effects (as described previously herein), which may negatively affect his or her functioning on the job. Second, medication blood levels should be monitored closely, in order that *minimum* therapeutic dosages may be maintained. Third, the personnel department should be notified of possible side effects and the likely expected occurrence of such problems. Practitioners should develop, with the employer's and the consumer's input, a strategy for handling the episode. This may involve affording the employee an extra break or time off to visit the CMHC, which the employee may make up at a later time.

Financial Issues

For individuals returning to work who have been receiving social security income, there is often a profound mixture of joy at becoming self-sufficient, and fear of loss of financial support. The loss of medical entitlements can also be extremely unnerving, particularly if the consumer is not receiving medical benefits at work. It is imperative to be in close communication with the Social Security Administration to ensure that there are no surprises about when benefits will be reduced or eliminated. This will also ensure that large overpayments do not occur, or if they do, that adequate planning and forethought be put into notifying and setting aside any extra money the consumer may receive.

Many consumers will find themselves without medical coverage after the cessation of social security benefits, either because they are not eligible for benefits as hourly workers, or because they have a pre-existing condition that precludes their receipt of benefits. This is a complicated area requiring much individual attention. The lack of medical benefits is not just the concern of persons with severe and persistent psychiatric disabilities. In many cases, local or state governments have programs that are beginning to assist low income workers to obtain basic medical insurance. The reduced rate insurance policies in many cases are subsidized by both employers and insurance companies. The National Alliance for the Mentally Ill (NAMI) has undertaken a similar tack of advocating for insurance reforms for people with serious mental illness.

Another way of dealing with medical insurance and medical programs (for those people who qualify for the SSI and/or Social Security Disability Insurance [SSDI] programs) is to address the issue of employment related work expenses (ERWE). ERWEs are extremely useful in reducing the overall gross income that is counted by the SSI and SSDI programs. A recipient of these government benefits may deduct expenses that are directly related to the person's disability but also required to maintain employment.

Personal and Psychological Factors

People who begin to earn money experience positive changes that can create disequilibrium. This disequilibrium may cause side effects that may result in problems that could be unforeseen or may create an impediment to maintaining employment. Extra money to spend, moving to a better apartment, getting a checking account, buying a car—all are positive things, but they add a level of complexity to life that can require some assistance. The car will need to be serviced, the checkbook balanced, and the apartment maintained. It is the authors' experience that even positive changes should be processed carefully with each individual, to facilitate a comfortable move into the new niche.

The down side of the increased financial freedom of the new worker is that there may be more disposable income for undesirable items, such as alcohol and illicit substances. Understandably, in an effort to fit in with the rest of the work group, some consumers may join TGIF (thank God it's Friday) trips to local bars. Whether this activity will work for the individual consumer is best discussed be*fore* the situation arises. How to socialize without the use of alcohol can be quite challenging in some occupations and local areas.

It must also be recognized that people will have relapses and will suffer discouragements on the job. It is very important to provide opportunities for people to discuss these issues and to get support for continuing the struggle to work. For some consumers, the discouragement of starting all over can seem insurmountable. Peer support, as well as professional support, must be available for these situations. It is critical that the ancillary aspects of rehabilitation be coordinated holistically in the treatment plan.

Role of Community and Employers

In order for persons with severe and persistent mental illness to be successful in the community and in employment settings, significant supports and modifications will be required (Mancuso, 1990). Mancuso (1990) has indicated that employment obstacles can be mitigated by developing accommodation efforts that attempt to allow the individual with severe and persistent mental illness to perform the "essential functions of the job." Mancuso (1990) also indicated that most accommodations for persons with psychiatric disabilities are either "inexpensive or free." However, the cost for the usual accommodations for persons with psychiatric disabilities tends to be sustained over a long period of time and cannot be implemented or constructed only once and then forgotten. Further, Mancuso indicated that the accommodations that are needed to include persons with psychiatric disabilities are "simply good management practices" and would or should be implemented by employers to benefit the employers' businesses. It is this latter tack that the authors feel is the most logical in addressing employers and their concerns with hiring persons with severe and persistent mental illness.

Simmons and Flexer (1992) outlined a variety of factors relevant to approaching employers in implementing supported employment services for persons with disabilities. Simmons and Flexer have indicated that rehabilitation programs must implement strong marketing campaigns, which address issues related to employer needs. Simmons and Flexer refer to the need to systematically "*tap* into the needs of employers and to describe the capability of the population of persons the employment service is representing."

The following concepts and practices were key:

1) persons with disabilities are productive employees, and a labor resource with the employer receiving additional benefits beyond that of a qualified pool of potential employees; 2) employers need to be "systematically cultured" to participate in the process of hiring persons with disabilities; 3) employers must be provided strong factual information dealing with workman's compensation and related concerns; and, further, 4) that employers who have participated in the process of hiring persons with disabilities are the most credible communicators of the viability of other employers hiring persons with disabilities. (p. 39)

Inclusion of employers into the process also requires systematic methods and strategies in informing employers of services and benefits within the community that might assist in the process of hiring persons with psychiatric disabilities. This should include developing an employer advisory board, which would address issues of employing, marketing, and providing input for the improvement of employment options for persons with psychiatric disabilities. This advisory board should consist of a variety of employers who, in total, represent the diversity of employers in the community. Programs should be developed to educate and inform these employers in order that the board members may become conduits to effect change within their workplaces. Further, the advisory board should be encouraged to include other employers in the process and to pass on information and successes the board has experienced.

In conjunction with advisory board development, combining the efforts of the multitude of disability related employment agencies would provide employers with a unified front in addressing employers' concerns about hiring persons with disabilities. Employers have indicated that they have been approached many times, relative to hiring persons with disabilities and that they are confused and apprehensive of implementing specialized employment programs. It has been the authors' experience that when turf issues and program implementation concerns can be addressed by all of the agencies providing vocational services, employers become more willing to be participatory in the process.

To support these concerted efforts, information must be presented to employers, which will extol the incentive programs that will, as Simmons and Flexer (1992) indicated, "seal the deal" with respect to hiring persons with disabilities. The programs that do benefit employers in regard to the hiring of persons with severe and persistent mental illness are On the Job Training (OJT) Funds, Targeted Jobs Tax Credits (TJTC), The Second Injury Rule, which (a) allows employers to utilize special Worker's Compensation funds when an injury has occurred as a result of a specific pre-existing disability, (b) offers the availability of an employment specialist to assist in the hiring process, (c) makes available funding for skill training through local VR and Private Industry Council (PIC) programs, and (d) permits sub-minimum wage certification, which enables employers to pay to persons with disabilities wages that are commensurate with their production.

Beyond the aforementioned array of efforts and practices, the practitioner should be prepared to offer a wide range of specific services that include the following:

1. *Education of employers about psychiatric disabilities.* Employers may be interested in working with people who have disabilities, but they are usually not informed about the illness. It can be especially useful to provide fact sheets about the illness itself, especially myth/stigma dispelling information, as part of any package of job development materials. The authors have found that employers are sometimes embarrassed about their own lack of knowledge and do not ask pointed questions. Employers want to know, among other things,

   a. What is the difference between mental illness and mental retardation?
   b. What kind of acting out behavior might they expect?
   c. What, if anything, will happen to their insurance rate if they hire people with psychiatric disabilities?

2. *Support for the employer before, during, and after placement.* Employers often have very humanitarian motives for hiring an individual with a disability, which may help to carry them over some rough patches; however, to sustain a long-term association, the employers must be convinced that their basic business needs will be met. There are a variety of ways to assess these needs and meet them, and a full discussion is beyond the scope of this work. Some of the most frequent concerns relating to support are the following—

   a. What do I do if the person decompensates at work?
   b. What about absences? Will a substitute worker be provided? Enclave and group options avoid this issue, of course, but individual placements must address it, depending on the nature of the work. The issue of absences is often best handled by encouraging the employer to treat the issue the same as they would other workers, especially in skilled jobs.
   c. Who will train the person? In some settings with high turnover, it is a selling point if the agency staff learns the job well enough to do training and retraining. Other strategies would include coworker training and mobile job support.

3. *Provision of thanks and feedback to employers, related to their importance to the process.* Employers benefit enormously from knowing that they are a valuable part of the community support

network, and that they are part of a cadre of other employers. Appreciation banquets, recognition newsletters, and so forth. are all important ways to cement the relationship. Inviting *prospective* employers to such gatherings with the individuals who are successfully employed offers powerful evidence that VR *works* and can help generate new jobs.

4. *Consultation regarding ADA.* Employers will be looking for assistance in figuring out how to comply with the ADA, and rehabilitation practitioners should be ready to brainstorm with them about the issue of reasonable accommodation in particular. A large number of low or no cost alternatives can assist people with mental illness to stay on the job. To name a few,

a. Flex-time to see psychiatrist/therapist

b. Frequent short breaks (for the bathroom, to get water) to deal with medication side effects

c. Multiple ways of giving instructions (e.g., orally and written; step by step fashion rather than all at once)

d. Flex-time to accommodate medication changes such as increased drowsiness

e. Permission to wear headphones to help control hallucinations

f. Elimination of non-essential functions of the job that might be causing the employee problems

ter), the programs that have developed have not yet found or fully put together the puzzle pieces to meet the needs of persons with psychiatric disabilities.

The authors have proposed that more recent development of models which emphasizes consumer involvement and the development of ongoing supports appear to have the most promise for providing appropriate employment services for persons with severe and persistent mental illness. Approaches that attempt to meet this dual emphasis are the choose–get–keep model proposed by Anthony; the PACT model discussed by Russert and Frey (1991); the SE/job club approach proposed by Simmons (1985); or the Thresholds approach. The authors attempted to present examples of how one would implement individualized services, based on providing for career development, individual interests, appropriate job matching, and ongoing supports (consumer and employer based).

In total, the authors have attempted to provide an overview of the aspects of implementing employment options for persons with severe and persistent mental illness. The authors feel it is important that all persons who want to work do so, and all people who can work should be provided this opportunity. The pieces to the puzzle are many and varied in shape and size. However, vocational programs can be implemented that are individualized, meet the needs of the consumer, and benefit the community as a whole.

Conclusions

It is evident that if persons with severe and persistent mental illness are to become full participants in the community, employment has to be an outcome that must be emphasized. One can see that a wide variety of vocational programs and options have developed over the years. However, not all vocational models have produced equally in terms of long-term outcomes for persons with psychiatric disabilities (Bond et al., 1988). In effect (to continue the analogy of this chap-

References

Anthony, J. L., & Lustig, P. (1968). A workshop experience for posthospitalized schizophrenics. In G. N. Wright & A. B. Trotter (Eds.), *Rehabilitation research* (pp. 72–78). Madison, WI: University of Wisconsin Press.

Anthony, W. A., Cohen, M. R., & Danley, K. S. (1988). The psychiatric rehabilitation model as applied to vocational rehabilitation. In J. A. Ciardiello & M. D. Bell (Eds.), *Vocational rehabilitation of persons with prolonged mental illness.* Baltimore, MD: Johns Hopkins University Press.

Azrin, N. H., & Besalel, V. B. (1979). *A behavioral approach to vocational counseling.* Baltimore: University Park Press.

Azrin N. H., & Besalel, V. A. (1980). *Job club counselors manual.* Baltimore: University Park Press.

Azrin, N. H., & Philip, R. A. (1979). The job club method for the handicapped: A comparative outcome model. *Rehabilitation Counseling Bulletin, 23,* 144–155.

Barbee, M. S., Berry, K. L., & Micek, L. A. (1969). Relationship of work therapy to psychiatric length of stay and readmission. *Journal of Consulting and Clinical Psychology, 33,* 733–738.

Black, B. J. (1988). *Work and mental illness: Transitions to Employment.* Baltimore: Johns Hopkins University Press.

Bond, G. R. (1991a). Vocational rehabilitation for persons with severe mental illness: Past, present, and future. In R. Liberman (Ed.), *Rehabilitation of the psychiatrically disabled.* New York: Pergamon.

Bond, G. R. (1991b). Vocational rehabilitation outcomes for persons with psychiatric disabilities. *Journal of Vocational Rehabilitation, 1*(3).

Bond, G. R., & Boyer, S. L. (1988). Rehabilitation programs and outcomes. In J. A. Ciardiello & M. D. Bell (Eds.), *Vocational rehabilitation of persons with prolonged mental illness* (pp. 231–263). Baltimore: Johns Hopkins University Press.

Bond, G., & McDonel, E. (1991). Vocational rehabilitation outcomes for persons with psychiatric disabilities: An update. *Journal of Vocational Rehabilitation, 1*(3), 21–29.

Botterbusch, K. F. (1991). Community-based assessment of persons with serious mental illness. In R. Fry (Ed.), *Fifth national forum on issues in vocational assessment: The issues papers* (pp. 197–201). Menomnie, WI: University of Wisconsin–Stout. Materials Development Center.

Brown, D. (1985) Career counseling: Before, after or instead of personal counseling? *The Vocational Guidance Quarterly, 33*(3), 197–201.

Cohen, L. (1976). A hospital's sheltered workshop as a rehabilitative and supported resource for discharged patients. *Hospital and Community Psychiatry, 27,* 559–60.

Davies, M. H. (1972). The rehabilitation of psychiatric patients at an industrial therapy unit outside the hospital. *International Journal of Social Psychiatry, 18,* 120–126.

Dellario, D. J., Goldfield, E., Farkas, M., & Cohen, M. (1984). Functional assessment of psychiatrically disabled adults: Implementations of research findings for functional skills training. In A. S. Halpern & M. J. Fuhrer (Eds.), *Functional assessment in rehabilitation.* Baltimore: Paul H. Brookes.

Federal Register (May 12, 1988). Rehabilitation Act Amendments of 1986. The state of supported employment service program; Final regulations. *Federal Register* (May 12, 1988) (34 CFR Part 363), *53*(92), 16981–16986. Washington, DC: Department of Education.

Gray, J. (1980). A follow-up study of psychiatric patients in a sheltered workshop program. *Hospital and Community Psychiatry, 31,* 563–566.

Greenleigh Associates. (1975). *The role of sheltered workshops in the rehabilitation of the severely disabled.* New York: U.S. Department of Health, Education, and Welfare.

Halpern, A. S., & Fuhrer, M. J. (1984). *Functional assessment in rehabilitation.* Baltimore: Paul H. Brookes.

Herr, E. L. (1989). Career development and mental health. *Journal of Career Development, 16*(1), 115–120.

Kiernan, W. E., & Payne, M. (1982). Hard to train: A history of vocational training for special needs youth. In K. P. Lynch, W. E. Kiernan, & J. A. Stark (Eds.), *Prevocational and vocational education for special needs youth.* Baltimore: Paul H. Brookes.

MacDonald-Wilson, K. L., Revell, Jr., W. G., Nguyen, N., & Peterson, M. E. (1991). Supported employment outcomes for people with psychiatric disability: A comparative analysis. *Journal of Vocational Rehabilitation, 1*(3), 30–44.

Mancuso, L. L. (1990). Reasonable accommodations for workers with psychiatric disabilities. *Psychosocial Rehabilitation Journal, 14*(2), 78–80.

Menchetti, B. M., & Udvari-Solner, A. (1990). Supported employment: New challenges vocational evaluation. *Rehabilitation Education, 4,* 301–317.

Neff, W. S. (1988). Vocational rehabilitation in perspective. In J. A. Ciardiello & M. D. Bell (Eds.), *Vocational rehabilitation of persons with prolonged psychiatric disorders.* Baltimore: Johns Hopkins University Press.

Prieve, K., & Depoint, B. (1988). *Making it work: Supported employment for persons with severe and persistent mental illness.* Spring Lake Park, MN: Rise Inc.

Rogers, E. S., Anthony, W. A., Toole, J., & Brown M. A. (1991). Vocational outcomes following psychosocial rehabilitation: A longitudinal study of three programs. *Journal of Vocational Rehabilitation, 1*(3), 21–29.

Rogers, E. S., Sciarappa, K., & Anthony, W. A. (1991). Development and evaluation of situational assessment instruments and procedures for persons with psychiatric disability. *Journal of the Vocational Evaluation and Work Adjustment Association, 24*(2), 61–67.

Roomey, D. J. (1984). Therapy for the chronically mentally ill: The therapeutic program at Portal. *Psychosocial Rehabilitation Journal,4,* 24–36.

Russert, M. G., & Frey, J. L. (1991). The PACT vocational model: A step into the future. *Psychosocial Rehabilitation Journal, 14*(4), 56–64.

Selleck, V. (1987). *Social network and dropping out of psychiatric rehabilitation: Exploring the relationship*. Unpublished dissertation, Northwestern University, Evanston, IL.

Simmons, T. J. (1985). *A job club approach to serving hard to place persons with disabilities* (Final report to the Private Industry Council). Lexington, KY.

Simmons, T. J., & Flexer, R. W. (1992). Business and rehabilitation factors in the development of supported programs for persons with developmental disabilities. *Journal of Rehabilitation, 57*(3), 29–42.

Stein, L. I., & Test, M. A. (1980). An alternative to mental health treatment: Part I. Conceptual mode, treatment program, and clinical evaluation. *Archives of General Psychiatry, 37*, 392–397.

Strauss, J. S., & Carpenter, W. (1974). The prediction of outcome in schizophrenics II. *Archives of General Psychiatry, 27*, 739–46.

Strauss, J. S., Harding, C. M., Silverman, M., Eichler, A., & Lieberman, M. (1988). Work as treatment for psychiatric disorders: A puzzle in pieces. In J. A. Ciardiello & M. D. Bell (Eds.), *Vocational rehabilitation of persons with prolonged psychiatric disorders*. Baltimore: Johns Hopkins University Press.

Strauss, J. S., Hafez, H., Lieberman, P., & Harding. (1985). The course of psychiatric disorder III: Longitudinal principles. *American Journal of Psychiatry, 142*, 289–296.

Wehman, P., & Moon, M. S. (1988). *Vocational rehabilitation and supported employment*. Baltimore: Paul H. Brookes.

Wesolek J. S., & McFarlane, F. R. (1991). Perceived needs for vocational assessment information as determined by those who utilize assessment results. *Vocational Evaluation and Work Adjustment Bulletin, 24*(2), 55–60.

Whitehead, C. W. (1977). *Sheltered workshop study: A nationwide report on sheltered workshops and their employment of handicapped individuals* (Workshop Survey, Vol. I, U.S. Department of Labor Service Publication). Washington, DC: U.S. Government Printing Office.

Will, M. (1984). *OSERS programming for transition of youth with disabilities: Bridges from school to working life*. Washington DC: Office of Special Education and Rehabilitative Services, U.S. Department of Education.

Zunker, V. (1986). *Career counseling: applied concepts of life planning*. Monterey, CA: Brookes/Cole.

Chapter 9

Supported Education

DAVID P. MOXLEY
CAROL T. MOWBRAY
KAAREN STRAUCH BROWN

Higher education is increasingly recognized as social capital, the possession of which becomes a principal means to achieve occupational mobility within the United States. Access to higher education, which leads to a well-trained work force, is seen by many state governments as a strategic asset, useful in attracting growth companies (Osborne, 1988). Education is seen as a primary means of offsetting the unemployment, underemployment, and downward mobility experienced by many workers during the 1980s (Oxford Analytica, 1986). Given the importance of higher education for the individual and the community, there is a concern about access to postsecondary education for people who often are overlooked as potential candidates for such education, including ethnic minorities (Reich, 1991) and those individuals challenged by disability. Large numbers of individuals in both these groups are likely to experience unemployment or underemployment.

Although participation in higher education has been seen as the purview of the young, who—upon completing high school—have moved on to community colleges, 4-year colleges, and universities, the United States has traditionally had multiple entry points for these institutions. The community college system has been particularly hospitable to the nontraditional student. Some adults have been able to enter community colleges to complete their Graduate Equivalency Degree (G.E.D.) and, then, to go on to complete college degrees. Others use community college courses to explore new careers, master new technologies now necessary to keep a job current, and/or continue their education as part of ongoing personal development. Four year colleges and universities have been reaching out more and more to adult learners, frequently with a special emphasis placed on recruiting women, individuals from ethnic or racial minorities, and persons with disabling conditions.

Many of these post-secondary institutions recognize that some students come into their programs unprepared to take advantage of course offerings and unable to meet academic demands. Developmental education has become institutionalized in many of these settings, offering diagnostic testing, enrichment courses, and courses designed to strengthen study and self-management skills.

The Carl Perkins Vocational Act of 1984 has provisions designed to assist in the vocational education of individuals needing accommodation, special assistance, or services, including the establishment of offices for students with special needs as part of supportive programs. Community colleges that receive funds under this act must provide the following services to their students who are disabled or are otherwise considered disadvantaged:

1. An assessment of the interests, abilities, and special needs of students with respect to completing successfully a vocational education program.
2. Special services, including adaptation of curriculum, instruction, equipment, and facilities, designed to meet the needs established through assessment.
3. Guidance, counseling, and career development activities conducted by professionally trained counselors who are associated with the provision of such special services.
4. Counseling services designed to facilitate the transition from school to postschool employment and career opportunities.

As post-secondary institutions have begun to serve students with special needs, they have become more hospitable places for these students. This chapter focuses on students with severe and persistent psychiatric disorders and the development of educational and rehabilitation supports within post-secondary educational settings. In addition to defining supported education and clarifying its foundation and rationale, we describe and contrast existing models. We describe some of the critical factors in service delivery within these models, which all emphasize, under a variety of auspices, collaboration among educational personnel, service providers, and people with psychiatric disabilities in the delivery of supported education. Finally, we summarize the major benefits of supported education, address its critics, and propose issues for future development and application of this programmatic concept.

Supported Education: Definition and Goals

Given our society's emphasis on the importance of higher education, providing support to individuals seeking higher education as a psychosocial rehabilitation (PSR) option should be no surprise (Unger, 1989). Mental health consumers, family members, advocates, educators, and researchers are becoming increasingly interested in organizing, implementing, and demonstrating relevant programmatic alternatives that make post-secondary education accessible and appropriate (Community Support Network News, 1990).

Thus, supported education has recently been added as a component of PSR. It involves the provision of ongoing supports to assist people with psychiatric disabilities to take advantage of skill, career, educational, and interpersonal development opportunities within post-secondary educational environments (Unger, 1989). From a psychosocial perspective, supported education allows participants to have alternative means of self-definition, from psychiatric patient to student (Unger, Anthony, Sciarappa, & Rogers, 1991). Supported education addresses the following PSR objectives:

1. Immersion in normalizing social and interpersonal environments within which individuals with psychiatric disabilities can come into contact with a range of different types of people, social situations, and interpersonal experiences.
2. Access to leisure, recreational, and cultural resources that are readily available through educational settings.
3. Opportunities to address and strengthen basic educational competencies related to successful completion of course requirements, including self-study skills, attendance, time management, planning, and self-management.
4. Opportunities to explore individual interests relating to career awareness, career development, and vocational choice.
5. Support from educational and PSR staff who are available to help students navigate the educational environment, to troubleshoot stressful situations, and to assist students to develop natural and/or ongoing supports within the educational setting.
6. Peer support from other participants in the supported education program.

Basis for the Development of Supported Education

Supported education as a programmatic alternative is an initiative, the development of which reflects principles and practices from a number of areas: (1) normative adult development, (2) the rehabilitation assets of higher education environments, (3) psychiatric rehabilitation, (4) the clubhouse model, (5) supported employment, and (6) the consumer movement. Each of these areas is discussed next and their implications for supported education are identified.

Normative Adult Development

Gould's (1978) model of adult life stages emphasizes the importance of separation from parents and from the family of origin during late adolescence and young adulthood. For many people coping with psychiatric disabilities, this separation may not occur according to a normative social clock because they may continue for some time to be dependent on family members, especially parents, during this period of their lives (Hatfield, 1987). Specific tasks during young adulthood, according to Gould, involve physical separation from the home and moving on to work or to school. The milestones of young adulthood include getting a job, sharing a residence with peers, paying rent, and laying the foundation, educationally and through training, for a subsequent career.

Havighurst (1974) identifies the developmental tasks of young adulthood as involving the establishment of both family and household. Basic to the achievement of these tasks is success in starting an occupation, a task that consumes a great proportion of the time of a young adult (Havighurst, 1974). Achievement of these tasks enables the young person to enter the adult world successfully, normatively between the ages of 22 to 28 (Levinson, 1978), although there is growing evidence that successful mastery of these tasks may actually take longer.

The importance of occupation and occupational choice during young adulthood is a salient feature of these normative developmental models. From a vocational development standpoint, however, occupational choice does not occur without time spent in exploration (Danley, Rogers, & Nevas, 1989; Super, 1953). During this period, the individual is involved in a process of self-examination in regard to various occupational possibilities. Exploration of different occupations occurs through school activities, leisure, peer involvement, observation of other people, and temporary or part-time work. Tentative choices are made, additional training is sought, and choices are explored by talking with others before making a decision about a career direction. Several years can be devoted to this process even before there is commitment to the first job. The normative ages for accomplishing developmental tasks may not be relevant to people coping with psychiatric disabilities, as for many other adult students. Specifically, in the case of students with psychiatric concerns, they may have their own age trajectory influenced by issues pertaining to their illnesses and the supports and other resources available to them.

For all adults, it is important to underscore the importance of occupational fantasy, exploration, and choice for the achievement of other developmental milestones (e.g., household formation). The post-secondary educational setting provides a milieu in which almost everyone is exploring occupational possibilities and in which tentativeness about occupational choice and career is not part of a deviancy cycle but rather is expected and acceptable. In an educational milieu, such exploration for persons with psychiatric disabilities can occur within the role of student rather than in the more stigmatizing role of patient.

Rehabilitation Assets of Higher Education

Higher education settings offer a richness of opportunities for personal development and social integration, which are difficult to attain in other areas of our society. Some personal development opportunities may be solely academic in character, while others enhance key developmental areas such as athletics, culture, socialization, and recreation. Activities such as musical and stage performances, political events, and athletic competition may be more accessible on a campus than they are in the general community. With the requisite supports, people with psychiatric disabilities may experiment with a variety of roles, including student worker, learner in a regular university or college classroom, or participant in an extracurricular activity.

Involvement in campus opportunities based on the preferences of students may lead to higher levels of social integration (Segal & Aviram, 1978). From a standpoint of normalization, social integration requires achievement in five dimensions (Wolfensberger, 1972): First, normalization requires *presence* in a regular community, and second, *participation* in socially valued activities. A supported education program can place people with psychiatric disabilities in the mainstream of campus life while providing requisite supports to enable individuals to take advantage of what the campus has to offer. Guided and supported participation in campus activities can result in *skill enhancement*, a third dimension of normalization. Mastery of different skills that result in success on campus can, in turn, provide *image enhancement*, the fourth dimension of normalization, which then can lead to higher levels of *autonomy* and more independent action, the fifth dimension of normalization.

Psychiatric Rehabilitation

Two intervention concepts are basic to the philosophy of psychiatric rehabilitation (Farkas, Anthony, & Cohen, 1989): first, an emphasis on the development of tangible and useful skills that enable individuals to master the requirements of specific roles of their own choosing; a supported education program assists people in mastering the role requirements of a student who is exploring and making tentative choices concerning vocational, social, and personal development. Second, emphasis must be placed on the augmentation and implementation of environmental supports involving interpersonal, material, and instrumental resources, designed to support the role functioning of people in specific situations. A supported education program becomes truly supportive when students have access to financial assistance, transportation, social and interpersonal interactions, tutoring, and books and academic materials—all of which are basic to functioning successfully as a student. The logic of supported education is to provide skill development and environmental supports within an academic setting, with resources designed to assist students in achieving success (Farkas et al., 1989; Hutchinson, Kohn, & Unger, 1989).

The basic rehabilitation concepts of skill development and environmental support are means by which the mission of psychiatric rehabilitation is achieved. The guiding mission involves the achievement by individuals of enhanced functioning so that the persons are satisfied and successful in an environment and in roles of their own choosing (Farkas et al., 1989). It is within the context of the mission of psychiatric rehabilitation that supported education realizes additional relevance.

The Clubhouse Model

The clubhouse, a PSR alternative, places emphasis on the acquisition by members of pragmatic independent living and work related skills within a supportive environment (Beard, Propst, & Malamud, 1982). According to standards formulated by Fountain House, one of the original clubhouses, providing members with opportunities to continue their education is an important feature of this program. A clubhouse offers opportunities for its members to advance their education in basic areas such as literacy and computation. However, according to Fountain House standards, the program also offers members opportunities to advance their education with the support of their peers and staff and to learn pragmatic skills necessary for attainment of educational outcomes (Taylor, Piagesi, McNaught, & Nielson, 1989).

Supported education is very compatible with the aims of the clubhouse. In fact, the clubhouse can offer a supportive environment in which students who are participating in higher educational settings can obtain (a) support from peers, (b) linkage to community resources and services that will help the student to realize educational goals, and (c) access to leisure and recreational outlets during weekend and evening hours. Supported education, however, occurs best in the actual university or college environment, with the clubhouse serving as a backup long-term support system.

Supported Employment

Supported work in actual employment settings has created positive outcomes for people with psychiatric disabilities (Anthony & Blanch, 1987), although there is some question as to the long-term effectiveness of this type of vocational rehabilitation alternative (Bond & Boyer, 1988). Despite its limitations, supported employment (SE) does place an emphasis on the social integration of people coping with psychiatric disabilities into community work settings. Full time employment may not be a sole measure of success, however. Bond and Boyer (1988) emphasize that a more reasonable indicator of success may lie in creating a portfolio of productive activity in the community, which can include part-time work, participation in education, volunteer involvement, and participation in a PSR alternative. Thus, it may be feasible to link part-time involvement in both work and education.

Yet, one problem frequently noted concerning jobs obtained through SE is that they may set limits on people's growth and development. Many jobs involve so-called food

and filth—placements in service related occupations involving food preparation, janitorial, or maintenance positions. Systematic needs assessments of people coping with psychiatric disabilities demonstrate these persons' desire to obtain relevant vocational training and education so they can move into a wider variety of productive work and career roles (Freddolino, Moxley, & Fleishman, 1988).

Therefore, SE offers an additional alternative within PSR. On the one hand, SE has demonstrated the usefulness and importance of individualized supports provided by VR staff, coworkers, and family in sustaining people with psychiatric disabilities on the job. On the other hand, if we are to assist people with psychiatric disabilities to move toward relevant, valued, and more diverse work in our changing society, then assisting people to realize positive outcomes from educational opportunities may prove to be a vital aspect of future PSR practice.

The Consumer Movement

PSR practice prioritizes the importance of consumer involvement in the identification of rehabilitation needs and goals (Farkas et al., 1989). Self-determination and client influence and control over service delivery are visible aspects of PSR as clients become increasingly vocal about what they want to achieve for themselves (Chamberlin, Rogers, & Sneed, 1989; Moxley & Freddolino, 1990). The relevance of PSR and community support services have become important issues in the design of service systems (Cohen & Anthony, 1988). PSR professionals are likely to interact with individuals who are increasingly vocal and assertive in their own programmatic preferences (even though these preferences may not be consistent with the diagnostic conclusions of professionals). Achieving educational, vocational, personal, and social development outcomes within postsecondary environments is a preference of many clients, as well as family members. The movement toward PSR within normative environments, such as a community college or university campus, is often fueled by the preferences and desires of consumers themselves.

Models of Supported Education

There are several different models of supported education. Following a rehabilitation philosophy, we are most interested in those models that provide opportunities for learning and support within normalized educational environments, such as community colleges, 4-year colleges, and universities. Three major approaches to supported education can be identified in the current literature: (1) the self-contained classroom; (2) the on-site model; and (3) the mobile supported education model (Unger, 1990a). They are distinguished both by the degree to which they integrate participants in the ongoing academic, social, and recreational life of the campus, and by the location of support services. Supports may include career development opportunities; ongoing access to guidance, counseling, and support from professionals; availability of peer supports; and case management activities, including linkage to benefits, crisis intervention, and coordination of the supported education program with mental health services.

All supported education models incorporate principles of hopefulness with a focus on achieving a person–environment adaptive balance. As participants struggle with real life processes in valued settings, they begin to acquire skills in the environments in which these skills will be used.

Self-Contained Classroom Model

Among the campuses where this model has been implemented are Boston University and George Brown College in Toronto (Community Support Network News, 1990; Unger, Danley, Kohn, & Hutchinson, 1987). These programs have a strong vocational focus, helping participants to develop career goals and then providing skill building and support so that they may enter or reenter the work force in the occupation of their choice or may enter a post-secondary educational institution.

The Boston University model is designed to modify the environment of participants and to help them develop skills in the context of a supportive relationship with designated rehabilitation staff members. All the participants complete a structured four semester curriculum, which prepares them for the normalized classroom. In addition, this program focuses on helping participants take charge of their disability rather than letting their disability define their entire lives.

The core programmatic element of this alternative is the curriculum, which involves students in choosing, exploring, testing, and implementing a career plan. This curriculum helps students develop a profile of vocational potential to identify their aptitudes. They then go on to examine occupational alternatives that match their interests and aptitudes. This is followed by the identification of a specific career goal and the resources, supports, and skill building necessary to reach that goal. Career planning is accompanied by professional and peer support both inside and outside the classroom. The outside support helps participants meet their income, housing, leisure, and mental health needs. After completion of the program, many students go on to other education, training, or employment situations. A unique aspect of the Boston University program is the ongoing linkage among graduates, peers, and staff through alumni meetings and job clubs.

A 1991 report on the Boston University program (Unger et al.) illustrates the necessity of choosing students likely to succeed in a post-secondary environment—that is, those young adults between the ages of 18 and 35 who possess average or above average intelligence and who can demonstrate the ability to use a classroom based program for career planning. In addition, participants must be stabilized on medication. Unger and her colleagues report that the Boston University program has a positive impact on subsequent competitive employment rates and on further involvement in additional education. Like many other PSR alternatives, supported education lowers hospitalization rates and elevates the self-esteem of its participants.

The George Brown program, under the auspices of a community college in Toronto, combines supported education and SE into one program, thereby demonstrating the portfolio approach to PSR. This approach helps participants combine work and training or education to reach vocational goals, alternating experiences in the classroom with experiences in the community. Students first experience self-contained classrooms, which have established curricula. This experience is followed by a 10-week supported work phase, which is expanded for another 5 months for those ready to move into the workplace. Mental health case management and counseling services are provided throughout the program. Entry is predicated on an assessment of motivation and ability to work in and with groups.

On-Site Model

This model has been implemented on a variety of community college campuses—Quinsigamond Community College in Massachusetts, Mott Community College in Michigan, and the California community college system. It serves students with psychiatric disabilities who want to achieve post-secondary education goals within integrated settings. Supports are located in existing campus programs, such as academic advising, special needs, and developmental education programs. Mental health services are provided by existing community mental health programs, which have linkages to their respective community college campuses.

Unlike self-contained classrooms, the on-site model does not immerse participants in a special program designed to prepare them for higher education but rather seeks to assist mental health consumers to make use of the array of resources available to all students on a community college campus. This model appears to emphasize integration over support, although the Quinsigamond program

uses peer support groups as an ongoing environmental resource strategy. The Mott alternative makes use of faculty mentors and provides individualized advising for students coping with psychiatric disabilities. The California community college system admits mental health consumers who can meet the requirements of all students, with appropriate support, and locates this support in the Office of Special Student Services, thus expanding the traditional roles of that office.

The on-site model is based on the assumption that enriching the special student services located on community college campuses can make them more relevant, appropriate, and accessible to students who have disabilities as a consequence of psychiatric illness. Unlike the self-contained classroom model, mental health services are not provided as part of the program. Linkages to existing mental health programs are emphasized. This model builds on existing services both in post-secondary institutions and in the existing mental health system, and so, it is the most economical of supported education models.

Mobile Supported Education Model

This model is generally implemented as part of a larger PSR program able to provide support, symptom management, and academic skill development to those participants who want to pursue higher education opportunities. The mobile supported education model integrates these educational opportunities and psychiatric rehabilitation in a more individualized and flexible manner than either of the other two models. Students can select their own post-secondary education site or training situation. They then can obtain flexible program supports that troubleshoot specific difficulties or particularly stressful or challenging life events.

The Community Scholar Program, located at Thresholds in Chicago, has one of the most elaborate examples of this approach to supported education. This program combines remedial educational and vocational awareness programs with case management and advocacy, to help consumers gain access to academic programs. Participants are educated about their rights as students, and staff members provide educational faculty with in-service training on how to address classroom issues that may arise with consumers. The program provides subject-specific tutoring and peer tutoring to help maintain students in the classroom successfully. Finally, the program has mobile education workers (MEWs), who operate on an outreach basis, providing support, educational counseling, and case coordination activities. As part of their support function, MEWs help participants build self-confidence and self-esteem in their roles as students. The MEWs validate dreams and fears about this role, and they demystify the campus and the higher education structure and process. Last, the MEWs act in a crisis intervention role. Support also is provided through peer support and a between semesters group, which offers a means to sustain the motivation, interests, and work of participants.

Summary of Supported Education Models

These three models reflect the diversity of supports included within the programmatic umbrellas of these different supported education initiatives. These supports include the integration of vocational and career development opportunities, professional guidance and case management, peer support, involvement of faculty, and linkage to other services. All of these models integrate PSR or mental health services with educational opportunities. They also emphasize the importance of career preparation and additional schooling for students coping with psychiatric disabilities. There is a spirit of hope and optimism communicated by these programs, based on the belief that, despite the difficulties created by psychiatric disabilities, students who are otherwise prepared to take advantage of post-secondary education, can, in fact, do so successfully.

Critical Factors in the Delivery of Supported Education

Consistent with the grass roots character of many PSR programs, supported education programs can be conceptualized, developed, and implemented using a broad based community planning effort involving primary consumers, family members, advocates, university faculty, and researchers. Such an effort has been undertaken in Michigan since the late 1980s, the aim of which is the development of a flexible, comprehensive approach to supported education that addresses the expressed needs of many young adults coping with psychiatric disabilities. Rather than describing this specific model, we have identified what we consider to be the most critical features of this approach, including the (1) specification of the participants, the outreach, and the supported education site(s); (2) inclusion of core services; (3) specific intervention approaches; and (4) evaluation of supported education.

Participants, Outreach, and Site

The literature on serious mental illness and on supported education suggests that participants should have a G.E.D, high school diploma, or some college experience, a history of severe and persistent disability consistent with current definitions in the psychiatric literature (i.e., severe mental disability of long duration, functional deficits in role performance, and/or severe problems relating to role performance), be involved in ongoing services and support or—if not—be willing to become involved in mental health services. This final criterion ensures that participants will have enough assistance in following through on their individualized learning and career plans and ensures ready access to crisis assistance, medication, and specialized therapeutic services. Given the possibility of stress introduced by the novelty of the campus and by academic and environmental demands, provision of available, responsive, and flexible crisis assistance is a critical feature of a supported education program. Linkage to mental health services strengthens follow through on individualized learning and career plans when crisis support, medication assistance, and specialized therapeutic services are readily available to participants.

Existing supported education programs have found greater benefits to their participants who are currently involved in mental health services (Community Support Network News, 1990). Participants themselves—not solely family members, case managers, or counselors—should be motivated to pursue post-secondary education. Potential participants can indicate an interest in the program during a screening interview. Of course, those individuals who have already started post-secondary education and who need additional supports or who want to switch to a different educational program are also appropriate candidates for a supported education initiative.

Avenues for recruiting consumers as potential supported education participants include contacts with consumer groups, family support groups, advocacy organizations such as the National Alliance for the Mentally Ill (NAMI), and professionals from mental health, social service, and rehabilitation agencies. Informational workshops targeting program administrators from community mental health organizations and from rehabilitation agencies, NAMI members, family members, and consumers can disseminate basic information about supported education, provide an overview of the program, and discuss the provision of support to supported education participants. This same material can be provided as inservice training sessions for case managers and other relevant program staff members recruited from a diversity of agency auspices, including the post-secondary sites themselves. This approach to outreach widens the recruiting net and, most important, begins to socialize a wide range of professionals, family members, and consumers into basic supported education and PSR principles.

Because educational needs, desires, and preferences of consumers vary, implementa-tion of supported education can be undertaken by either 4-year universities or community colleges. Community colleges are frequently attractive because they offer a wide range of courses and programs, as well as more flexibility in the scheduling of classes. The most appropriate post-secondary education sites are accessible, offer a full range of vocational, professional, and liberal arts degrees, and offer services for special students, including financial aid information and assistance, career counseling, individualized counseling, remedial and developmental programs, tutors, and note takers. A diverse student population may also be important because it may increase the chances that faculty, staff, and students have more tolerance of people from different backgrounds and with different behaviors.

Core Services

In supported education, interventions must be offered on campus. The PSR literature indicates that interventions must be environmentally specific and geared to the environment in which participants are functioning. In addition, the benefits of supported education accrue, in part, because of the non-stigmatizing educational environment. This environment can improve self-image and the sense of personal dignity.

Five environmental supports, available on campus and geared to the individualized needs of consumers, can compose the core of the supported education initiative, although these supports are not seen as a replacement for ongoing mental health and rehabilitation opportunities delivered off campus: informational resource packet; on-site mentorships; facilitated eligibility determination, entry, and processing; facilitated contacts and services; and contingency funds.

An *informational resource packet*, available to participants, professionals, and significant others, can provide detailed information on registration, enrollment procedures, special student services, financial aid, and support available through public and nonprofit agencies. Orientation to the packet can be included as part of a kickoff workshop, which offers presentations by college officials and representatives (especially staff members of special student services), agency personnel, and the staff of the supported education initiative. A workshop could offer an opportunity to all participants, their significant others, participating agency personnel, college staff, and project staff to form initial relationships based on face-to-face interaction.

On-site mentorships are the second core service. Opportunities to work with mentors who are experienced and with successful student peers can assist participants to increase their personal support, increase social learning, and increase problem-solving efforts. These peers, from the general student population, can be available to supported education participants for note-taking, tutorials, and advice within specific courses taken by supported education students. Recruitment, training, and ongoing support of these mentors may need to be coordinated by supported education staff members and the staff of the special student services office.

Facilitated eligibility determination, entry, and processing through the state rehabilitation program is a third core service. Given the importance of integrating supported education with career and vocational development, early involvement with the state rehabilitation program is an important aspect of the supported education initiative. The resource information packet must include the most accurate, comprehensive information available about gaining access to resources and services offered by the state rehabilitation program. The availability of state VR counselors who are well oriented to the supported education program and to working with people who have psychiatric disabilities is a critical component of the supported education initiative. The possibility of coordinated casework among supported education staff, staff from the college's special student services office, and state VR counselors is another important programmatic feature.

A fourth core service, *facilitated contacts and services*, assists all supported education participants in making use of on-campus offices of special student services and college academic advising offices. Students can be apprised of the services offered by these offices during the kickoff workshop. Again, coordinated efforts among supported education staff, staff of the special student services office, mental health professionals, and state VR counselors can help participants to realize a more consistent and supportive on-campus experience.

The final core service addresses the precarious economic life of many people who live with long-term psychiatric problems. The availability of *contingency funds* will assist students to meet expenses so that they can take full advantage of the post-secondary educational environment and avoid unnecessary stress. These funds should be used to cover costs not met through other sources or costs that must be covered while students are waiting for loans, other financial support decisions, or eligibility determinations. The funds—which are available to students quickly without red tape—can be used flexibly for such needs as transportation, books, socialization activities, or clothes. They can be used to pay for tuition costs until regular enrollment or student aid is received.

Intervention Approaches

The core services identified herein are supports available to all supported education students. However, given the diversity of approaches to the actual delivery of supported education, choices can be made about the form of supported education, based on the needs and desires of consumers. Given the need for evaluation research in this area of PSR, multiple models can be offered to evaluate the types, levels, and durability of outcomes produced by each approach. For example, a *structured curriculum model*, consistent with the Boston University model, may offer a formal classroom on the grounds of a community college, staffed by a career development teacher and assistant. Prioritizing a nonintegrated educational experience, the structured curriculum model offers skill development, stress management, information, study skills and self-management training, and a supportive classroom environment.

The *group support model*, a second approach, can offer mutual support groups for people with psychiatric problems who are involved in their own self-arranged post-secondary educational programs. Facilitated by both consumers and mental health professionals, these groups may offer structured and open discussion about career development, social support, stress management, study and academic skills, decision-making, and anxiety reduction. Speakers who can address participants' interests in post-secondary academic and career development topics can make presentations to these groups.

A third alternative focuses on enabling supported education participants to obtain *information from and referral to* the special student service offices. This model targets intervention resources on the staff of these offices, based on the rationale that many special student service staff members lack experience with and knowledge of students who are coping with psychiatric problems. Training and consultation to the staff members of these offices may result in the delivery of more relevant and appropriate counseling services to students with psychiatric disabilities. Supported education students can receive enhanced information (i.e., information and assistance beyond that provided as a core service) about these offices with the aim of helping them to expand their use of the existing resources offered by special student services.

Evaluation of Alternative Supported Education Approaches

These three alternatives reflect the many ways of incorporating supported education into higher educational settings. Also, this diversity illustrates the many purposes and potential outcomes of supported education. As part of program evaluation, supported education initiatives can identify a broad array of relevant outcomes, all of which are consistent with the evaluation of the broad aims of many PSR programs. Solely basing evaluation of supported education on educational and employment indicators fails to recognize the important psychosocial aims of these programs. Relevant outcomes include changes in the following:

1. *Perception of self.* Outcomes in relationship to self-esteem, self-concept, empowerment, self-confidence, and self-image are important here.
2. *Social networks and social support.* Through participation in supported education, participants can have more contact with peers, faculty, and other adult students. It is expected that students will develop new relationships and achieve higher levels of social integration and support, although they also may experience more stress.
3. *Employment related activities and outcomes.* To some degree, all supported education alternatives address career awareness and the selection of a career goal. Yet, the structured curriculum approach formally places the most emphasis on building career awareness and making career choices. Therefore, from a comparative perspective, the question of which alternative produces the strongest and most salient career outcomes, as well as employment outcomes, may become very important. The extent to which participants continue their educational careers and the form in which they choose to do this (e.g., participation in a vocational program through community college or through a vocational school; subsequent involvement in 4-year curricula) are important themes for the evaluation of supported education.
4. *Living status.* Rehabilitation effects can also be investigated in relationship to more distal outcomes such as quality of life, symptomatology, difficulties expe-

rienced in everyday life, and role performance.

Arguments Against Supported Education

Many arguments might be mustered against supported education as a tenable PSR alternative. The community psychiatry literature has characterized young adults with mental illness as having serious psychological problems involving impulsiveness, lack of insight, and impoverished judgment. They have also been characterized as having deficits in socialization and in social and interpersonal skills (Beardsley, Kessler, & Levin, 1984; Gruenberg, 1982; Pepper, Kirshner, & Ryglewicz, 1981; Stein & Test, 1982). Isolation and related deficits in social networks may compound the difficulty that young adults with mental illness may experience in relation to the achievement of social integration and full social participation (Harris & Bergman, 1987).

Repeated crises resulting from stress and from deficits in coping skills may prevent young adults from taking advantage of rehabilitation opportunities (Gruenberg, 1982; Gruenberg & Archer, 1983). Deficits in independent living skills (Harris & Bergman, 1987) may mean that young adults with mental illness should concentrate on the acquisition of basic living competencies rather than on higher education. Indeed, psychiatric illness may create barriers to learning. Stress arising from environments with high expectation demands may result in recurrent hospitalizations (Gordon & Gordon, 1981). Critics may emphasize that successful campus life requires the very motivational, social skill, and cognitive competencies that young adults coping with psychiatric disabilities lack. Also, because many resist participation in formal rehabilitation opportunities, these individuals will, therefore, not make good candidates for supported education.

However, the literature concerning the functional abilities of young adults with psychiatric disabilities is not consistent. Several studies have found that younger, as opposed to older, clients who are seriously mentally ill have better community living skills, higher cognitive functioning, and better adaptation (Mowbray, Herman, & Hazel, 1992). In a statewide study of 2075 clients in the community who meet criteria for serious mental illness, Hazel, Herman, and Mowbray (1991) found that 20% already had some college education and another 40% had earned a high school diploma. This total of 60% of the sample with a high school diploma or better is not very different from that for the Michigan population, at 68%.

Other critics point to the success of SE and make an argument for the refinement of this programmatic alternative, instead of developing a new PSR alternative. Training that leads to immediate vocational outcomes may be seen as a higher priority than education; furthermore, training that leads to SE may create the same types of outcomes as those produced by supported education. These critics may raise arguments that supported education (1) is unrealistic and that it will only result in failure, frustration, reduced self-confidence, and a strengthening of learned helplessness; (2) fails to recognize that many young adults will not be ready for higher education because many experience their first major illness—cognitive or affective—during the very years (e.g., 20–34) in which their peers will be involved in higher education (Egri & Caton, 1982); and (3) fails to recognize the importance of titrating the demands placed on young adults with mental illness (Pepper et al., 1981).

Many of these criticisms may be accepted as constraints on, and as caveats for, the implementation of a supported education program. Yet, research demonstrations illustrate the strengths of supported education as a rehabilitation alternative, as well as its success for people coping with psychiatric disabilities (Hutchinson, et al., 1989; Unger et al., 1991). Descriptions of model supported education programs indicate that people coping with severe and persistent psychiatric problems can be successful in post-secondary environments, thereby exploring and developing career interests and directions through participation in campus based programs; in addition, these students have the opportunity to interact with students who are themselves in the process of learning about different kinds of appropriate social relationships and who are struggling to define their own career directions. Given the relative novelty of supported education, sufficient research on these programs has not been undertaken to date, in order to identify the specific population of people with long-term mental illness who are most likely to benefit from this rehabilitation alternative.

Young adults with severe and persistent mental illnesses struggle with the developmental tasks of all young adults: the development and pursuit of vocational goals and the development of work and personal relationships with adults outside of the family, in addition to the struggles created by psychiatric illness. Post-secondary educational settings, in combination with work sites and rehabilitation supports, can provide important opportunities for the mastery of developmentally appropriate tasks. Although 1985 survey data reported by the NAMI indicated that 54% of young adult relatives of members have had college experiences (Spaniol, Jung, Zipple, & Fitzgerald, 1985), mental illness frequently has interfered with the completion of degrees and with the exploration of careers that comes from various work and interpersonal experiences. The ultimate effect is that commitment to career is postponed or never realized, and the young adult fails to develop basic social and problem solving skills that are so fundamental to successful living in the community.

We see higher education, implemented in conjunction with a supportive rehabilitation approach, as extremely relevant to working with young adults. Success, however, need not be defined solely in terms of the completion of a degree. Not all students who start higher education remain to complete degree requirements in a fixed time period or after the first try. Success should reflect addi-

tional benefits of postsecondary education: the extent to which participants strengthen their personal development (e.g., self-esteem, self-concept, self-awareness, social and interpersonal skills), strengthen their career development (e.g., vocational maturity, career awareness), increase their social integration and development (e.g., social network, social involvement) and realize improved career, vocational, and personal outcomes.

Future Directions

Despite the support and promotion received from consumers and family members, supported education has been struggling to develop and to become established as a consistent option in mental health and college environments. However, major barriers to these programs exist in the areas of philosophy, resources, and attitudes.

Integration and Other Philosophical Issues

A major philosophical problem revolves around the issue of integration. The PSR literature endorses environmentally specific interventions. Yet, existing supported education models diverge substantially in the extent to which students are truly integrated with their peers in campus settings. The self-contained classroom is obviously the most segregated of the models. This supported education intervention provides classroom experiences only with project staff and with other participants who have psychiatric disabilities. There is no practice phase involving participation in degree or nondegree classes and interactions with regularly enrolled students or regular college faculty. Using VR as an analogy, the self-contained classroom model might be akin to the work crew or enclave in industry, wherein disabled individuals are placed in normal settings but work together on specific tasks and not with other regular and nondisabled employees.

This approach to VR has often been criticized as stigmatizing and nonnormalizing, representing only a minor variation from the traditional facility-based approach to employment of workers with disabilities.

The most integrated approach, the on-site model, could be seen as providing insufficient supports that students with psychiatric disabilities need and possibly leading to more failure experiences rather than greater independent functioning. In comparison to VR, this approach may parallel that of merely providing job search assistance or job clubs, which seem insufficient to meet the vocational assistance needs of many people coping with psychiatric disabilities.

To truly follow the vocational example of the clubhouse might involve a combination of several SE models. An initial brief segregated phase would utilize the self-contained classroom (akin to the clubhouse's on-site work options); followed by a practice phase of enrollment in a nondegree, regular college course, with group support provided and availability of project staff members for assistance (akin to the clubhouse transitional employment program); then finally, entry into a degree program with regular enrollment and continuation of group and project staff support on a less intensive basis, as needed (akin to independent, competitive employment).

Resource Development

Of course, the issue of integration, intensity, and duration of supported education services may involve resource questions as much as philosophical questions. That is, the greater the extent to which specialized staff and other services are required for supported education of psychiatric consumers, the more expensive the program becomes. Traditional mental health reimbursement mechanisms (such as Medicaid or other third party payors) are not available and probably would not be desirable because supported education is a rehabilitative not a therapeutic intervention. However,

rehabilitation agencies are often reluctant to support higher education pursuits, limiting funding only to short term training that is directly job-related (i.e., required for a specific job). Institutions of higher education could help sustain supported education initiatives, theoretically, at least. Yet, given decreased federal support and skyrocketing costs, it is unlikely that they could or would fund much of the intensive preparatory (e.g., choice or skill building components) or individual or group support aspects of the models.

Optimally, a mix of funding streams could be tapped for supported education, secured from a partnership of mental health and rehabilitation agencies and universities and community colleges. Mental health and rehabilitation agencies may contribute, on an in-kind basis, specialized staff members who have backgrounds in psychiatric rehabilitation. Universities and community colleges may contribute classroom space, meeting rooms, and staff members from special student services and counseling offices. Involvement of students from various human service disciplines can supplement the staffing of such coordinated initiatives and give these students essential training in PSR practice (Anthony, Cohen, & Farkas, 1988). Widespread expansion of supported education approaches may depend substantially on changes in federal funding regulations that encourage the development of prototypes for how supported education models may gain access to and mix these funding sources, either at the program level, through grants and contracts or at the individual client level through fees for services.

Attitudinal Barriers

As important as they are, however, resources and philosophical clarification are probably not enough to ensure the future of supported education initiatives. Irrespective of funds available, significant attitudinal problems must be addressed. Institutions of higher education have been historically reluctant to accept students with a history of psychiatric disturbance. In fact, the existence of psychiatric problems, in and of itself, has been an accepted criterion for student suspension or expulsion (Psychiatric Disabilities Special Interest Group, AHSSPPE, 1991).

Unger (1990b) pointed out that faculty members need guidance by the institution implementing an appropriate code of conduct, vis-à-vis student responsibilities, and providing clarification to faculty members on how problematic behaviors are handled: setting limits with students, making referrals to medical and treatment personnel, and taking appropriate disciplinary action when required. Faculty and students both need support and assistance through special student services or counseling offices.

While acceptance of students with a psychiatric history has historically been problematic for higher education, this situation may be changing. That is, because university populations are becoming more diverse and nontraditional, they are finding large numbers of students who present some mental health problems. This need, combined with requirements under Section 504 and Public Law 94-142, as well as the Americans with Disabilities Act (ADA) (West, 1991) requires institutions of higher education to become more accessible to a variety of students with disabilities. Thus, institutional norms and culture may become more amenable to the matriculation of students with psychiatric disabilities, as they become more responsive to the individualized learning needs of all students.

Unfortunately, higher education personnel are not the only relevant staff members with problematic attitudes toward supported education. Mental health professionals often establish even greater barriers for adults with psychiatric disabilities entering higher education. Some have not adopted a rehabilitation philosophy and express disbelief in the ability of many clients to participate even in VR programs. Others adopt a deficit orientation and see their clients' vocational and career potential strictly limited to routine, structured employment in part-time, temporary, and low status positions. These attitudes appear more strongly entrenched than those of higher education personnel, in that they probably reflect fundamentals acquired in professional training and subsequently considered to be verified through substantial experience, based on selective perception.

Research Directions

The growth of supported education is dependent on more demonstration and more research that establishes the benefits of this form of PSR and that challenges deficit orientations of professionals. We need more research overall, which establishes the feasibility and effectiveness of the models. We also need opportunities to test models in increasingly diverse settings and to establish which components are contributing most to positive outcomes—peer support, skill development, or resource availability? Further refinements could address whether one approach or one set of supported education components works better for a specific group of consumers than another; or in one geographic location compared to another. Research can then play a role in fine tuning the delivery of supported education. It can also examine implementation issues and provide some keys to success (e.g., identification of effective pre-enrollment strategies; how to interface most effectively with mental health personnel, university administration, or rehabilitation staff; and identification of optimal methods of providing ongoing personal support to students).

We can also add to this list issues pertaining to sustaining the motivation of students, effective instructional strategies, obtaining the support of faculty members who are teaching regular classes in which supported education participants are enrolled, and strengthening interagency collaboration among the supported education program, mental health, consumer groups, and other organizations.

Conclusion

Supported education should play a role in PSR systems of the future. It represents an important alternative for people coping with psychiatric disabilities in providing an array of services and supports that will assist them to meet their own goals. Post-secondary education and career development will be important assets to the workers of the future. The availability of educational programs that are sensitive to the needs of people with psychiatric disabilities and that will assist consumers to take advantage of knowledge intensive jobs and employment will be one more step toward the creation of consumer relevant mental health and rehabilitation systems.

References

Anthony, W. A., & Blanch, A. (1987). *Supported employment for persons who are psychiatrically disabled: An historical and conceptual perspective.* Boston: Boston University Center for Psychiatric Rehabilitation.

Anthony, W. A., Cohen, M., & Farkas, M. (1988). Professional preservice training for working with the long-term mentally ill. *Community Mental Health Journal, 24,* 258–269.

Beard, J. H., Propst, R. N., & Malamud, T. J. (1982). The Fountain House model of psychiatric rehabilitation. *Psychosocial Rehabilitation Journal, 5*(1), 47–53.

Beardsley, C., Kessler, R. C., & Levin, E. (1984). Education for the young chronic client. *Psychosocial Rehabilitation Journal, 8,* 44–52.

Bond, G. R., & Boyer, S. L. (1988). Rehabilitation programs and outcomes. In J. A. Ciardiello & M. D. Bell (Eds.), *Vocational rehabilitation of persons with prolonged psychiatric disorders* (pp. 231–263). Baltimore: Johns Hopkins University Press.

Chamberlin, J., Rogers, J., & Sneed, C. (1989). Consumers, families, and community support systems. *Psychosocial Rehabilitation Journal, 12*(3), 93–106.

Cohen, M., & Anthony, W. (1988). A commentary on planning a service system for persons who are severely mentally ill: Avoiding the pitfalls of the past. *Psychosocial Rehabilitation Journal, 12*(1), 69–72.

Community Support Network News (1990). *Special issue on supported education.* Boston: Boston University Center for Psychiatric Rehabilitation.

Danley, K. S., Rogers, E. S., & Nevas, D. (1989). A psychiatric rehabilitation approach to vocational rehabilitation. In M. D. Farkas & W. A. Anthony (Eds.), *Psychiatric rehabilitation programs: Putting theory into practice* (pp. 81–131). Baltimore: Johns Hopkins University Press.

Egri, G., & Caton, C. L. (1982). Serving the young adult chronic patient in the 1980's: Challenge to the general hospital. In B. Pepper & H. Ryglewicz (Eds.), *The young adult chronic patient* (pp. 25–31). San Francisco: Jossey-Bass.

Farkas, M. D., Anthony, W., & Cohen, M. R. (1989). Psychiatric rehabilitation: The approach and its programs. In M. D. Farkas, & W. Anthony (Eds.), *Psychiatric rehabilitation programs: Putting theory into practice* (pp. 1–27). Baltimore: Johns Hopkins University Press.

Freddolino, P., Moxley, D., & Fleishman, J. (1988). Daily living needs at time of discharge: Implications for advocacy. *Psychosocial Rehabilitation Journal, 11*(4), 33–46.

Gordon, R. E., & Gordon, K. K. (1981). *Systems of treatment for the mentally ill: Filling the gaps.* New York: Grune & Stratton.

Gould, R. (1978). *Transformations: Growth and change in adult life.* New York: Simon & Schuster.

Gruenberg, E. (1982). Social breakdowns in young adults: Keeping crises from becoming chronic. *New Directions for Mental Health Services, 14,* 43–50.

Gruenberg, E., & Archer, J. (1983). Preserving chronic patients' assets for self-care. In I. Barofsky & R. Budson (Eds.), *The chronic psychiatric patient in the community: Principles of treatment* (pp. 29–48). New York: MTP.

Harris, M., & Bergman, H. C. (1987). Differential treatment planning for young adult chronic patients. *Hospital and Community Psychiatry, 38,* 638–643.

Hatfield, A. B. (1987). Families as caregivers: A historical perspective. In A. Hatfield and H. Lefley (Eds.), *Families of the mentally ill: Coping and adaptation.* New York: Guilford.

Havighurst, R. J. (1974). *Developmental tasks and education.* New York: David McKay.

Hazel, K. L., Herman, S. E., & Mowbray, C. T. (1991). Characteristics of adults with serious mental illness in a public mental health system. *Hospital and Community Psychiatry, 42,* 518–525.

Hutchinson, D., Kohn, L., & Unger, K. (1989). A university-based psychiatric rehabilitation program for young adults: Boston University. In M. D. Farkas & W. Anthony (Eds.), *Psychiatric rehabilitation programs: Putting theory into practice* (pp. 147–157). Baltimore: Johns Hopkins University Press.

Levinson, D. (1978). *The seasons of a man's life.* New York: Knopf.

Mowbray, C. T., Herman, S. E., & Hazel, K. L. (1992). Subgroups and differential treatment needs of young adults with long-term severe mental illness. *Psychosocial Rehabilitation Journal, 16,* 45–62.

Moxley, D., & Freddolino, P. (1990). A model of advocacy for promoting client self-determination in psychosocial rehabilitation. *Psychosocial Rehabilitation Journal, 14*(2), 69–82.

Osborne, D. (1988). *Laboratories of democracy.* Boston: Harvard Business School Press.

Oxford Analytica. (1986). *America in perspective.* New York: Houghton Mifflin.

Pepper, B., Kirshner, M., & Ryglewicz, H. (1981). The young adult chronic patient: Overview of a population. *Hospital and Community Psychiatry, 32,* 463–469.

Psychiatric Disabilities Special Interest Group, AHSSPPE. (1991). Examples of role clarification: Dealing with disruptive behavior. *P.D., Newsletter of the Association of Handicapped Student Services Programs in Postsecondary Education,* Summer, 6–8.

Reich, R. B. (1991). *The work of nations: Preparing ourselves for 21st century capitalism.* New York: Knopf.

Segal, S. P., & Aviram, U. (1978). *The mentally ill in community-based sheltered care: A study of community care and social integration.* New York: Wiley.

Spaniol, L., Jung, H., Zipple, L. A., & Fitzgerald, S. (1985). *Needs and coping strengths of families of the mentally ill: Report of a national survey* (reprint). Boston: Boston University Center for Psychiatric Rehabilitation.

Stein, L. I., & Test, M. A. (1982). Community treatment of the young adult patient. *New Directions for Mental Health Services, 14,* 57–67.

Super, D. (1953). A theory of vocational development. *American Psychologist, 8,* 185–190.

Taylor, D., Piagesi, D., McNaught, J., & Nielson, M. (1989). A psychiatric rehabilitation approach in a clubhouse setting. In M. D. Farkas & W. Anthony (Eds.), *Psychiatric rehabilitation programs: Putting theory into practice* (pp. 136–146). Baltimore: Johns Hopkins University Press.

Unger, K. (1989). Psychiatric rehabilitation through education: Rethinking the context. In M. D. Farkas & W. Anthony (Eds.), *Psychiatric rehabilitation programs: Putting theory into practice* (pp. 132–161). Baltimore: Johns Hopkins University Press.

Unger, K. (1990a). Supported postsecondary education for people with mental illness. *American Rehabilitation, 16,* 10–14.

Unger, K. (1990b). Serving students with psychiatric disabilities. *P.D., Newsletter of the Association of Handicapped Student Services Programs in Postsecondary Education, Psychiatric Disabilities Special Interest Group,* Spring, 3.

Unger, K., Anthony, W. A., Sciarappa, K., & Rogers, E. (1991). A supported education program for young adults with long-term mental illness. *Hospital and Community Psychiatry, 42*(8), 838–842.

Unger, K., Danley, K., Kohn, L., & Hutchinson, D. (1987). Rehabilitation through education: A university-based continuing education program for young adults with psychiatric disabilities on a university campus. *Psychosocial Rehabilitation Journal, 10,* 35–49.

West, J. (1991). The social and policy context of the act. In J. West (Ed.), *The Americans with Disabilities Act: From policy to practice.* New York: Milbank Memorial Fund.

Wolfensberger, W. (1972). *Normalization.* Toronto: National Institute on Mental Retardation.

Chapter 10

Development of Support Through Case Management Services

MARTHA HODGE

JEFFREY DRAINE

While transporting a woman who was leaving a state hospital to a community mental health center, a case manager was telling the former patient about services and therapies available there. During the conversation, the woman asked her case manager to "get me some help this time instead of therapy". While uncomfortably revealing how clients sometimes see mental health services, this anecdote says something about how case managers can function in the lives of persons who experience serious mental illness. Many professionals understand that a person who is worried about having a place to live, something good to eat and something to do for fun will not have much patience for psychotherapy as a solution. Some of these professionals have recognized that in order for the best therapeutic treatments to work for persons with mental illness, attention needs to be directed toward meeting basic needs first.

In supporting the treatment of human problems faced by individuals, some form of case management is usually involved. In this sense, while case management, or intensive case management, may be among the newest trends in the planning of mental health services, it is as old as the experience of families who have lived with their ill relatives throughout the human experience. All people have organized safety nets around (or under)

themselves for times of ill health or other crises. The family is a primary safety net for most people. Families meet needs of individuals as they change and grow. A functional family is "an agent of socialization and control, mediating between society and its members. Through guidance, direction, and feedback the family unit practice provides collective strength, skills, experience, practical service and crisis intervention to each member," and can be considered a "traditional case management system" (Savarese, Detrano, Koproski, & Weber, 1990, p. 288). Outside of the family, functioning individuals establish networks of affiliations that can be activated in a time of crisis. Components may include relationships with a general physician and other service providers, with professional colleagues, and with social groups and community organizations such as religious congregations and civic clubs.

A common characteristic of the lives of persons with serious mental illness is the lack of these safety nets or the inability to develop supports in times of need. It is ironic that during acute illness, the relationships and routines that make up safety nets may be in great jeopardy. Case management is a professional activity working with the social environment of people with serious and persistent mental illness. The case manager builds safety nets and may be an integral part of the safety net.

Definitions of case management vary, mostly depending on preferred models and ideological priorities. The definitions generally include the assessment of service problems: provision of access to knowledge, resources, and support; and assurance of continuity and quality of care. Case managers help address the social problems of the person with mental illness (Rapp & Chamberlain, 1985). *Intensive case management* particularly refers to work done with small caseloads, usually with 10 to 20 clients and 24-hour on-call responsibility. Sometimes, this responsibility is carried by case managers as part of a team, supporting and backing up one another, but more often, intensive case management is done by individuals with no formal team support.

In introducing case management to mental health and rehabilitation professionals who want to understand its function and its potential for supporting rehabilitative and mental health services, an outline of the environment from which case management developed is provided, with a review of the problems it was meant to address. In the first section, the concept of case management and its specific goals and strategies are expressed in different models. Then follows a picture of what case management looks like in practice—the nuts and bolts. The experienced reader may notice a lot of the familiar in new language, as much of what is known about case management practice evolved from a social casework tradition. The chapter concludes with a summary of issues in case management. It is hoped that some readers will find a new way of viewing persons with serious mental illness as consumers of professional services and of seeing case managers as their guides and advocates.

The Origin of Current Interest in Case Management

Deinstitutionalization has been blamed and credited for much, including the current interest in case management (Intagliata, 1982).

The process of creating community-based services for ex-mental hospital patients resulted in a system that has grown tremendously and is often fragmented, discontinuous, and insensitive to the needs of persons with serious mental illness (Isaac & Armat, 1990; Johnson, 1990; Mechanic, 1989). Mental health systems deal with unpopular, vulnerable clients, while resources for social programs are shrinking. Client needs frequently get lost in an environment concerned about system survival. The case manager promotes a client centered approach to serving the person with serious mental illness by "assisting clients in negotiating for services that they both want and need" (Cohen, Farkas, Cohen, & Unger, 1990). The case manager is the connection between the mental health services consumer and a complicated service environment.

Some attention has always been paid to coordination and continuity of care, whether it was cooperative relationships with physicians and nurses in a state hospital or casework by other human service professionals. What makes case management different today is the intensity of the service provided. Case managers, by the services they provide, are invited into the daily lives of clients. The intensity of services ranges from the more involved forms of basic casework to models that include an array of treatment and support professionals hired to work as a case management team. While case management is generally a supportive service, not a treatment, intensive case management services can include various kinds of treatments that enhance social functioning, such as skills training in activities of daily living (ADL) or interventions for symptom management.

Recent interest in case management as a particular mental health service is facilitated by a systemic interest in streamlining services. While not shown to reduce the overall cost of care, interest remains in the role that case management plays in reducing inpatient hospitalization days. Case management for persons with serious mental illness is now reimbursable by Medicaid, largely with hopes that it would accomplish these goals.

Purpose and Principles of Case Management

Case managers coordinate services to improve quality of life and to develop skills of daily living (Modrcin, Rapp, & Chamberlain 1985); to prevent hospitalization (Friday, 1986); and to enable effective client participation in medical treatment (Modrcin et al., 1985), including compliance with medication regimens and management of symptoms that may be harbingers of crisis.

Principles common to most models of case management include

- *Individualization*—There is no perfunctory service plan; services and supports are individualized, using the concept of service fit, tailored to meet the specific objectives of the client.
- *Community-based*—A portion of every case manager's time is spent out of the office, especially in the environment where clients live, work, and learn.
- *Open-ended*—Case management is not a time limited service; it is available for life, if needed.
- *Accountability*—The "buck stops here." The case manager is a single, identifiable point of accountability for services to a person with serious mental illness in the context of a personal, purposeful relationship.

To support case management practice based on these principles, some operational principles are imposed on the supporting agency as well. In traditional services, the caseworker role serves to fit the client into existing services. In client-centered case management with a strong advocacy role, the services are designed to fit the client. Some have seen that the case manager's knowledge of client needs could be placed at the center of an inverted hierarchy organizational structure of mental health services (Altshuler & Forward, 1978)(also, see Rapp, Chapter 11, in this volume). Some case managers are vigorous advocates, creatively leveraging resources and services for their client, while others are more willing to encourage clients to accept system

constraints. There is tension between the roles of case manager as advocate and as service coordinator (Rose & Black, 1985). Carragonne (1980) outlines the organizational differences that accommodate case management:

Traditional services	Case management
8 A.M. to 5 P.M.	Indeterminate
Routine schedule	Flexible schedule
Routine work tasks	Nonroutine work in response to client need
Operates in office	Community based, *in vivo*
One service emphasis	Multiservice emphases
Little or no interagency contact	Extensive and varied interagency contact
Authority on caseload only	Authority to represent agency
Limited decision-making	Extensive decision-making
Limited freedom to operate	Extensive freedom to operate

Case Management as Support

Support is a concept frequently associated with case management. Client and professional perceptions of support needs are frequently different. Money and love are at the top of many clients' lists of needs (Estroff, 1987). Other readily identified needs include relief from bad feelings, compassion, friends, homes, and jobs. In several recent conversations with clients, transportation has been identified as a major need. At the top of lists developed by professional staff are psychiatric treatment and medication. Closely following are ADL, entitlements, case management, and crisis services (Campbell, 1989). The coordination of seemingly unrelated support activities leads some to conclude that case management is the glue that holds a comprehensive service system together. Components associated with support can be identified as follows (Hansell, 1976):

Group—People need attachment to a repeating activity that involves a cluster of people who regard each other as members.

Role—People need the opportunity/capacity to perform at least one role valued by society.

Money—People need money to have the basic essentials of life (i.e., home, food, etc.).

People—People need a persistent (lasting) attachment to at least one other person.

Identity/meaning—People need a picture of themselves, a way to integrate all their attachments.

An operationalization of support such as this is broad enough to include client defined needs with those supports traditionally offered by professionals. Because these support components are those generally common to all individuals, emphasis can be placed on the individual with mental illness rather than on the debilitations affecting a person. The case manager integrates treatment concerns with basic human needs, allowing professional and informal support activities to complement one another.

Because people with mental illness have so often lost social support networks in the course of their illness, constructing and shoring up natural support systems is often a priority at the initiation of case management relationships. In the first stages of the relationship, the case manager may provide primary support, as atrophied social skills and competence in daily living develop. Some have pointed out that case managers may constitute the majority of a client's social support system (Savarese et al., 1990).

Models of Case Management

Models of case management are tools that organize the complexities of serving clients. Useful models prescribe case manager and client roles, how the client will be assessed, what individual goals may be, strategies for meeting those goals, and means for evaluat-ing success. The four models of case management in common practice are the expanded broker, personal strengths, rehabilitation, and full support models (Robinson & Bergman, 1991; Solomon, 1992).

While models are guides in structuring case management practice, case managers do not necessarily adopt a single model to the exclusion of the strategies and goals of the others. Obviously, there is overlap in these areas among models. Models help the case manager focus assessment and service planning. Models assist agencies in determining both the goals for case management programs and the methods of evaluating them. Regardless of what model is used, engaging, assessing, planning, actively connecting, following along, and intervening when necessary are the case manager's methods of ensuring that supports are in place.

The Expanded Broker Model

The expanded broker model is closest to the traditional view of casework. In this model, the case manager role is that of a professional familiar with the mental health system, providing access to information and services. The client's needs and available resources are assessed, and then the client is linked with services. Because caseloads in this generalist model are high, individual attention cannot be given to linking and monitoring services, as is the case in other models. If the caseload is particularly large and agency supports limited, case managers in work situations using this model may only have the time to see those clients who are more assertive or are in crisis situations (Intagliata & Baker, 1983). Goals are stabilization in the community and the successful use of services available. Success is evaluated on the basis of stability in the community and the absence of crises.

The Personal Strengths Model

The personal strengths model highlights client achievement (Robinson, 1991). In this model, the case manager is a mentor who assists the client in identifying the personal strengths that can be maximized to meet client directed goals. Individual goals are driven by clients' desires (Modrcin, Rapp & Poertner, 1988). Strategies include cooperation of a team of case managers for creative problem solving and resource development, the use of a variety of resources, including those outside of the mental health system, and aggressive outreach (Rapp & Chamberlain, 1985). Evaluation of success is based on the client's ability to identify and meet personal goals, and the array of resources made available to clients.

Two assumptions are the foundation for the personal strengths model. First, persons who succeed are those who know and develop their potential. Second, success is largely determined by access to resources. In the case management relationship, a dual focus results from these assumptions, one having therapeutic goals toward self-assessment, and the other having social and brokering goals (Rapp & Chamberlain, 1985). The strengths-based character of the assessment drives the dually focused case management relationship.

A strengths assessment often provides a new perspective about people with serious mental illness. People with mental illness may find it difficult to begin thinking about themselves from a strengths perspective. Culturally, humility is highly valued, and most people have been taught not to talk much about what they do well, lest they be seen as braggarts. Additionally, people with mental illness have been given so many implicit messages (they look around and see their brother with a business and family and compare their lot in life) or explicit messages ("you'll never be able to . . ., you aren't ready; you need 24-hour supervision") that they do not see themselves as people with strengths. The mental health system has historically invited people to tell about their troubles and problems, with a perfunctory—at best—look at their capabilities. The personal strengths model underscores a systematic, functional emphasis on personal strengths.

The Rehabilitation Model

The rehabilitation model identifies barriers to achieving goals and works to overcome those barriers. This model builds on previous models, in that case management is put into a specific context—the larger service model of psychiatric rehabilitation. In the psychiatric rehabilitation process, the case manager has been described as a "social prosthesis" (Schade, Corrigan, & Liberman, 1990, p. 7), a buffer to the stresses of negotiating the service systems around the client. The client is assessed based on functions, strengths, and deficits in skills, abilities, and available resources. Individual goals are driven by clients and are likely to focus on strengthening some specific skills and making adjustments in the living and working environment to facilitate independence. Evaluation is based on the client's satisfaction in the social environment of choice, with minimal reliance on professional involvement (Anthony & Liberman, 1986; Robinson, 1991).

The functional assessment is a contribution of the rehabilitation model to case management. While fairly new in mental health settings, functional assessment has long been used in the general rehabilitation field. The difference between a functional assessment and other diagnostic assessments is more easily understood when the principal difference between treatment and rehabilitation is considered. Treatment in mental health deals with the management of symptoms and the development of therapeutic insights. The most important psychiatric treatment for serious mental illness currently available is medication. On the other hand, psychiatric rehabilitation also includes helping people to get and keep the skills and supports necessary for community life. These interventions include the professional help of social workers, counselors, housing providers, occupational and activities therapists, and vocational specialists. The Center for Psychiatric Rehabilitation (Cohen et al., 1990) describes a functional assessment process as identifying skills and resources for succeeding in a particular environment. Environmental specificity is critical because all environments have their own requirements.

Using a stress–diathesis model for understanding mental illness (Nuechterlein & Dawson, 1984; Zubin & Spring, 1977), psychiatric rehabilitation interventions focus on both physiological and behavioral factors. While neuroleptic medications act to reduce the impact of physiological problems (impairment), case managers may be involved with social and behavioral interventions targeting sources of stress and any functional impairment in the environment (disability). Intervention goals may include mastery of new behavioral responses to daily living situations or adaptations in the social environment. Activities toward these goals are the teaching and rehearsal of new skills or the training of family members and coworkers in a working knowledge of mental illness and in the ways in which to cope with any difficulties of living with the client.

The Full Support Model

The full support model gives case management a place in a comprehensive system of care. It stresses the course of the symptoms of psychiatric illness and their impact on behavior in a community setting. The case manager is part of an interdisciplinary team containing most of the professional resources and expertise needed to serve the client. The client is led in activities and therapies to understand the illness and its symptoms and how to compensate for them. Goals focus on the reduction of symptoms and their impact on functioning. Strategies are assertive outreach; *in vivo* (in the environment where the client lives, works and socializes or recreates) service delivery and training in living skills— including symptom, medication, and money management; the use of varied professional expertise within the case management service team; and round-the-clock–7-day crisis availability. The success of the full support model is evaluated in terms of the degree to which the client participates in treatment of the illness and the reduction of symptoms and

enhancement of skills in compensating for the illness.

The concept of full support can be equated with transferring all the supports of a hospital ward into the community. The treatment team includes social workers, nurses, physicians, therapists and other professionals who interact with each other in the process of providing services to the client in the community. Services may be based in a center where clients are monitored and evaluated and where care is coordinated and where crisis care is accessible. The central point of coordination enhances the appropriateness of treatment decisions, as professionals aware of client needs share responsibility for decisions, such as the use of inpatient alternatives (Thompson, Griffith, & Leaf, 1990). This is how the full support model is made operational at PACT (Program for Assertive Community Treatment) in Madison, Wisconsin. Stein (1990) asserts that PACT is not limited to being a case management model, as it is intended to be a total system of care. Case management activities, however, are a central component of its operation (Stein & Test, 1980).

Assertive Community Treatment (ACT) is derived from the PACT model, but the totality of the system of care at PACT is not replicated (Bond, Miller, Krumwied, & Ward, 1988). The similarity of the programs lies in the provision of total care by a team. ACT teams are small teams of case managers who focus on *in vivo* services, ADL and coordination of a total system of care, relying as much as possible on resources available within the team. ACT teams differ, in that they have been implemented in environments where the whole range of coordinated PACT services is not feasible, due to financial or system constraints, leading to a version of the model that coordinates services outside of those provided directly by the team.

CASE STUDY

A hypothetical case study may illustrate the differences among these models and how they build on one another. An elderly client has just been told he will be moved because his home for many years has been condemned. The man has a major mental illness and has been hospitalized for psychiatric problems within the past year. The case management question is, what supports are needed in this situation?

First, it should be pointed out that a case manager providing *in vivo* services would have noted that condemnation was imminent for a building in such disrepair and would have begun looking for an alternative living arrangement prior to any formal notification. In reality, however, people often are only assigned case managers when there is a crisis, or case managers serve so many people that they must limit their contact and service to people who are in crisis.

The simple solution seems to be to help find another place to live. However, what if the elderly person felt very frightened of moving and thought perhaps someone was "out to get him" and decided that the case manager might be part of such a conspiracy? Also, what if there were friends and family in the immediate neighborhood who talked to him each day but who felt they could not take him into their homes? What about the several year waiting list at nursing homes and senior citizen apartments? Working with the client, the case manager works through the maze of issues constituting social support and creates a plan. The emphasis of such a plan and its starting point and priorities are a product of what model of case management services is being employed.

In the example, the expanded broker model, emphasizing linkage with other providers/people, prompts the case manager to focus on assistance from the landlord for some temporary repairs while another home is found. There may be a new linkage with the senior citizens agency. Another option may be advocating for priority on waiting lists for emergency cases.

The strengths model adds the dimension of client potential to the expanded broker model. The assessment of this client will characteristically focus on what is going well in his life. The case manager may want to build on an already strong relationship with another per-

son for social support and to help him with problem solving. The interventions will be more client directed and will treat the abilities of the client as a resource.

Using a rehabilitation model would build further on the expanded broker and personal strengths models, coordinating services toward new skills and environmental supports that allow the client to live independently. The possibility of a home health aide to facilitate living with a family member could be explored. We may ask how ties to informal support can be strengthened—could the client move closer to friends, near his religious congregation, or another center of his social life? Could the client be trained to recognize problems in his living environment and seek solutions to them?

The full support model would add a focus on psychiatric symptom management. Are the paranoid feelings and thoughts out of control? Are role functions impaired because of the symptoms? Is medication a need or a possibility? Is more *in vivo* attention needed to monitor the client's living environment and its impact on symptoms?

Case Management Process

In addition to medical needs, the person with serious mental illness faces common subsistence needs—such as housing, clothing and food—social affiliation, and meaningful activity. Case management can be understood to have both cross-sectional and longitudinal factors (Schade, Corrigan, & Liberman, 1990; Test, 1979), assisting with a cross section of supports (family, medical treatment, and social agencies, etc.) and ensuring their continuity over time (longitudinal). As discussed earlier, models shape the focus of an assessment and in turn the goals and evaluation standards for the case management relationship.

Assessment

Two components of assessment are information gathering and engagement. Information gathering is not only to arrive at a diagnosis, but also to glean a complete picture of the client, including strengths and personal resources, as well as problems. The principles of a specific model may determine the scope of information needed.

Biopsychosocial information includes a detailed history with emphasis on patterns related to the person's illness. Descriptions of successful interventions and evaluations of those that have failed are useful. A history of medication strategies is helpful if the case manager is a source of information for the psychiatrist. A full picture includes information from the client, family members, and medical and social service professionals. Thus also begins coordination of a paper trail, with releases of information and documented consent.

Engagement is more than passive maintenance of positive regard; it includes assertive activities, such as involving the client as a key source of information. Client involvement ensures the client's commitment to the success of a plan. Interpersonal difficulties associated with mental illness can put case managers in the position of making a greater investment in the relationship. In the course of being flexible, nonjudgmental, and sensitive, case managers can demonstrate interpersonal skills that clients may need to learn or relearn.

The client is the best source of information about the individual experience of mental illness. Case manager responsibilities regarding psychiatric symptoms include knowing the client well enough to recognize a change in symptoms. Most people and their families know the signs associated with a recurrence of symptoms and can tell case managers what to expect. The signs most frequently associated with relapse include change in personal hygiene or grooming, a change in mood, a change in sleeping or eating habits, or withdrawal. These are monitored by the case manager involved in the client's social environment. Over time, physicians and case managers can help clients to monitor their own signs of decompensation, which may be a specific goal.

Statements about aspirations are important information. Case managers work together with clients to articulate personal goals. There may be a need for reeducation to work in this manner (Kisthardt & Rapp, 1989). Many persons with serious mental illness have learned to passively accept staff opinions and could learn to assert their own opinions. With confidence built in the engagement process, clients can learn not only to express aspirations, but also to value them.

Service Planning

A good, thorough assessment will make service goals and plans seem obvious and, with adequate client involvement, desirable. The success of later linking, monitoring, and evaluating hinges on the strength of the plan. Plans enumerate the goals, objectives, and interventions—components that interact in specific ways.

Goals are broad, general, long-term (12–18 months) statements of desired outcomes. Service planning goals will be more action based than the aspirations discussed in assessment. *Objectives* are outcome statements that indicate more short-term, measurable, and specific activities. "Make friends" is a goal, and "joining and participating weekly in a basketball league" is an objective. Objectives are not merely goals with shorter time spans, nor are they a list of steps. They are best thought of as a list of independent indicators that the broader goal is being accomplished. With the aforementioned goal of making friends, other objectives attached to that goal could be "is able to identify one new acquaintance in whom the client can confide" or "the client introduces self to new persons." With the objective of joining a basketball league, possible interventions include assisting the client in finding a league, playing basketball with the client, or advocating for a free or reduced membership fee at an athletic club. "Live in the community" is a goal, and "No hospitalizations in 6 months" is an objective. Interventions to accomplish the objective and ultimately achieving the goal might include daily medication drop-offs, participation in a medication education and support group, or transportation to weekly Alcoholics Anonymous (AA) meetings. Objectives are specific and measurable. They lead easily to criteria for evaluating success toward meeting goals.

Some tend to confuse interventions with goals. For example, attending day treatment is not a goal. Having more friends or educational aspirations are goals, but linking a client with day treatment is an intervention. Goals and objectives are targeted to the experience of the client. The confusion arises when mental health and rehabilitation professionals project system goals related to service usage onto clients. Client-centered service means that the goals are related to social functioning, reduced symptoms, improved income, and better housing. These are goals that relate to the life of clients, not to their use of services or the activities of case managers.

Well-defined goals, with clear, specific, and pertinent objectives, lead the case manager to relevant intervention strategies. Intervention plans clarify time frames and persons responsible for implementation. These are the details of who, what, where, and how. Intervention activities are actions altering the life situation of a client toward a defined objective. Counseling and skill training are interventions, so are establishing a support plan with an employer, going shopping with a client, or taking the client on a strictly leisure activity if goals include enhancing these realms of community living. With a well conceived plan, intervention activities make sense for the individual client. Rather than being shuttled into a set of cookie-cutter-style interventions planned for a mass of agency clients, an individual can identify goals that are meaningful for his or her life situation and aspirations and can link daily activities to those goals.

Monitoring and Evaluation

Case managers use a plan for consistent support and monitoring. If progress begins to slow down or if objectives are not being achieved, the case manager, staff members, and client can use the plan as a guide in solving service problems. Monitoring considers these basic questions:

Is the person having second thoughts about the goal?
Is the goal/objective reachable?
Is there a psychiatric complication (e.g., a side effect from the medication)?
Has the person lost some support?
Is the task attainable (e.g., is there a need for smaller steps or more time for completion)?
Has the person moved faster than expected?
Is substance use or abuse involved?
Are additional supports necessary?

Most programs have requirements for regular quality assurance reviews of plans and progress, including physician review and peer review. While these kinds of reviews are important to administrators and to those who fund case management services, it is not necessarily most useful in determining the success of case management. The client and case manager set meaningful goals, which reflect expected outcomes and are used to monitor success. As in the other steps of the case management process, the client can participate in evaluating the success of case management. Information gathered in monitoring can be discussed, and clients can contribute to modifications in plans. Rigorous evaluation of case management programs informs program development as well as individual performance. Such evaluation efforts are possible, particularly if staff members are involved in the planning and implementation of such evaluation (Boydell, Trainor, & Intagliata, 1986) or if the evaluation mechanics are designed into a program from the start (Hansberg, Solomon, & Meyerson, 1990).

Substance Abuse and Homelessness

Substance abuse significantly affects the lives of seriously mentally ill clients (Drake, Osher, & Wallach, 1989; Safer, 1987), and persons with mental illness are disproportionally represented among the homeless (Isaac & Armat, 1990; Roth & Bean, 1986). These problems complicate stigma and misconceptions about persons with mental illness. Case managers may spend as much time with services targeted to addiction and destitute poverty as they do in mental health and rehabilitative service systems.

Substance Abuse Awareness

Substance abuse can have a negative impact on professional relationships, on the course of psychiatric symptoms, on client participation in treatment and rehabilitation plans, and on the success of those plans (Bergman & Harris, 1985; Drake et al.,1990; Test, Willisch, Allness, & Ripp, 1989). Because this phenomenon has an impact on the success of interventions, the case manager needs a clear assessment of client substance abuse history, status, and treatment. A substance abuse assessment that relies on information from the client could test the strength of the case management relationship, in terms of the degree of honesty expected. As in the strengths or functional assessments, useful information is not limited to the negative history of abuse and relapse but also includes personal qualities or situations that contributed to times of successful recovery from dependence.

Disorienting symptoms of mental illness and the effect of substances contribute to unreliability of client reports of their past. The habits of binge users may mask minimal changes in substance tolerance and make it difficult to evaluate. Substance induced psychotic withdrawal symptoms are easily confused with psychiatric symptoms, making them difficult to evaluate. Also, client perceptions of use and abuse are different from staff or professional perceptions. Expectations about what may be recreational consumption of alcohol among persons with mental illness, a group of persons with a high incidence of alcoholism (Test, Knoedler, Allness, & Burke, 1985; Test, Willisch, Allness,

& Ripp, 1989), may bias perceptions of acceptable consumption.

Recognizing the difficulties in obtaining accurate information on substance use, blood and breath tests are sometimes used to corroborate client reports. The Michigan Alcoholism Screening Test (MAST) (Selzer, 1971) and the Addiction Severity Index (McLellan et al., 1980, 1985) are scales that have some usefulness to case managers. While limited to alcohol problems, the MAST is "readily incorporated into a semistructured interview and, though test items are quite direct, it effectively stimulates candid interchange about drinking habits" (Zung & Charalampous, 1975, p. 131). The Addiction Severity Index is limited because it was developed and standardized for use with inpatients in substance abuse treatment and is of questionable value with persons who are in denial of alcohol and drug problems. However, it can serve as a guide to deciding what questions to ask in an assessment. Given the prevalance of denial, though, some assessment resources, such as Drake's Case Manager Rating Scale for Alcohol Use Disorder (Drake et al., 1990) or the CAGE (Mayfield, McClead, & Hall, 1974) are easy and accessible scales, based on an assumption that those working closely with persons with mental illness are often more reliable sources of substance abuse information than the clients themselves (Drake, 1990; Test, 1989).

Homelessness

Homelessness could be the ultimate loss of social support. Recent attention has been directed toward intensive case management as a strategy for serving homeless persons who are also mentally ill. Outreach and advocacy are particularly important in structuring case management services for homeless persons (Rog, Andranovich, & Rosenblum,1987). Assertiveness of services needs to be strong enough to overcome the effect of survival strategies that include avoiding contact with institutional settings or people who seem "official." Smaller case management caseloads facilitate more intensive relationships with homeless persons. The quality of the initial contact is important in developing trust. The primacy of basic needs before mental health treatment is important, and meeting these needs may be particularly difficult for persons at the margins of society. Once these basic needs are met, it is far easier for the homeless person to accept mental health treatment.

Advocacy concerns include availability of housing and financial resources and overcoming the double stigma of mental illness and destitute poverty. Homeless persons are frequently described as having "fallen through the cracks" of social service systems. Case management is uniquely capable of addressing this concern with its role of coordinating services for clients across agencies and ensuring continuity and accountability.

Community Resources and Advocacy

Case management involves a relationship both with the client and with the community in which that client lives, works, and recreates. Many case management activities enhance individual client functioning. Other activities enhance the social environment. Housing, employment, health care, and other issues have broader dimensions that require an understanding of interventions at a community level.

In a rehabilitation paradigm, mental illness has the distinct components of impairment, disability, and handicap. The *impairment* is the physiological part of the illness, and the *disability* is the limitation to individual functioning. *Handicaps* are those social structures or barriers that exist outside of the individual with mental illness, preventing full integration into the community. Examples of handicaps are stigma, bureaucratic hassles, and resistance to workplace adjustments. Case management assists in the amelioration of handicap through the use of community resources and thoughtful, effective advocacy.

Community Resources and Integration

Needs of clients can be met by many resources and supports that are not traditionally offered by the mental health system. To access these, case managers face a general social service system that is often overburdened. Some community agencies openly disagree with the policy of reducing state hospital admissions. The personal strengths model specifically encourages the case manager to look outside of the mental health system for the needed supports and resources (Robinson, 1991). The basic premise is that "community integration and adjustment can only occur once removed from the mental health system" (Modrcin et al., 1985). The expanded broker model relies more heavily on traditional mental health services. The full support model provides services that are not currently available in the system but relies on the skills of persons who are on the service team or who are part of the service program (Robinson, 1991).

Community integration begins with a view of the person who happens to have a diagnosis. Aside from mental illness, this person is likely to have housing problems, income problems, job problems, family problems, and problems with social relationships. There is a tendency for mental health systems to assume responsibility for addressing problems faced by their clients when other service systems have fallen through in their responsibility. Services created in this process run a risk of being focused on the mental illness in such a way that clients are never assisted by anyone who does not see them as primarily a person with mental illness. For example, when housing programs cannot help persons with mental illness, a mental health system may create housing units. New housing units become treatment modes and therefore part of a treatment system rather than simply a solution to the housing problem. In finding solutions to the basic problems of living, the case manager is in a position to take steps toward community integration by choosing to use community resources targeted for the general population.

System Advocacy

In the process of seeking and linking with community resources, the case manager is certain to run into barriers that prevent clients from having access to what is needed to meet their goals. Concurrent with trying to get services and supports for individuals, case managers need to work with clients, other case managers, and supervisors on system advocacy. A strategy matrix presented by Modrcin, Rapp, and Chamberlain (1985) describes a decision-making model that case managers can use in their role as advocates. Table 10.1 is a presentation of the model, given a situation where a client, Peg, wants to live at a particular residence but does not want to have to leave her home every morning for a scheduled activity.

While some case managers may want to be knights in shining armor, rescuing clients from the clutches of a cold, impersonal mental health service system, it needs to be understood that advocacy is not necessarily adversarial. Case managers may be surprised by the success of gentler initial strategies that seek common goals and clear understanding of client needs. Using the matrix shown in Table 10.1, decisions regarding which course to follow need to consider whether simpler, less adversarial options have been tried, how many clients are involved or could be helped, what kind of system changes may be involved, and the receptiveness of system staff members to different strategies in the past.

Identifying system needs is an assessment at a different level of analysis, and a positive, assertive engagement can effectively involve the appropriate parties. Complete information gathered in this process leads into clear setting of goals and objectives, and the meeting of these objectives is the means of evaluating the advocacy process. Throughout the process, both clients and system staff members who are parties to the process are involved. Clear communication across all lines leads to the availability of more information, and all are better able to understand and meet client needs. Being open to understanding the system constraints while making client needs clear can create positive outcomes for advocacy efforts, without adversarial tension.

Conflict Resolution

Advocacy exists in an environment of conflicting interests. Being able to handle conflict well can begin with accepting its inevitability. It is not a failure of case management to meet with conflict. An effective case manager can operate in an environment of conflict. A case manager may model problem solving skills for the system, as well as for the client.

Table 10.1 Strategy Matrix

	Individual Level	Administrative Level	Policy Level
Positive	Approach the group-home supervisor to allow Peg to spend most of her A.M.s at the residence.	Request an exception to Peg's case, in return for the case manager being available by beeper.	Make a request to the board to waive the "out-of-home rule" for Peg.
Neutral	Approach supervisor to discuss alternatives for Peg's A.M.s.	Present information on the need for a more flexible approach to time spent at the residence.	Collect data on the number of people who did not have access because of this rule.
Negative	Send letters complaining about the situation.	Arrange media coverage on the discrimination caused by the rule.	Approach the county to request that funding for the residence be cut.

Keeping the client central in discussions maintains the intent of conflict resolution to meet the needs of clients. Supervisors and administrators use conflict to get systems and regulations changed. Case managers encourage a client centered conflict resolution process that requires that the staff "stick to the issues" rather than get involved in office or personal politics.

Current Issues in Case Management

Even though much has been written recently about case management, a few issues deserve further consideration. Exploring these issues will help to make case management a more effective service and will enhance understanding of mental health services in general.

Who is the target client of case management? Although intensive case management was initially part of a service system for persons with serious and persistent mental illness, programs serving other clients have attempted to use case management models with mixed results. Particular difficulty has been found, for example, with persons who have personality disorders (Harris, 1990).

How do we protect the health and safety of clients and case managers? There are limits to the risks that case managers ought to assume in their work. It would be acceptable, for example, not to expect case managers to enter *crack houses* (where cocaine is sold and used), looking for a client. On the other side of this issue, how far can a case manager be expected to go to ensure that a client is in a safe environment, specifically when it may be against the expressed wishes of the client?

How can case management be culturally sensitive? Much is said about this, but often it is no more than an appendage tacked onto existing training programs or workshops. Agencies that operate in multicultural environments can commit to an assessment of the communities they serve. Such an assessment might include the identification and operationalization of communication patterns, norms of authority, perceptions of mental illness, and receptiveness to assistance in particular cultures. Evaluations of how these assessments may alter the function of case management would make a concrete contribution to addressing this issue.

How much responsibility is expected, for how much remuneration? In many mental health systems, case managers assume 24-hour responsibility for crisis intervention. Some require ownership of an automobile. Effective case managers are expected to understand service systems and to be able to advocate for clients in those systems. Salaries and benefits, however, do not match with these professional and life style expectations. How much is 24-hour supervision worth? Does this level of responsibility require a particular level of education? Do salaries need to be adjusted to attract persons at this level?

To what extent do case managers serve as agents of social control? Many would perceive that case managers are paid to make sure that persons with mental illness comply with prescribed service and treatment. Where there are inadequate services, it could be said that the case manager is not responsible for managing services, but rather the clients themselves.

Conclusion

Case managers help persons with serious mental illness to negotiate their social terrain. Case managers use an array of skills and resources to assess, plan, link, monitor, and evaluate services, and to advocate for the needs of clients. The case manager provides a focus of responsibility for meeting the medical, economic, and social needs of the client. The case manager often is an important source of social support.

Models of intensive case management organize systems of care including community services for persons with serious mental illness. The full support, rehabilitation, and personal strengths models build on each other and on the more traditional expanded broker model to offer an array of service alternatives. They represent different perspectives about the capabilities of persons with mental illness and their potential to be helped, either directly in terms of helping themselves. Because some models are more comprehensive than others, they also differ in resources needed to implement them. Each model specifies priorities for assessment, preferred intervention strategies, and criteria for evaluation or for service assurance.

Activities of case management follow the traditional human service paradigm of assessment, planning, monitoring, and evaluation. However, the delivery of these services differs in the intensity of involvement and the emphasis on accountability. The case manager is expected to be a strong advocate for the client, promoting community integration and assisting in conflict resolution. These differences hinge on a premise that case management can promote a client centered approach to treatment and care in an environment that is often system centered.

When a helping relationship such as this one exists, there is mutual respect between client and case manager, and there is a sharing of the tasks of living in the community, as the client copes with the difficulties of the illness. Empathy is expressed in such a way that the client feels supported and strengthened as a person. An important function of the relationship is to provide proof that the client is cared about and belongs to a community.

References

Altshuler, S. C., & Forward, J. (1978). The inverted hierarchy: A case manager approach to mental health services. *Administration in Mental Health, 6,* 57–68.

Anthony, W. A., & Liberman, R. P. (1986). The practice of psychiatric rehabilitation: Historical, conceptual and research base. *Schizophrenia Bulletin, 12,* 542–553.

Bergman, H. C., & Harris, M. (1985). Substance abuse among young adult chronic patients. *Psychosocial Rehabilitation Journal, 9,* 49–53.

Bond, G. R., Miller, L. D., Krumwied, R., & Ward, R. S. (1988). Assertive case management in three CMHC's: A controlled study. *Hospital and Community Psychiatry, 39,* 411–418.

Boydell, K., Trainor, J., & Intagliata, J. (1986). A participatory approach to the evaluation design of a case management program for the long-term mentally ill. *Canada's Mental Health, 34,* 11–13.

Campbell, J. (1989). *The well-being project report: Mental health clients speak for themselves.* Newhall, CA: The Well-Being Programs.

Carragonne, P. (1980). *An analysis of the function of case management in four mental health social service settings.* Austin, TX: University of Texas, School of Social Work.

Cohen, M. R., Farkas, M. D., Cohen, B. F., & Unger, K. V. (1990). [Trainer package]. *Psychiatric rehabilitation training technology: Setting an overall rehabilitation goal.* Boston: Boston University, Center for Psychiatric Rehabilitation.

Drake, R. E., Osher, F. C., Noordsy, D. L., Hurlbut, S. C., Teague, G. B., & Beaudett, M. S. (1990). Diagnosis of alcohol use disorders in schizophrenia. *Schizophrenia Bulletin, 16,* 57–67.

Drake, R. E., Osher, R. C., & Wallach, M. A. (1989). Alcohol use and abuse in schizophrenia: A prospective community study. *Journal of Nervous and Mental Disease, 177,* 408–414.

Estroff, S. (October, 1987). Renewal and Revision: Creating Authentic Communities. Address at the 10th Annual Learning Community, Madison, WI.

Evans, K., & Sullivan, J. (1990). *Dual diagnosis: Counseling the mentally ill substance abuser.* New York: Guilford Press.

Friday, J. C. (1986). *Case managers for the chronically mentally ill: Assessing and improving their performance.* Atlanta: Southern Regional Education Board.

Hansburg, F., Solomon, P., & Meyerson, A. T. (1990). Integrating a research agenda into a new psychosocial rehabilitation program. In A. T. Meyerson & P. Solomon (Eds.), *New developments in psychiatric rehabiliation: Vol. 45. New directions for mental health services.* San Francisco: Jossey-Bass.

Hansell, N. (1976). *The person in distress: On the biosocial dynamics of adaptation.* New York: Human Sciences Press.

Harris, M. (1990). Redesigning case management services for work with character disordered young adults. In N. L. Cohen (Ed.), *Psychiatry takes to the streets: Outreach and crisis intervention for the mentally ill.* New York: Guilford Press.

Intagliata, J. (1982). Improving the quality of care for the chronically mentally disabled: The role of case management. *Schizophrenia Bulletin, 8,* 655–674.

Intagliata, J., & Baker, F. (1983). Factors affecting case management services for the chronically mentally ill. *Administration in Mental Health, 11,* 75–91.

Isaac, R. J., & Armat, V .C. (1990). *Madness in the streets: How psychiatry and the law abandoned the mentally ill.* New York: Free Press.

Johnson, A. B. (1990). *Out of bedlam: The truth*

about deinstitutionalization. New York: Basic Books.

Kisthardt, W., & Rapp, C. (1989). *Bridging the gap between principles and practice: Implementing a strengths perspective in case management*. Lawrence KS: University of Kansas School of Social Welfare.

Liberman, R. P. (1988). *Psychiatric rehabilitation of chronic mental patients*. Washington, DC: American Psychiatric Association.

Mayfield, D., McCleod, G., & Hall, P. (1974). The CAGE questionnaire: Validation of a new alcoholism screening questionnaire. *American Journal of Psychiatry, 131*, 1121–1123.

McLellan, A. Lubursky, L., Woody, G., O'Brien, C., & Druley, K. (1980). An improved diagnostic evaluation instrument for substance abuse patients: The Addiction Severity Index. *The Journal of Nervous and Mental Disease, 168*, 26–33.

McLellan, A., Lubursky, L., Cacciola, J., Griffith, J., Evans, F., Barr, H., & O'Brien, C. (1985). New Data for the Addiction Severity Index. *The Journal of Nervous & Mental Disease, 173*, 412–423.

Mechanic, D. (1989). *Mental health and social policy* (3rd ed). Englewood Cliffs, NJ: Prentice Hall.

Modrcin, M., Rapp, C., & Poertner, J. (1988). The evaluation of case management services with the chronically mentally ill. *Evaluation and Program Planning, 11*, 307–314.

Modrcin, M. Rapp, C., & Chamberlain, R. (1985). *Case management with psychiatrically disabled individuals: Curriculum and training manual*. Lawrence, KS: University of Kansas School of Social Welfare.

Nuechterlein, K. H., & Dawson, M. E. (1984). A heuristic vulnerability/stress model of schizophrenic episodes. *Schizophrenia Bulletin, 10*, 300–312.

Rapp, C., & Chamberlain, R. (1985). Case management services for the chronically mentally ill. *Social Work, 30*, 417–422.

Robinson, G. K. (1991). Choices in case management. *Community Support Network News, 7*, 11–12.

Robinson, G. K., & Bergman, G. T. (1991). *Choices in case management: A review of current knowledge and practice for mental health programs*. Washington, DC: Mental Health Policy Resource Center.

Rog, D., Andranovich, G., & Rosenblum, S. (1987). *Intensive case management for persons who are homeless and mentally ill: A review of community support program and human resource development program efforts*. Washington, DC: Cosmos Corporation.

Rose, S., & Black, B. (1985). *Advocacy and empowerment: Mental health care in the community*. Boston: Routledge, Kegan, Paul.

Roth, D., & Bean, G. J. (1986). New perspectives on homelessness: Findings from a statewide epidemiological study. *Hospital and Community Psychiatry, 37*, 712–719.

Safer, D. J. (1987). Substance abuse by young adult chronic patients. *Hospital and Community Psychiatry, 38*, 511–514.

Savarese, M., Detrano, T., Koproski, J., & Weber, C. M. (1990). Case management. In P. W. Brickner, L. K. Scharer, B. A. Conanan, M. Savarese, & B. C. Scanlan (Eds.), *Under the safety net: The health and social welfare of the homeless in the United States*. New York: Norton.

Schade, M. L., Corrigan, P. W., & Liberman, R. P. (1990). Prescriptive rehabilitation for severely disabled psychiatric patients. In A. T. Meyerson & P. Solomon (Eds.), *New developments in psychiatric rehabilitation. New directions for mental health services, 45*. San Francisco: Jossey-Bass.

Selzer, M.L. (1971). The Michigan Alcoholism Screening Test: The quest for a new diagnostic instrument. *American Journal of Psychiatry, 127*, 1653–1658.

Solomon, P. (1992). The efficacy of case management services for severely mentally disabled clients. *Community Mental Health Journal, 28*, 163–180.

Stein, L. (1990). Comments by Leonard Stein [special section on the Madison model of community care]. *Hospital and Community Psychiatry, 41*, 649–651.

Stein, L., & Test. M. A. (1980). Alternative to mental hospital treatment: I. Conceptual model, treatment program, and clinical evaluation. *Archives of General Psychiatry, 37*, 392–397.

Test, M. A. (1979). Continuity of care in community treatment. In L. I. Stein (Ed.), *Community support systems for the long-term patient. New directions for mental health services, 2*. San Francisco: Jossey-Bass.

Test, M. A., Knoedler, W. H., Allness, D. J., & Burke, S. S. (1985). Characteristics of young adults with schizophrenic disorders treated in the community. *Hospital and Community Psychiatry, 36*, 853–858.

Test, M. A., Willisch, L. S., Allness, D. J., & Ripp, K. (1989). Substance use in young adults with schizophrenic disorders. *Schizophrenia Bulletin, 15*, 465–476.

Thompson, K. S., Griffith, E. E., & Leaf, P. J. (1990). A historical review of the Madison model of community care. *Hospital and Community Psychiatry, 41*, 625–634.

Zubin, J., & Spring, B. (1977). Vulnerability: A new view of schizophrenia. *Journal of Abnormal Psychology, 86*, 103–126.

Zung, B. J., & Charalampous, K. D. (1975). Item analysis of the Michigan Alcoholism Screening Test. *Journal of Studies on Alcohol, 36*, 127–132.

SECTION III

REHABILITATION AND MENTAL HEALTH SERVICE DELIVERY

Chapter 11

Client-Centered Performance Management for Rehabilitation and Mental Health Services*

CHARLES A. RAPP

Current mental health management practice is characterized by separation of management from clients. Buttressed by management theory and methods, management education programs, and public tolerance, mental health management has been systematically separated from the clients it is charged to serve. As Miringoff (1980) states,

> as social welfare has grown, there has been an increasing recognition that management is needed, but such management has often been perceived, even by its own practitioners, as an activity almost divorced from the quality of service itself. In this view management is concerned almost exclusively with an organization's maintenance and political functioning; the quality and substance of service provided is seen to be outside the purview of management. Hence managerial measures of efficiency and budgetary concerns have often been viewed by service practitioners as being counterproductive to service delivery. (p. 10)

This separation between mental health manager and the client with severe psychiatric disabilities has had severe consequences. It has produced chronic and acute goal displacement, whereby the organization's means become its end. "Thus the activities that the organization engages in (interviewing clients, supervising staff, managerial tasks such as budgeting and personnel selection, etc.) are used as criteria to judge the success of the organization" (Neugeboren, 1985, p. 28). This process is characterized by concern for survival or program expansion and the loss of purpose.

Another result of the separation has been that managers frequently engage in reactive management practice; in premature embracing of snazzy new management practices, which consume large amounts of resources before they atrophy and are discarded; and in employing problem solving modes that seem to solve problems but that never seem to lead to improved performance. The separation between management and clients also is a primary reason why management is seen either as being irrelevant or as posing an obstacle

*Much of the material in this chapter has been reprinted from *Social Administration: A Client Centered Approach* (1991) by Charles A. Rapp and John Poertner, with permission from Longman Publishing Group.

to better service delivery in so many agencies. Management continues to be seen as a major contributor to low morale and job satisfaction and as a major source of burnout (Karger, 1981).

The most profound consequence is felt by clients. Clients bring their problems, needs, pain, and suffering to the human service agency, seeking help, direction, relief, and an increased sense of control and power. Too often, their feelings of impotence are exacerbated in the face of rules, policies, and protocols that seem unresponsive to their concerns. At times, the process of receiving service is dehumanizing, whether through the physical setting of service or through the behavior of personnel. Also, too often, our services are ineffective, do not help, and fail to produce benefits for the clients.

This chapter presents a framework for management practice in mental health that promises to reduce the chasm between managers and consumers and between managers and direct service staff. It does so by (1) describing the assumptions and principles of client-centered performance management, and (2) proposing a new metaphor and resultant strategies for implementing client-centered management.

Assumptions of Client-Centered Management

One of the defining characteristics of management is that it does not directly produce or deliver goods or services. Instead, direct delivery or production of goods or services is accomplished by the teacher, the salesperson, the assembly line worker, or the direct service worker. A mental health consumer receives help through the efforts and interaction with the therapist, the case manager, or the nurse and psychiatrist in the medication clinic. A manager's contribution to client welfare is indirect, mediated through the efforts of direct service workers. By this definition, management would include positions such as administrators, supervisors, program directors,

coordinators, and so forth. It is hoped that the ideas in this chapter apply to all of these positions.

The first assumption of client-centered performance management is that the *raison d'être* of management is client well-being, and the principal task is to facilitate that well-being. The mental health manager is confronted with myriad constituencies (e.g., funders, licensing and regulatory organizations, advocacy groups, unions, media, staff, other agencies) that make demands on the organization. Clients are but one of these groups and often have the least power and influence; also, these varied constituent demands are often incompatible with client goal attainment and well-being. Client-centered managers, rather than succumb to external pressures and become diverted, never lose sight of their purpose and continue to make client welfare the centerpiece of their political activity.

The second assumption is that a manager's performance is virtually identical and inseparable from the performance of the organization or organizational unit to which the manager is assigned. This perspective assumes that managers are placed in those positions to be responsible for the performance of the domain under them, whether it is a team, an office, an area, a program, a division, or an entire agency. It assumes that this is why the organization is paying the manager. It is therefore rare to have a superior (in terms of capability) manager overseeing an inadequate program or a superior team being run by an inferior manager. They are interchangeable for 80 to 90% of managers and units. This notion is more prevalent in business, where excellence in top-level management is equated with organizational performance: profit, market share, and so forth. The late Sam Walton (of Wal-Mart), Stephen Jobs (formerly of Apple), and the most recently visible figure, Lee Iaccoca (of Chrysler) have achieved such high esteem in large part through the performance of their organizations. The process followed in *In Search of Excellence* (Peters & Waterman, 1982) was to identify first the high performing companies and then find the managers who made it happen.

The notion that management equates with performance is much more alien in the human services. The most typical initial response is to identify factors that seem to be beyond the influence and control of managers, which affect organizational performance. Common examples of such excuses include civil service or patronage appointments; less than adequate community services; unsympathetic judges, physicians, and other gatekeepers and decision-makers; and insufficient staff in terms of amount or quality. The most frequent response is, "We don't have enough resources." For each manager, the obstacles to performance are numerous and vary in terms of type of obstacle and degree of influence. Mental health managers, however, are responsible for either mitigating obstacles their units confront or taking such obstacles as unchangeable and seeking performance despite them.

If management equates with performance, then a clear definition of mental health service performance is necessary. The client-centered performance model posits five performance areas: client outcomes, productivity, resource acquisition, efficiency, and employees' job satisfaction. The client-centered manager is responsible for performance in each of these areas.

The centerpiece of agency and managerial performance is the benefits accrued by clients as a result of our efforts. The performance related to client outcomes focuses on the improvement in the *client's* situation or at least the curbing of a deteriorating *client* situation. Client outcomes act as the bottom line of mental health services in much the same way that profit serves business. The business executive needs to closely monitor production, acquisition of component parts, and employee morale but would never assume that happy employees who seem to be diligently working guarantee an adequate profit. In much the same way, human service managers need to perform in a variety of areas, but adequate performance in these areas is neither sufficient nor a proxy for client outcomes. It is this

notion that leads Patti (1985) to argue that effectiveness (client outcomes) should be the "philosophical linchpin" of human service organizations.

Principles of Client-Centered Management

Four principles act as the foundation for *client-centered performance management* (Gowdy & Rapp, 1988):

1. Venerate the people called "clients."
2. Create and maintain the focus.
3. Possess a healthy disrespect for the impossible.
4. Learn for a living.

Principle 1: Venerate the People Called Clients

Managers play a key role in communicating the values of the program to those who use it, to those who work for it, and to the community in which it operates. Whether consciously or unconsciously, managers communicate, in their daily words and actions, how people will be viewed and treated by the program. Managers whose programs show effective results for those it serves are managers who create helping environments wherein consumers are seen and treated as human—as people who are more than mere patients or clients (Gowdy & Rapp, 1988). They are seen as whole people; each individual has a life beyond the program, comprising a variety of interests, relationships, and histories. Although schizophrenia, for example, might bring a person to a mental health center, that person is much more than "a schizophrenic." She or he is a person who happens to experience schizophrenia, along with many other life events and processes. Central to seeing people as individuals is the view that people have strengths and can grow and change over time.

Among the ways in which managers manifest this principle are (1) knowing the clients, their stories, their history, their families, interests, and so forth; (2) having frequent contact with clients, characterized by courtesy, friendliness, and respect; (3) promoting clients as heroes; (4) assuming a client advocacy perspective toward their own jobs.

Principle 2: Create and Maintain the Focus

The organization that performs is the one that has clearly defined its mission, purpose, and performance, and that commits all its knowledge, resources, and talents to achieving those aims. The high performing agency is conscientiously myopic and single-minded. It systematically excludes the irrelevant and limits the domain of organizational concern. Basically, *the performers* set out to do one or two things and to do them well. For the client-centered performance manager, that focus is defined in terms of clients and client outcomes.

Organizational focus requires the following:

1. The management's job is to select and establish an organizational focus.
2. The management should define the focus in terms of client outcomes.
3. The management's definition of a focus dictates *the elimination* of other potentially worthwhile goals and activities.
4. Management embodies a commitment, a preoccupation, an obsession with achieving that focus.

Principle 3: Possess a Healthy Disrespect for the Impossible

Mental health services suffer from a chronic lack of funds, staff, community interest, and public support. This lack of resources is simultaneously coupled with incessant demands from the program's multiple constituencies (Martin, 1980). Thus, a manager's daily work life is often typified by a continual stream of needs and demands from consum-

ers, staff, funders, providers, courts, regulatory agents, and advocates. There are deadlines to meet, reports and grants to be written, meetings to attend, phone calls to take, questions to be answered, and crises to be resolved.

In the face of such a chaotic milieu, managers seem to evidence one of two responses: (1) surrender to such constraints and be satisfied maintaining the status quo; or (2) persist in finding opportunities to improve the program in the midst of chaos. *Both responses* mean that managers *work equally hard*, it seems, but they *work differently*. The effective managers are those who take the second course of action. Rather than remain inactive behind excuses of "not enough money," "not enough time," or "not enough staff," exceptional managers are those who say, "This is needed. Let's make it happen." They are people who instill a "make do" attitude in the workplace, in which program participants and staff members become actively involved in making good things transpire in the face of seemingly overwhelming odds. As such, the manager removes barriers to action: needless procedures, policies, meetings, and processes. The manager is willing to go with a promising idea and willing to drop one that has not worked, though the manager may have been pleased with the attempt. As Franklin D. Roosevelt stated, "But above all, try *something*." The result of this perspective is that such programs are flexible and changing, sprouting innovations based on emerging consumer needs.

Five characteristics seem to be at the root of these action oriented managers (Gowdy & Rapp, 1988, p. 57):

1. A perception of self as powerful and responsible in the situation at hand
2. Flexibility and invention, based on a clear focus on people's needs
3. Highly developed problem-solving skills, with a premium on partializing
4. Ability to blend agendas of seemingly disparate interests
5. Persistence (Gowdy & Rapp, 1988, p. 57).

Principle 4: Learn for a Living

Managers whose programs show effective re-sults are those who seem to "learn for a living" rather than "work for a living" (Gowdy & Rapp, 1988). They actively seek out input and feedback on program performance, from sources ranging from program participants and staff, to publications, performance reports, funders, and consultants. Their programs are open to visitors and observers; their offices are open to continual streams of clients and staff; their conversations are laced with sto-ries about what they have learned from re-flecting on their own practice. These managers evidence the critical skills of learning, in-cluding a total lack of defensiveness about evaluating their work; a drive to critically examine minute helping interventions and decisions, to glean their impact; and the ability to brainstorm with others so that truly creative ideas can be identified and pursued.

Rather than deifying existing interventions or program models, these managers are people who approach life with the question, "What can I learn today?" They are open to experi-mentation. They create learning environments for their staff by paying attention to client outcome data, by constantly putting the work of the program under a critical (but nonblaming) microscope, by encouraging contact with a diversity of people, and by providing support for risk takers.

The Typical Organizational Chart and the Inverted Hierarchy

Typical Organizational Chart

The most resilient symbol of management is the organizational chart. Originally devised for the military and borrowed by manufac-turing companies during the Industrial Revolution, the hierarchical and pyramidal organization chart (sometimes referred to as a table of organization) is ubiquitous in human service organizations. The basic configura-tion is portrayed in Figure 11.1. The chart

typically includes three types of personnel. The first is *line staff*, the people who actually make the product or deliver the service. The second type is *supervisory and management*, who are responsible for controlling and co-ordinating the work to be done. The third type of personnel is *support staff*, who perform specialized roles for the organization, such as budgeting and accounting, legal services, in-formation systems, housekeeping, etc. In the pure sense, these support personnel have no direct authority over the line and managerial personnel.

This traditional organizational configura-tion was designed to enhance the manufacture and distribution of products. Efficiency was the ultimate criterion, and control was the principal function of management. The or-ganizational chart portrayed what positions exist in the organization, how these are grouped into units, and how formal authority and communication flows among them (Mintzburg, 1979). This vertical hierarchy depicts the division of labor and establishes that power is centered at the top.

Criticisms of Top-Down Organization

The criticisms of this organizational con-figuration are legion. For the client-centered performance manager, the most pertinent consequence is the inherent separation of managers from frontline workers and clients. Furthermore, the larger the organization, the greater the distance between day-to-day cli-ent contact and the policy decisions affecting these clients. "The vertical, one-way hierar-chy tends to separate and give precedence to goals of organizational maintenance over client-oriented goals" (Altshuler & Forward, 1978, p. 58). While this seems to occur in business, with profound consequences (Peters & Waterman, 1982), mental health services—with their plethora of constituencies—make it that much easier to forget about the clients. The typical organizational structure reinforces the tendency to maximum nonresponsiveness to clients and their welfare.

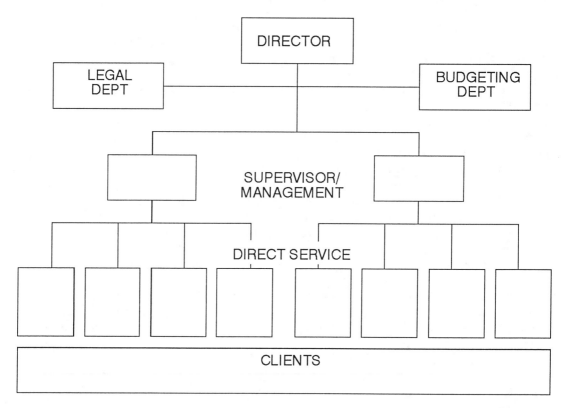

Figure 11.1. The organizational chart.

A second implicit consequence of this configuration is that control remains the major managerial function, with its implicit assumption that employees in the trenches will engage in actions that are wrong or bad or inadequate unless their behavior conforms to the letter of the management established policies and procedures, and that close monitoring is required. Unfortunately, many organizational rules (i.e., policies and procedures) were developed not based on the needs of clients, but rather, based on the needs of the organization. For example, most paperwork was not designed to help frontline workers provide better service, but rather, to control who is to receive what form of help for how long, in order to please other constituencies. Another problem with rules in mental health organizations is that they assume that clients are the same, or at least similar enough that a rule can be implemented uniformly, with rather uniform results. The worker trying to help a particular client knows how farcical this assumption is. The agendas for managers, workers, and clients are, therefore, widely discrepant. Managers seek to control and maintain adherence to the rule book, while workers seek to help individuals who are unique. It is no wonder that management in so many mental health organizations is seen as irrelevant or as the major obstacle to quality service.

A third consequence of the typical organizational configuration is symbolic. Clients are rarely included in the chart. The power is at the top, and all others are subordinate. Subordinate means "inferior to or placed below another in rank, power, importance, etc.; subservient or submissive" (*Webster's New World Dictionary*, 1972). These concepts are abhorrent to the client-centered performance manager. The need for a new symbol, a new metaphor for the human service manager is needed.

A New Metaphor

Mental health organizations that are producing superior rates of client outcomes seem to turn the typical organizational configuration upside-down in everyday practice (Gowdy & Rapp, 1988; Gowdy, Rapp, & Poertner, 1987). It is from this observation that the inverted hierarchy was created (Figure 11.2). This organizational configuration is a more accurate portrayal of a client-centered organization and has more fidelity with concepts underlying the client-centered performance model of management. First, at the pinnacle of the chart are the clients, and all organizational personnel are subservient to them. In fact, supervisors are subservient to frontline workers and the person who may be called the "boss" is subservient to supervisors and frontline workers.

The assumption central to the inverted hierarchy is that the principal function of management at any level is not to *control*, but to *help the next higher rung do their jobs more effectively*. *Subservient* then relates not only to power and authority but also to service. The service provided by management is to help others who want to do the best job possible to do their job better. How do managers help? There seem to be four major categories of organizational helping:

1. Clearly laying out the job to be done and the expectations of how it should be done
2. Providing the tools to get the job done
3. Removing obstacles and constraints to the desired performance
4. Creating a reward based environment

Providing Direction

One way in which managers can help those who provide direct services is to lay out

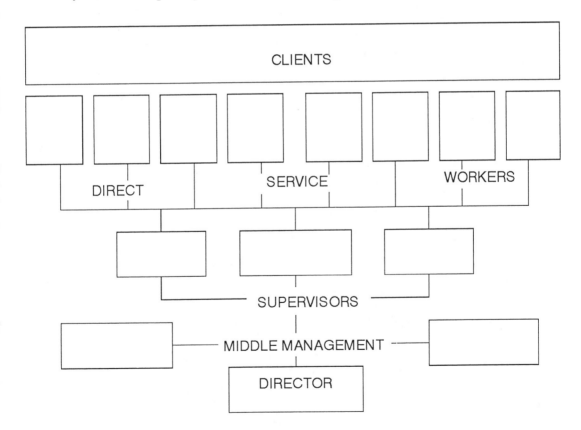

Figure 11.2. The inverted hierarchy.

clearly the job to be done and the expectations of how it should be done. This guidance also includes providing clarity about how a particular employee's job fits into a larger context of program, agency, and society. This cluster of managerial strategies can be subdivided into (1) vision and program design, and (2) managing people and information.

Vision and Program Design

> Vision is the key to leadership. Unless you have a vision of where you're going, you are not going to get there. (Reverend Theodore Hesburgh, President, The University of Notre Dame)

> Where there is no vision, the people perish. (Old Testament, Proverbs 29:18)

One of the most common elements cited in discussions of leadership is vision. As Henry Kissinger has stated,

> The task of the leader is to get people from where they are to where they have not been. The public does not fully understand the world into which it is going. Leaders must invoke an alchemy of great vision. Those leaders who do not are ultimately judged failures, even though they may be popular at the time.

Mental health managers, no less than others in leadership positions, need to develop and articulate a vision of the enterprise. Exceptional managers "deal in symbols and visions and shared understandings as well as the techniques and trappings of their own specialties" (Kanter, 1983, p. 305). The overreliance on management technology can stifle innovation, reduce creativity, and prevent the organization from doing the right thing (i.e., the things most effective in achieving their mission).

Visions that influence tend to have the following characteristics: First, the vision captures the central reason for the organization's existence and describes the fundamental business of the organization. It defines the client as the ultimate reason for the organization but does so by speaking directly to the interests of not only clients, but also staff and a larger society. Second, it is future oriented and has a timeless quality to it. It invokes

feelings of optimism and hope; it has a certain universality of appeal. It is both inspiring and realistic. Third, it uses language that eschews jargon and professional terminology, and it often employs analogy, metaphor, and personification. The use of symbols is prevalent. Fourth, it is personal. It is something the manager owns, and it derives its passion from that ownership.

At its core, a vision establishes and communicates the organization's values. It is shared values that Peters and Waterman (1982) found to be the principal control mechanism in exceptional companies, not hierarchy and policy and procedures manuals, which seem to be the mechanism of choice in human service organizations.

A vision can serve several important functions for both the manager and the organization. First, it can act as a guide to managerial and staff behavior. It provides another benchmark for selecting and identifying opportunities and for making decisions. Second, a vision can act as a tool for unifying potentially disparate agendas of multiple constituencies. The vision is something the manager seeks to share with others. It helps a manager act "integratively, bringing other people in, bridging multiple realities. . . . It outlines a pattern for the organization and its constituents" (Kanter, 1983, p. 305). Third, a vision should answer two important questions: (1) For clients, why would I want service from the organization? (2) For employees, why would a person want to work for the program? It seeks to create a shared meaning. Fourth, a vision is a symbol for the organization and is a basis for developing other symbols. In fact, the vision is quickly turned into symbols by the best managers (Peters & Austin, 1985). The vision is communicated in myriad ways; it becomes ubiquitous. It is a way of stating what the organization stands for.

A concrete method of providing and reinforcing direction is to create a storybook, an organic text of agency stories. These are short descriptions of events and worker actions that reflect the kind of work desired. Stories can be solicited from workers, colleagues, supervisors, or clients, or it can be generated by the manager. New additions could be included in newsletters or posted for some period before being formally entered into the storybook. The stories themselves can be used in speeches and training sessions and made a formal part of employee orientation. It could also be used as a recruitment device for new staff members. The storybook becomes one source of finding and describing the heroes and symbols of the organization.

A *mission statement* acts to formalize and make public the vision of an organization. It is a short statement that can help communicate the vision, values, and focus of the organization. Decide what the mission is to be, and avoid conflicting missions. For example, a mission for a girl's correctional facility is twofold: to protect society, and to habilitate juvenile offenders. This leads to a confusion of values because protecting society can be done simply by removing offenders from society and does not necessarily translate into or incorporate habilitation. If the mission was simply the care, treatment, and habilitation of clients, then protection of society could be inferred as a result of the mission, rather than a separate goal or mission.

The *program design* translates the mission statement by prescribing the minimum sets of behaviors required for goal achievement. A well-crafted program design provides a variety of direction-setting elements, including goals and objectives, the target population, and the service plan. The *service plan* itself describes where the help will be provided, what will be the natural flow of helping phases, what are the existing expectations of clients and workers, and how the emotional elements will be accommodated. It also prescribes the minimum behaviors required of key actors for the program to meet its goals. The client-centered performance manager would use this document as a ready source for directing behavior.

Managing People and Information: Techniques for Guiding Behavior of Staff

If done with precision and tied to client outcomes, *job descriptions* are the most direct source of job prescription for the individual employee. While direct service worker positions come to mind first, it is equally important to write supervisory and managerial job descriptions that are precise.

If "what gets measured gets done," the data that are collected by personnel and are reported also send a powerful message concerning what is important to the organization. The *selection and reporting of client outcomes* defines the priority domains of the work. The selection and reporting of those worker behaviors most influential in producing these outcomes establishes the most important behaviors. In this respect, the data help guide and direct behavior. Performance appraisal and interpersonal feedback similarly direct behavior and provide a set of tools for improving performance.

A powerful technique for directing behavior is the *modeling* of supervisors and managers. Does their behavior consistently embody the values of the organization? Are they models of client-centeredness? This modeling helps guide others in how to make decisions and how to behave. There is no more destructive element in an organization's culture than supervisors and managers who pronounce one set of values or prescriptions and then behave in incompatible, inconsistent, or opposite ways.

The modeling of client-centeredness is particularly important. The following are but nine examples that are often within the control of managers:

1. Interact with clients in the hallway or waiting rooms; find opportunities to do so—have an open-door policy concerning clients.
2. Institutionalize a variety of client feedback mechanisms (e.g., client satisfaction surveys, focus groups, suggestion boxes) and respond to them.
3. Insure client representation on the board of directors or advisory board.
4. Provide membership dues for staff and consumers so that they can join consumer organizations and advocacy groups.
5. Arrange for advocacy group repre-

sentataives to regularly address staff meetings.

6. Donate honoraria to consumer organizations.
7. Talk about clients in every interaction; make them heroes.
8. Ensure that the manager's personal staff acts as an extension of that manager, in treating clients with the highest degree of courtesy, respect, and dignity.
9. Hire former clients.

Another opportunity for providing direction occurs in many of the myriad day to day interactions. The most obvious are those in which staff come to you for advice and suggestions. Others are more subtle. A worker frustrated by a client who has not followed through on a series of agreements will have a natural tendency to be angry with or to blame the client. While acknowledging the frustration, the manager can reframe the client's behavior as being a result of fear or lack of confidence. The manager can emphasize the heroic mission the program has established to work with clients confronting the most difficult situations.

Helping a client to complete onerous financial assistance forms can be placed in a perspective that emphasizes the client's need for money and the importance of the worker arranging it. Once the assistance is arranged, the worker and client can begin work on job training or parent education and so forth.

Providing the Tools

With expectations clarified and a variety of mechanisms established to reinforce them, the tools required to meet the expectations must be provided. It is often the discrepancy between expectations and tools that causes job dissatisfaction and low levels of effectiveness—for example, setting ambitious goals for clients and workers and then requiring services on 50 clients at one time.

For the client-centered manager, there are two general strategies for facilitating employees in their meeting of expectations. First,

the client-centered performance manager seeks to place as many resources as possible in the trenches, where the help occurs. Overhead costs should be kept to the minimum, which usually means reducing the levels of managerial and staff positions. In many agencies, especially public bureaucracies, there are simply too many employees who do not provide service as their primary responsibility. Second, the client-centered performance manager should constantly be asking employees, "How can I help you with your job?" Furthermore, the employees responses should be written down, and the manager should find a way to implement their requests. An eminently worthwhile question that the manager could ask every day while driving home is, "What did I do today that made the jobs of my workers more effective or easier?" Tools can be categorized into three groups: (1) information, (2) structural supports, and (3) tangible resources.

Information

Training. Am I asking the staff to do something they do not know how to do? The answer is too often yes. Training includes such activities as orientation and preservice training, continuous inservice training, continuing education, and so on. Given the inherent difficulty of human service work and the fact that the lowest credentialed, most inexperienced personnel are placed in direct helping roles, the training imperative is clear. We simply cannot provide too much training.

Technical Assistance and Consultation. This refers to the provision of help in the technical application of helping strategies to particular clients or groups of clients. It is one thing to know how to do a specific method of assessment or intervention and another to skillfully apply that methodology to the myriad case situations that a frontline worker confronts. Ready and continuous access to a person who has such expertise can help ensure that training is applied in practice. The most continuous source of such help is the immediate supervisor or peers, but access to outside experts is often valuable. The focus of the work is to place individual cases and situations under the microscope.

Interpersonal Feedback. Informational tools also include feedback from clients and significant others—coworkers, supervisors, and upper-level management. Interpersonal feedback is information that is provided concerning some action or actions on the part of the worker. People's behavior is in large part determined by the reactions of others; we grow and learn. Therefore, the organizational culture must encourage and facilitate ongoing exchanges and specific mechanism for this must be established. Focus groups and exit interviews with clients, group and individual supervision, written notes and evaluations, and even conversations while standing by the coffee pot can be opportunities for feedback.

Information-System Feedback. Another tool for feedback is review of the data reports provided by the organization's information system. If designed to capture client outcomes and critical service events, frontline workers would receive critical information on the results of their Herculean efforts.

Structural Supports

Caseload Size. A frontline worker's caseload must allow for the established expectations to be met. Caseloads of 70 for community mental health case managers are common. Improving the community integration of people with severe mental illness is both too important and too demanding to be prohibited by unworkable caseload size. The simple truth is that the goals we seek to achieve simply cannot be achieved under such a yoke. Managers' creativity and courage are often needed. For example, suppose a team of four frontline workers is expected to provide case management services to 200 people with severe mental illness. Instead of having each worker having responsibility for 50 clients, whereby they can only respond to day to day crises, assign 20 clients to one or two workers, and assign the other clients to the remaining

workers. This configuration provides at least one worker and 20 clients with a chance to receive the benefits promised by the service without significantly lessening the service to the others (they were hardly being served anyway).

When caseloads are reduced, it may not be possible to serve everyone who is eligible or who could benefit from the service. Rather than being seen as irresponsible, this choice is often the most responsible decision. This requires straight talk to elected officials, funders, and other constituencies.

Interagency Agreements. The increasing specialization of our service programs, combined with the complexity of human life and problems, means that clients can rarely have their needs met through one agency. Many client problems are, in fact, not client problems but problems regarding the transactions between clients and societal institutions (e.g., schools, courts, employers). This means that help is provided by multiple agencies and the targets of change are often institutions, not the clients.

Close working relationships among agencies are indispensable for effective and efficient helping. One tool for such collaboration is the provision of interagency agreements. We are not referring to agreements with vague references to cooperation and collaboration, nor are we referring to 26-page continuity of care agreements. Rather, 1- or 2-page working documents, which detail the reciprocal responsibilities in behavioral language, is the recommendation. The document should answer the question, Who will do what when? This is a document that can literally—if needed—be placed on the table between workers of two agencies, to guide their work around a client.

Forms. Paperwork is the bane of a direct service worker's existence in mental health. Later in this chapter, reduction of paperwork is discussed, but for now, attention is given to "forms as tools." The two forms ubiquitous in every agency are the case assessment and case (treatment) plan. These forms should, more than any other forms, be supportive of good helping. For example, a case plan should be designed to have the client goal, tasks needed to accomplish the goals, time frames for accomplishment, name or job title of person responsible for achieving the goals, and a place for worker and client signatures. It should act as an a*genda* between worker and client, laying out the areas to be discussed and the agreements needing to be reached. It should be a document that both worker and client can work from, and each should have a copy. It should not have to be burdened by additional information requirements not central to the client–worker nexus.

Similarly, assessment recordings should help to structure the information collection. It should help a worker and client identify the information needed to develop a case plan and to organize it in a way that conclusions and directions become clear. It should not include information that is not going to be used. For example, some agencies still require rather long social histories as part of the assessment process, but little of the information is ever used to form a case plan. Assessment should be relevant to the form of help the agency is offering. For example, a genogram (McGoldrick & Gerson, 1985) is of little use to a worker who is helping someone to choose, get, and keep a job, or to find housing for the homeless.

Both case plans and assessments should be designed to be as dynamic as actual helping. Assessment is ongoing in our work, not a one-shot event. Workers are learning something about clients with each encounter. Case plans change as situations change, and often, tasks are added or timelines are altered weekly. Forms and policies that do not allow or facilitate changes actually detract from the helpfulness of these documents. For example, agency policies requiring update of a treatment plan every 3 or 6 months are simply not reflective of actual helping.

Helpers for the Helpers. Many workers have too much to do for too many people, and some of the work is recurring and involves little skill (e.g., clients needing emergency trans-

portation, clients needing a reassuring phone call, clients needing specific help in balancing a checkbook). Managers who arrange for volunteers, casework extenders, emergency transportation services, or student help and who adequately structure their work may free workers for tasks requiring their skills and assist in managing the workers' workloads. The use of task analysis will help guide the meaningful structuring of such roles.

Supportive Policies and Procedures. Organizations often develop policies and procedures in response to a perceived problem that no longer exists, or these policies and procedures are contradictory to expectations the same organization has for its workers. For example, the agency may expect workers to be available for crisis situations after hours but then places limits on the use of compensatory time. If the expectation is for an outreach mode of service delivery, yet billable service hours do not include transportation time, major disincentives are created. The best source of identifying organizational anomalies is the workers themselves. If we *listen* to them, we will be able to identify the areas of change.

Tangible Resources

For the Worker. These can vary widely, depending on the agency and the particular job, so a few examples will have to do. A classic situation concerns the case manager who is expected to do work outside of the agency. Resource supports would include cars, adequate travel reimbursement, liability insurance, a beverage holder and trash bag for the car, clipboards or laptop computers for recording in cars or parks, a roll of quarters to check in with the agency, and either cellular phones or beepers. For many workers, easy to use resource guides, Rolodex® files, adequate office supplies, and so on, would help them to do their jobs more effectively or efficiently.

For the Client. These, too, can vary widely, but in many agencies, access to a slush fund for emergencies would be critical. These are monies not tied to bureaucratic controls (e.g., forms, permissions, meetings, and several layers of review) but almost immediately available for such things as rent deposits, food, clothing, registration fees for community activities, and so forth. It could mean a *lending closet*, where clients who could not afford to buy could borrow some item, such as vacuum cleaners, kitchen supplies, furniture, or even fishing poles.

Removing Obstacles and Constraints

The third category of managerial behaviors required by the inverted hierarchy is the constant and conscientious removal of barriers to performance. In a sense, the lack of any of the previously mentioned tools acts as an obstacle. For example, inadequate job descriptions detailing work expectations is an obstacle. Large caseloads is an obstacle. This section does not repeat these managerial ideas but rather focuses on a few of the most ubiquitous obstacles in mental health organizations. The major theme in this section is "less is more": less paperwork, fewer meetings, fewer priorities, fewer permissions, fewer organizational levels, fewer excuses, less noise. The obstacles are addressed in two categories: (1) organizational structures, and (2) psychological obstacles.

Organizational Structure

This category of obstacles concerns those that are created by the organization, often as an attempt to solve a previously defined organizational problem.

Hierarchy. The performance manager must remove needless organizational levels. The goal is to push responsibility, authority, resources, and problem solving to the lowest possible level of the organization. This can only be done by removing managerial levels, the major purpose of which is control. The test must be: How does this position directly enhance performance? How do people at this level help the people above them in the inverted pyramid? What responsibilities are redundant with other levels? Where is authority shared where it could be vested in one person at the next higher (subordinate) level? The author's position is that in many human service organizations, managers are not helping but in fact get in the way, and therefore their jobs should be redesigned to be helpful and the remainder of their tasks let go. Not only does this remove an obstacle to performance, but also it allows the organization to commit the resources to frontline positions where the help to clients occurs. The result is a more efficient and effective organization.

Paperwork. Paperwork within human service organizations has reached crisis proportions, with studies and estimates suggesting that over 30% of a worker's time is consumed by such requirements (Jydstrup & Gross, 1966; Richart, 1970). Paperwork is a major factor in reduced productivity, efficiency, job satisfaction, and even effectiveness. The reduction of paperwork, however, seems particularly incorrigible. What follows are some strategies that work.

First, the manager should establish a benchmark such as, "paperwork can consume no more than 10% or 15% of a frontline staff member's time." The burden then falls on the organization to set documentation requirements that would accommodate such a goal.

Second, the manager can analyze the paperwork demands on frontline staff by creating two lists. The first list contains all of the assumed data and forms required by external agencies (e.g., accreditation, granting agencies, legislature). The goal with the first list is to meet (or change) the requirements of the external agencies at the minimum acceptable level. This means that the manager talks directly with people from these agencies. What are the minimum requirements? How often must it be completed? What is the intent of the information? What is done with it, and why is it important? Many human service agencies are laboring under false assumptions about such requirements. Once this information is gathered, the manager orders people not to complete forms above the minimum and then takes what is left and designs the simplest, least redundant way of collecting the necessary information and completing the paperwork.

The second list contains the forms and data requirements developed by the agency itself. With this list, the manager tests each data element and each form in terms of its presumed effects on the performance areas. Basically, the questions are as follows: How is this piece of information helpful to the work? What decisions or actions need to be informed by these data? If the answers do not meet *explicit* tests of helpfulness, performance, action, and decision, they are automatically dropped. Another approach with this list is to do a zero-based paperwork review, in which staff are to pretend there are no requirements and to develop needed forms as if the agency is new.

Another paperwork reduction strategy is to exploit the power of the microcomputer. With adequate programming, these machines can remove much of the redundancy of recording and can produce reports tailored to a wide range of constituencies internal and external to the organization (Taylor, 1981).

Meetings. Peter Drucker (1967) states that every meeting is a waste of time.

> Meetings are by definition a concession to deficient organization. For one either meets or one works. One cannot do both at the same time. In an ideally designed structure there would be no meetings. Everyone would know what he needs to know to do his job. (p. 45)

There is no perfectly designed organization, and Drucker realizes that. Meetings are a reality of organizational life, and much of our precious time gets expended in meetings. Keeping Drucker's admonition in mind should be a first step in using our meeting time more constructively. However, this is not enough. Managers also need to know how to evaluate meeting time and what to do about utilizing it. The first step is to decide how much intra-organizational meeting time you are willing to tolerate, knowing that whatever time spent cannot be used to serve clients. Ten percent of a worker's time seems like a reasonable amount

to shoot for. Guidelines for when not to have a meeting, how to prepare for a meeting, what to do when a meeting starts, and what to do after a meeting can be found in Rapp and Poertner (1991).

Psychological Obstacles

This entire client-centered performance model is about new managerial methods and new perspectives. Given this, it is logical to identify obstacles that reside in the minds of managers. Many of these are created and sustained by structural features of the human service organization, but etiology is not the concern here. Rather, the concern is that there are personal and psychological stances that greatly impede organizational performance.

The absence of the managerial perspective reflected in the basic principles acts as a major barrier. For example, it is simply impossible to manage according to the inverted hierarchy if one does not have a "healthy disrespect for the impossible." If you think that you cannot reduce paperwork, you will not. If you believe that you cannot arrange training opportunities with such a limited budget, you will not.

Blaming and Excusing. Many of the negative descriptors (e.g., *complacent*, *defensive*, *rigid*) of organizations, specific organizational units, or people reflect a particular psychology characterized by feelings of impotence and insecurity at its roots. The most prevalent behavioral manifestations are in blaming or excusing. Common excuses for not performing are "not enough money," "not enough time," "not enough staff," "not enough community resources." Blame is often focused on families, court personnel, other agencies, funders, administrators, and most disturbingly on the client. Some mental health services have even developed professional sounding phrases for blame, such as "the client is resistant to therapy." Blaming and excusing deflect responsibility from the agency and its personnel therefore and reinforce feelings of impotence.

High performing managers simply will not

and do not tolerate blaming and excusing. The perspective is to identify obstacles such as the behavior of court personnel. Obstacles, however, are meant to be attacked, removed, circumvented, or attenuated. Where excuses and blame lead one to passivity, obstacles are susceptible to analysis, problem-solving, and intervention. Every small increment of success can therefore produce an increment of confidence, control, and empowerment.

Detachment. Organizations unresponsive to employee needs, organizations that place a premium on control and permissions, organizations that ignore or punish extra effort or risk-taking behavior on behalf of clients, and organizations that place a premium on form rather than results come to be viewed as the enemy by its employees or workers. Employees, especially those in frontline positions who have the least power and responsibility, often become psychologically detached from these programs or organizations. It is a coping strategy, a protective device to shield the worker from feelings of low self-worth and of hostility toward the organization. The organization is not "me" but is personalized as upper management or the board of directors.

The goal for the client-centered performance manager is to have all employees see themselves as the agency. They share responsibility for each success and each disappointment. In their contacts with clients and key actors, they realize that they not only represent the agency but also *are* the agency. Their names could just as easily be placed on the agency letterhead as that of the executive director. Part of their work identity is the organization, much like a part of a person's identity may be the family or church.

Strategies for creating such feelings include the constant sharing of credit for agency successes, maintaining nurturing work environments, treating employees as adults by giving them responsibility and authority, permitting autonomy, encouraging failure and interdependence, creating winners, rewarding risk-taking behavior, and establishing an inspiring vision and concomitant values. The manager can also create other opportunities for linking personal and organizational identities: Have frontline workers do some public speaking on behalf of the organization; arrange for workers to do presentations at statewide conferences on the agency's programs; encourage workers to attend board meetings or legislative hearings; involve workers on temporary task forces and work groups; have the organization be a regular source of prestige and rewards for the worker; place pictures of workers in annual reports; include stories of workers in newsletters; regularly ask everyone for their opinions and take these seriously; give frontline workers business cards; fill their offices with agency awards.

Reward Based Environment

The fourth cluster of management behaviors composing the inverted hierarchy concerns creating a reward based environment in which to work. Mental health practice provides an opportunity to touch others—to make a difference in people's lives. It provides rich opportunities for learning and collegiality. Work should be a source of satisfaction, esteem, achievement, and pride. Work should be enjoyable. Yet, for too many human service personnel, work is frustrating, depressing, punishing, and joyless. The agency environments are often oppressive, and management is often perceived to be part of the problem. Clients and employees *require* a reward based environment, which contributes to each person feeling that he or she is a winner.

The old adage is "nothing succeeds like success." It turns out to have a sound scientific base. Researchers studying motivation find that the prime factor is simply the self-perception among motivated subjects that they are in fact doing well. Whether they are or not by any absolute standard doesn't seem to matter much. In one experiment, adults were given puzzles to solve. All ten were exactly the same for all subjects. They worked on them, turned them in, and were given the results at the end. Now, in fact, the results they were given were fictitious. Half of the exam takers were told that they had done well, seven out of ten correct. The other half were told they had done poorly, seven out of ten wrong. Then all were given another ten puzzles (the same for each person). The half who had been *told* that they had done well in the first round really did do better in the second, and the other half really did do worse. Mere association with past personal success apparently leads to more persistence, higher motivation, or something that makes us do better. (Peters & Waterman, 1982, p. 58)

Positively reinforced behavior slowly comes to occupy a larger and larger share of time and attention, and less desirable behavior begins to be dropped. Yet, most managers appear not to understand the power of this concept; the reward structure is inadequate in terms of the amount and the way in which it is implemented. The first rule of reinforcement is that the rewards need to be valued by the person being rewarded. While it is true that all persons have their own sets of job values and unique reinforcement menus, there are probably more similarities among people than differences. For example, most of us respond positively to written and verbal praise, and to formal recognition through awards. Based on the work of B. F. Skinner, Peters and Waterman (1982) observed that high-performing managers follow five additional rules in using positive reinforcement:

1. The reinforcement should be specific as to the behavior being rewarded.
2. The reinforcement should have immediacy—close time proximity between the behavior and the reward.
3. Small achievements (e.g., one client got a part-time job) warrant rewards (try to make everyone a winner).
4. The reinforcement should be unpredictable or intermittent (this happens naturally in large organizations because no manager can be aware of all behavior that warrants reward).
5. A fair amount of the reinforcement comes from top management (not just from your immediate supervisor).

What this portrays is an environment where people are receiving many rewards for many different behaviors at a variety of times from many different sources. This also suggests that those reward systems that are at set times (annual reviews or employee of the month) and are based on general criteria (made the greatest contribution to the agency) are less potent for meeting personal or organizational needs. The most prevalent obstacle to the creation of reward based environments is the manager's belief that money, promotions, and other tangible rewards are the only or the most powerful rewards. The problem is that these rewards are limited, delayed, and often not under the manager's control. The evidence, however, is that the aforementioned rewards are as powerful as tangible rewards and are controlled by the manager. William Manchester, in describing his World War II experiences as a foot soldier, said, "A man wouldn't sell his life to you, but he will give it to you for a piece of colored ribbon." Not only are they powerful, but they have a nice effect on the giver as well.

Sources of Rewards

There are numerous ways that the mental health administrator can directly use rewards. In fact, sources of rewards for people include the work itself, coworkers, and other people within the agency, in addition to the direct supervisor. The mental health administrator constructing the reward based environment takes responsibility for orchestrating rewards from all of these sources.

Rewards from the Work. Rewards can be orchestrated from the work itself. Information systems that provide frontline workers with feedback on their successes are rewarding. The open-ended responses from a client satisfaction survey that ends with, "Is there anything else you would like to tell us about receiving service here?" tend to be disproportionately positive and enormously rewarding. Designing work so that task completion is evident and results in a product can be extremely rewarding.

Rewards from Peers. Mental health administrators can establish the expectation that coworkers reward each other. This expectation can be established through modeling or direct request. "Joe, will you tell Jerry what a good job he did on that project with you." In other cases, peers could nominate colleagues for awards. The manager should make a habit of saying good things about people's work "behind their backs."

Rewards from Supervisors. Others in the agency, particularly higher-ups, (actually, lower in the inverted pyramid) are potent sources and targets for rewards. Mental health administrators at one level seek out those above to reward other staff members. They also identify behavior of frontline workers to be rewarded. A call to a frontline worker from the agency director can be a powerful reward. The board president can be asked to drop by and tell Mary about what a great job she did last month in improving the vocational status of her caseload. Each year, Pam Hyde, the Ohio Commissioner of Mental Health, arranges for Governor Richard Celeste to sign certificates awarded to exceptional case managers. The reward based environment is one in which everyone can feel like a winner and where rewards are varied and frequent.

On the way home from work each evening, a manager may well want to ask the question, "What did I do today to make my people feel like winners?"

Having Fun in a Mental Health Agency

Beyond these ideas, however, is a simple notion that work should be fun! Ideally, the fun should come directly from the work or should be symbolic of the work. This does not preclude birthday parties, agency softball teams, or Friday afternoon happy hour gatherings. They, too, can help build camaraderie and make people feel special. However, fun that comes from the work offers the added benefits of increasing performance and making the *work itself* enjoyable.

The authors have been particularly im-pressed with the results of celebrations and gag awards. An annual conference of state and local mental health managers in Kansas focused on community-based care for people with severe mental illness always includes an awards ceremony recognizing exceptional performance. Awards have included

1. "Hospital Buster" T-shirts for the programs that have the lowest utilization of state psychiatric hospitals
2. An American flag for getting clients registered to vote and involved in elections
3. The Reaganomics Award for the program with the greatest number of employed clients
4. The "Bag Lady" award for the program that can scrounge (mobilize) the most community donations (e.g., time, money, jobs, housing, recreation, space)
5. A pair of gloves for the "Hands-On Management Award" for the manager who gets most personally involved in the program

These awards not only provide public recognition of meaningful achievement but also are a source of much laughter. The power is seen in the response of one mental health center executive director whose agency had not received an award, "What do you think we need to do in order to receive an award next year?"

Every organization should have a "Perfect Failure Award." One agency calls it the "Boner Award," which is a large bone with a yellow ribbon around it. The indeterminate nature of human service work means that despite Herculean efforts by workers, clients will still not achieve all their goals and will endure other apparent "failures." Workers who do everything correctly and go beyond normal efforts deserve as much recognition as those who achieve obvious "success." Two other highly recommended awards are the "Extra Mile Award" and the "Mission Impossible Award." The former would recognize effort well beyond the call of duty. The latter award would recognize the solution of some chronic or seemingly incorrigible problem (e.g., a client who has made significant gains, about whom everyone else had given up; getting an uncooperative judge to follow agency recommendations). Such awards would help encourage risk-taking behavior and extra effort by organizational members.

Fun and celebrations should also include clients. Award ceremonies for client achievements, pictures on walls, and alumni involvement in current programs. Why not enshrine the heroes in an agency hall of fame? Our mental health programs should have an element of joy to them.

The prerequisite of recognizing and celebrating achievement is observation and listening. Managers must simply place themselves in a position where they can see or hear instances of good or superior work and achievement. One cannot hide in an office and still identify performance worth rewarding. The use of client satisfaction surveys, focus groups, information system reports, and contact with key actors are traditional sensing devices.

THE CASE OF ESTELLE RICHMAN: PROVIDING TOOLS AND REMOVING OBSTACLES

Case management had been a lower-level priority in this Ohio community mental health center for several years. Case managers were given little support and recognition. In early 1986, the executive director, Estelle Richman, identified case management as a number one priority and became committed to providing case management effectively.

Various stakeholders were first identified: the county mental health board, the agency's board of trustees, agency administrators, and case managers. Each group of stakeholders was seen as a team that needed to interact with another group of stakeholders or team. Ms. Richman acted as a facilitator between the county board of mental health and the agency board of trustees, and between agency board of trustees and the agency administrators. The case manager supervisor acted as a facilitator between the agency ad-

ministrators and the case managers. Once stakeholders had been identified, the process of education began.

Educating the board of trustees was effective, due to its simplicity and honesty. First, case management was added as an agenda item every month, as part of the director's report. Topics included: meaning of Community Support Program (CSP); importance of case management, the need for case management, evaluation based on outcome rather than productivity standards, empowerment versus enablement. The result of this education process was the board's approval of a new organizational structure, creating a case management unit separate from the outpatient department. The unit was staffed with a supervisor and sixteen case managers.

Second, both the executive director and the case management supervisor took advantage of every opportunity to attend county and state conferences, workshops, or seminars on case management. Articles, books, and other materials on case management were collected, read, and discussed. Policies and procedures began to develop. Simultaneously with their self-education program, Ms. Richman and her program director began an energetic education program for the case managers. This training included teaching a model for effective case management and making workers feel like stakeholders with a voice in determining how the program would function. After a couple of months, these workers were able to contribute invaluable feedback.

The following items were presented by the case managers and, with Ms. Richman's influence, policies were successfully adopted or changed to make the program more effective:

1. *The case managers expressed a need for an agency-owned vehicle for them to use if their own car were not available.* Ms. Richman requested that the finance committee of the board of trustees approve leasing a car. The committee learned that aggressive outreach was the preferred mode of treatment and availability of an agency-owned vehicle would facilitate this. Further, statistics showed that

case managers spent 50% of their direct service time in the field. The committee was impressed by the data and the commitment of "meeting the client on the client's turf" and recommended approval to the board. The leased car arrived 2 months after the request. The finance committee has continued its support by approving the leasing of a second vehicle.

2. *Punching a time clock acted as a barrier to case management work.* The time clock had been placed in the agency by the board of trustees, and all staff were required to punch in except the highest level administrators. Data were presented to the personnel committee by the director, showing that case managers were frequently needed by clients prior to 9:00 A.M. and after 5:30 P.M. Each time they came in early or left late, special recordings needed to be done. Large accumulations of compensatory time developed. The paperwork flow through the personnel department tripled. The personnel director and Ms. Richman requested that case managers be permitted to work flexible hours. The personnel committee of the board enthusiastically endorsed flexible time and removal of the time clock for case managers. This was achieved in 3 months. The removal of the time clock for case managers not only removed an obstacle to their work, but also became a visible symbol of the organizational importance assigned to case management services, case managers, and their chronically mentally ill clients.

3. *Visual display pagers became a necessity, as case managers spent an increasing percentage of time out of the agency.* Pagers cost the agency $200 per pager plus air time. The fiscal director had not planned for them in his budget and was apprehensive as to their value. Ms. Richman's program director spent time explaining case management, aggressive outreach, and community resources. The budget director began to understand that case managers working with clients and collaterals in the community were more productive than when in the agency. All 16 case managers now have their own pagers.

4. *Case managers frequently complained about required paperwork.* They noted that some forms were redundant and others appeared useless. All paperwork not relevant to the client was reviewed by the county mental health board and the agency quality assurance coordinator. All paperwork that could not be documented as necessary by a primary funding body was eliminated. If the only funding body requesting the document was the county mental health board, negotiations were held to eliminate the document. Required paperwork frequently is reviewed. An agency goal to maintain documentation time at less than 20% remains strong. Clerical workers have been retained to help with nonclinical documentation and routine paperwork.

5. *Caseload size was an immediate problem as the agency sought to do effective case management.* It was apparent that caseload size had to be reduced. The board of trustees made the commitment to shift resources and to hire additional case managers to effect an overall caseload ratio of 43:1 from the original 75:1. With the identification of priority clients, 3 case managers have 10 to 12 clients, 10 have 35 clients, 2 have 60 to 80 clients, and 1 has 150 clients. (Clients on the 150-person caseload require only medication monitoring. Clients on the 60–80 caseloads are currently stabilized and working but have periodic needs for support. These caseloads are the next priority to be reduced to 35:1.)

6. Many clients have a payee for their disability checks, which is frequently an outside agency with minimal understanding of the mental health system. The program director and billing coordinator approached Ms. Richman and the fiscal director about the feasibility of the agency becoming representative payee for clients requesting this service. Case managers felt strongly that they would be better able to advocate for clients in the community if the agency was the payee. While very new territory, Ms. Richman and the fiscal director determined that clinically it would be worth the risk. Financially, the agency loses money on this project, but case management successes have far outweighed any fiscal negatives. Currently, the agency is the representative payee for 100 clients.

In conclusion, the agency has been successful in implementing a comprehensive case management system, and this is due to an executive director who was single-minded in her pursuit, who set the direction (e.g., specify client outcomes, job descriptions, designed a model of intervention), provided the tools to do the job (e.g., training, leased cars, pagers, quality supervision), and assertively removed obstacles to performance (e.g., paperwork, time clock, caseload size).

References

Altshuler, S. C., & Forward, J. (1978). The inverted hierarchy: A case manager approach to mental health. *Administration in Mental Health, 1*, 57–68.

Drucker, P. F. (1967). *The effective executive.* London: Pan Books Ltd.

Gowdy, E., & Rapp, C. A. (1988). *Managerial behavior: The common denominator of effective community-based programs.* Lawrence, KS: University of Kansas.

Gowdy, E., Rapp, C., & Poertner, J. (1987). *Managing for performance: Using information to enhance community integration of the chronically mentally ill.* Lawrence, KS: University of Kansas School of Social Welfare.

Jydstrup, R. A., & Gross, M. J. (1966). Cost of information handling in hospitals. *Health Services Research, 1,* 235–271.

Kanter, R. M. (1983). *The change masters.* New York: Simon & Schuster.

Karger, H. J. (1981). Burnout as alienation. *Social Service Review, 55*(2), 270–283.

Martin, P. Y. (1980). Multiple constituencies, dominant social values, and the human service administrator. *Administration in Social Work, 2,* 15–27.

McGoldrick, N., & Gerson, R. (1985). *Genograms in family assessment.* New York: Norton.

Mintzberg, H. (1979). The nature of managerial work. Englewood Cliffs, NJ: Prentice-Hall.

Miringoff, M. L. (1980). *Management in human service organizations.* New York: Macmillan.

Patti, R. (1985). In search of purpose for social welfare administration. *Administration in Social Work, 9*(3), 1–14.

Peters, T., & Austin, N. (1985). *A passion for excellence.* New York: Random House.

Peters, T. J., & Waterman, R. H. (1982). *In search of excellence.* New York: Harper & Row.

Rapp, C. A., & Poertner, J. (1991). *Social administration: A client-centered approach.* White Plains, NY: Longman.

Richart, R. H. (1970). Evaluation of a medical data system. *Computer and Biomedical Research, 3,* 415–425.

Taylor, J. B. (1981). *Using microcomputers in social agencies.* Beverly Hills, CA: Sage Publications.

Webster's new world dictionary. (1972). New York: World Publishing.

Chapter 12

Interagency Collaboration Among Rehabilitation, Mental Health, and Other Systems

ROBERT I. PAULSON

For more than 3 decades, there have been serious concerns about the effectiveness of human service delivery systems, particularly for multiproblem individuals and families. The community mental health system has not managed to escape these problems. The development of the Community Support Program (CSP) at the National Institute of Mental Health (NIMH) and the Robert Wood Johnson (RWJ) Foundation Chronic Mental Illness Program were responses to the fragmented and poorly coordinated human service delivery systems for consumers who are severely mentally disabled. Inadequate responsiveness to consumer needs and issues in accountability and effectiveness are just a few of the results of these problems. The lessons that can be learned from these prior efforts and the interorganizational literature are the issues that must be addressed in the development of coordinated and integrated systems of care.

System coordination is critically important to mental health practitioners. There is broad acceptance that case managers and other practitioners working with persons with major mental illness are subject to high burnout rates. Not the least of the burnout causing frustrations they face is the difficulty in accessing services from multiple organizations

and persuading them to provide services in a consistent, coordinated fashion. Part of the case managers' frustrations are caused by their reasonable outrage at how organizations appear to operate in their own self-interest rather than that of the client's, and by case manager naiveté regarding organizational realities. For many of these workers, their reasonable, yet naive, belief that an organization *should* behave in a particular way justifies their judgment of the morality of others whose behavior deviates from their expectations. This moral exhortation or "you really oughta wanna" approach is never effective in changing human behavior (Mager & Pipe, 1970); nor does it change organizational behavior. Similarly, social planners take the rational, logical approach and assume, much as line workers, that logic is sufficient motivation for an organizational leadership to cooperate with planners and adopt their plan.

The approach to effective interorganizational collaboration is based on two major assumptions. First, one must comprehend the forces that operate on organizations, in light of the available incentives and sanctions—that is, the constraints and opportunities faced by organizations. Second, an analysis of interagency collaboration should adopt the point of view of the world as it is, rather than how it could or should be. Appreciating political realities of organizational life is essential in designing coordinated systems of care.

The chapter is divided into three parts. In the first section, the rationale for integrated and coordinated systems of care is presented, followed by an analysis of the different models that have been developed to achieve system integration. The second section explores the implementation literature and the lessons that can be learned in designing and implementing integrated systems of care. The final section presents a conceptual framework for looking at the issues in securing interagency collaboration and uses a case study of a community mental health system to illustrate its application.

An Overview of Service System Coordination

In the aftermath of deinstitutionalization, the responsibility for fulfilling the needs of persons with major mental illness, which were once provided by one total institution was transferred to various community agencies, each responsible for differing aspects of the individual's needs. Community support systems (CSS) necessitate the collaboration of a variety of agencies in meeting the needs of persons with severe mental disabilities and—consequently—are subject to the same potential pitfalls and problems of other human service systems. These system problems usually are manifest as fragmentation, discontinuity, and the lack of coordination and accountability.

Collaboration and Coordination Outcomes

Coordination is a special kind of interorganizational relationship, which is a major concern of mental health and rehabilitation practitioners and one of the desired outcomes of interagency collaboration. Reid (1964) observed that coordination among organizations depends on (1) shared operational goals, (2) complementary resources, and (3) a mechanism for controlling the exchanges. It is important to note that agencies can share general goals without sharing operational goals—that is, the way services are delivered. For example, a state psychiatric hospital, a community mental health center (CMHC), a transitional employment program, a crisis center, and a club house may all have a common goal of alleviating the symptoms of mental illness and restoring a person's functioning but may differ so radically in their approaches that cooperation becomes difficult, if not impossible. Not infrequently, the client is left caught among conflicting services, philosophies, and expectations. To illustrate, hospital staff may encourage a seriously mentally ill person to be a compliant "patient" and discourage patient initiative and independence; the CMHC might emphasize medication compliance and attendance at agency programs, while the transitional employment program and club house encourage citizenship and independence.

The prerequisite of having complementary resources is the simple notion that two organizations must have resources to exchange, which the other wants (e.g., clients or services), or there is little reason for them to enter into a relationship. It is often overlooked that interorganizational relationships such as coordination are costly in terms of time, effort, and the loss of some autonomy and control. Even if two agencies share operational goals and have complementary resources, there needs to be some agreed upon mechanism (e.g., standard operating procedures, referral agreements) to facilitate and monitor the exchanges, or the relationships could easily break down.

Reid (1964) also observed that coordination can take the form of ad hoc case coordination, systematic case coordination, or program coordination. In ad hoc case coordination, workers in different agencies communicate with each other concerning a specific case without the benefit of any formal mechanisms or procedures to facilitate this coordination. In systemic case coordination, formal mechanisms—such as joint case conferences, standardized referral criteria and procedures, or dispute resolution processes—are established, to provide a more consistent and systemic framework for the coordination, and they usually involve formal interagency agreements. Finally, program coordination adds joint planning and decision-making, and perhaps even joint operation of programs with the cooperating agencies.

It is also important to distinguish whether program and services, resources, clients, or information is being coordinated. Much of what case managers face on a regular basis is ad hoc case coordination, while the CSP notion calls for movement toward program coordination, the most complex and involved type of coordination. Furthermore, there are degrees of comprehensiveness, compatibility, and cooperation that characterize any of these exchanges (Aiken, Dewar, DiTomaso, Hage, & Zeitz, 1975). The level at which each of these elements should most appropriately be coordinated depends on the circumstances and the desired outcome. For example, ad hoc case coordination is most appropriately coordinated at the line worker level, while program coordination can only be accomplished at a top management level, where the necessary organizational commitments can be secured.

Coordination also depends on an organization's awareness of its interdependence, the degree of standardization (i.e., predictability, or routine nature) of the units to be exchanged, the type of organization, and the resources that can be committed to maintaining the interorganizational relationships (Litwak & Hylton 1974). To illustrate the principle of the extent of standardization, in cases where client exchanges involve similar people who need essentially the same services and whose needs remain stable, the interchange is more predictable, disputes are less likely, and it is therefore easier to maintain the relationship. However, if the clients, such as persons with major mental illness, are very different in their conditions and needs, and if these needs fluctuate rapidly over time,

then the case coordination between the two organizations is much more complex and difficult.

Coordination among agencies is predicated on shared goals, complementary resources, and a method of making exchanges. Once agencies and staff identify these components, the exchanges can have varying degrees of formality (e.g., informal relationships through joint planning). Organizations (agencies) often differ in awareness and commitment to interagency relationships and in their perspectives on the desirability of coordination.

Three Models of Program Coordination

Initially, most social services were provided by private voluntary agencies funded primarily by charitable contributions, frequently under religious auspices. Two solutions to service coordination, which are very much in use today, were developed during this time. Settlement houses, charged with the responsibility of integrating immigrants into the community, relied on coordination through caseworkers, who were expected to provide individualized, comprehensive services in much the same way that case managers are expected to function today.

With the increased complexities and problems of urban life and the competition for private donations, agencies joined together and formed community chests, to coordinate fundraising and health and welfare councils, and to coordinate planning (in many communities, both functions were combined into one organization). As these organizations brought agencies together to study a common social problem or target population, interorganizational agreements were frequently developed to enhance coordination. Lacking fiscal resources and statutory mandates as leverage to force agencies to coordinate, health and welfare councils had to rely on persuasion to effect greater coordination because participation was purely voluntary. In the 1960s, public funding of social services increased dramatically with the passage of Title XX and the War on Poverty legislation.

There was increasing recognition that for many individuals—such as children, the elderly, or severely mentally disabled persons—no single agency could provide all the services needed. Three different but related strategies emerged during this time period. These three strategies were (1) the creation of central coordinating agencies such as community action programs (CAPs) or "model cities" programs, (2) the consolidation of a number of separate human service agencies (e.g., welfare, health, employment, corrections, and mental health) into one superagency at the state or local level, and (3) the development of one-stop neighborhood service centers, where a variety of human service agencies were colocated under one roof. Each of these three strategies of centralization, consolidation and colocation proved to be insufficient to create integrated service systems and unified approaches to solving social problems.

Centralized Coordination

The central coordinating strategy was a response to the observation that no single agency was responsible for overseeing the coordination of services to a particular target population or for a particular social problem. It was assumed that if a single agency was created with the task of coordinating other services (an organizational case manager as it were), the result would be a fixed point of accountability, responsibility, and information, which would lead to improved coordination.

An example of this was the Office of Economic Opportunity (OEO), which was established to administer the War on Poverty with programs in the local communities. Through OEO, community action agencies (CAA) were created and charged with coordinating local, state, and federal resources in a unified strategy to reduce poverty. However, OEO's essential function was to provide funding for the CAP administrative organization. The expectation was that program funding would occur through those CAAs that were successful in competing for categorical federal funds from multiple federal agencies. This proved to be more difficult than anticipated. The result

was that the CAAs were seriously underfunded, compared to the magnitude of the problems they sought to solve and compared to well-established and well-financed agencies (e.g., housing authorities or school boards). Consequently, the CAAs had relatively few resources to induce other organizations to collaborate. Furthermore, as the "new kids on the block," most CAA programs did not have the credibility, power, or authority to persuade others to cooperate. The alternative goals of "power to the poor"—more commonly known as "maximum feasible participation"—often led to intense political conflicts with established agencies. This provided additional reasons for established agencies to be reluctant to cooperate.

In response to some of the political problems created by the CAAs, the "Model Cities Program" altered the OEO strategy by insisting that the model cities agencies become part of the local government. It was hoped that the added clout, expertise, and resources of the local government would overcome some of the problems of the OEO programs. However, the basic funding strategy of relying on other federal departments (which were supposed to give model cities applications priority, but which did not do so in practice) for program funding and the general lack of resources to induce other agencies to collaborate resulted in the same problems.

Consolidation

The second strategy sought to get around the problem of lack of authority and power by consolidation. Here, the assumption was that by having previously independent agencies reporting to a single higher authority, the administrator of this higher authority would have the incentives and sanctions to bring about coordination. Greater efficiencies, it was asserted, would occur by developing common forms and procedures and eliminating duplication and overlap. These umbrella agencies usually consolidated mental health, health, substance abuse, and welfare services. What was often overlooked was the fact that the constituent agencies were not likely to voluntarily give up their power without a fight, nor were agency directors willing to resign their positions to enable new and "more cooperative" leadership to replace them.

The results were mixed and depended heavily on whether the new agency director had the charisma or power (which usually depended on backing by the chief elected political official) to persuade or force these previously independent agencies to change the way they did business. When this did occur, substantial improvements resulted. In many instances, however, these agencies and their directors had independent power bases and constituencies and were able to maintain the status quo within the new structure. In the worst cases, the agencies (now departments or divisions) operated much like their former independent selves, only with another layer of bureaucracy. In other situations, interunit rivalries among the constituent agencies led to constant internal power struggles, which diverted the energy and resources of the agency from its main task of delivering services. It should be noted that all too often, the mental health division was one of the least powerful divisions in such agencies.

Colocation

The multiservice center strategy presents a somewhat parallel situation to the consolidation approach. In this case, social welfare agencies agreed to colocate workers or create satellite offices in a single location to serve a defined neighborhood. The success of these centers depended to a large extent on whether the agencies that were colocated gave the on-site workers a degree of independence and authority to make their own decisions, whether there were interagency protocols that allowed for central intake and flexibility in the rules and procedures, and whether the service center administrator was granted supervisory authority by the agencies involved over their outstationed workers. Otherwise, the employees were still oriented toward their central offices and could not make service plans and decisions without first clearing

them with the central office and observing its chain of command. Similarly, the probability of conflicting procedures and regulations was unlikely to be diminished, thus thwarting the idea of a multineed client being helped in one visit. Mental health centers were likely to be participants in such colocation strategies.

Assessing the Three Strategies

More recent endeavors at service integration and coordination including those in mental health have essentially been variations on these same basic themes. Comprehensive CMHC swere initially conceived as specialized examples of one-stop multiservice centers for their catchment area. The CSP strategy, which fixed responsibility for a complete package of services in a new specialized CSP agency (or as a new program in a mental health agency), was essentially a variant of the central coordination strategy used in the CAPs. The CSP have faced similar problems of insufficient funds, authority, and power to bring about the desired coordination.

The most comprehensive approach in mental health to the problems of coordination of services to persons with major mental illness has been the RWJ Foundation "Chronic Mental Illness" Project. The RWJ approach essentially replicates the model cities strategy of creating a central fiscal, administrative, and clinical authority (although these authorities are not a direct part of local government), which is responsible for the planning and coordination of services to a specific target population. These mental health authorities could either provide services directly or contract out for services. Initial indications are that these projects have experienced many of the same problems that model cities agencies faced.

None of these strategies have proven to be panaceas for effecting interorganizational collaboration or service system integration. Instead, they have had varying degrees of success, depending on a wide variety of circumstances and factors. How can this mixed record be explained, and what can be done to improve the chances for success? The basis of any explanation comes from an understanding of the factors that influence an organization's willingness to cooperate and establish interorganizational relationships with other agencies. For this, we need to look at interorganizational theory and the implementation literature.

Interorganizational Program Implementation

The implementation framework used in this chapter is based on three interconnected parts: (1) the elements of an implementation system, including the complexities of joint action; (2) implementation structures; and (3) the multiple incentive system model. The first part is concerned with those factors that are involved in any implementation process and must be taken into account when analyzing or designing program implementation strategies. Regardless of how well controlled and integrated these factors are, there are always implementation problems that result from the difficulties inherent in interorganizational relationships. These strategies assume that programs are implemented by a focal organization, through a formal administrative structure. As such, they cannot adequately describe or explain programs that are implemented through more informal multiorganizational processes, which characterize much of social program implementation. The concept of implementation structures fills this gap. Finally, to make any implementation model complete, the factors that motivate and direct the behavior of individuals and organizations must be explained. This is the function of the multiple incentive system model. Together, these three elements form a conceptual framework that can guide practitioners in analyzing and implementing collaborative systems of care.

The Elements of an Implementation System

Van Meter and Van Horn (1975) developed a model of policy implementation, which is suitable for analyzing program implementation. The elements in their model are program standards and objectives, program resources, interorganizational communication and enforcement activities, characteristics of the implementing agencies, economic-social and political conditions, and disposition of the implementers (Van Meter & Van Horn, 1975).

The implementation's success depends on the implementers knowing and agreeing on what they are to implement. For this reason, the degree of *clarity and specificity of program/policy objectives and standards* is essential. While the principles and services outlined in the NIMH CSP appear to be very straightforward, they have not proven to be easy to make operational in a consistent fashion. For example, the disparity in interpretations of just one function, case management, has been well documented (Chamberlain & Rapp, 1991), and this disparity is true of most of the other CSP elements as well (Brekke, 1987). Similar problems have occurred with respect to PSR programs (Anthony, Cohen, & Farkas, 1990; Farkas & Anthony, 1989).

The greater the extent of vagueness and ambiguity around objectives, the more likely there is to be conflict among the various implementers. Decisions about program interpretations are made and conflicts resolved through a political bargaining and mutual adjustment process, which can change the shape of the final program considerably. Implementers of different aspects of the program may have different interpretations, causing obstacles and delays in implementation. Implementations with the greatest power are more likely to make their interpretation stick. Program clarity and specificity impose constraints on this type of process.

The second factor that must be considered in the implementation of any program is the *availability and adequacy of new resources* to implement a new program. If there are both program specificity and new resources, then implementation success will probably hinge on the technical feasibility of the program. These resource issues interact with the previous considerations about objectives and are illustrated in this chapter, using Ohio's experience in implementing statewide case management mandates.

In Ohio, initial discussion of case management mandates did not describe how such programs should be structured and operated. Under such conditions of program ambiguity and new resources, the decision-making elites of the implementing organization are likely to shape the program to further their own view of existing organizational aims. CMHC directors who felt their traditional outpatient therapist models were effective for persons with major mental illness tended to use these new funds to expand these services. In other cases, agency leadership used the money to establish new specialized programs for seriously mentally ill persons, with case management as the cornerstone.

If there are no new resources and program expectations are vague, one would expect little new activity because to initiate new activity, resources would have to be taken from existing programs. Instead, the organization is likely to claim that the new program is really no different from what is already being done. There might be superficial changes in organizational processes and some name changes to give the appearance of compliance. This happened in a number of instances in Ohio, where agency directors asserted that their therapists had always provided case management services when necessary for this population, and therefore, there was no need to change how they delivered services. Their titles, however, were frequently changed to therapist case managers.

In response to inconsistent implementation, the Ohio Department of Mental Health began to insist that case management be carried out by designated case managers, which was initially defined as a person who spent more than 50% of her or his time on case management. Later, for reimbursement purposes, the directives were changed to include case management services delivered only by full-time case managers. Because insufficient resources to fully implement the case management mandates existed, full implementation meant that therapist positions had to be eliminated and converted to case management positions. Hence, full implementation was resisted in agencies that did not embrace the new model, until such compliance pressure occurred and agency directors were forced to make such conversions at great cost to the morale of the agency (although the negative attitude of agency leadership contributed to the morale problems).

Implementation studies consistently indicate that resource inadequacy is an important source of implementation problems. This is particularly true when the cooperation of other agencies is needed for the implementation. Without resources to offer others as an incentive for participation, there is little reason for others to agree to participate. Resource adequacy is a relative concept, however. In few instances have sufficient resources been allocated for the implementation of a comprehensive CSP. Resistance to the implementation of CSP components (due to differences in interpretation, ideology, or absence of new resources) on the part of traditional mental health programs or supportive service agencies (e.g., vocational, housing) can be heard at almost any meeting concerning services to persons with major mental illness.

Even if there are agreed on program goals and adequate resources, programs will not be implemented correctly in the absence of adequate mechanisms to communicate the goals and to enforce the appropriate use of the resources. Therefore, the third element in the model, *interorganizational communication and enforcement activities*, is vital for implementation success. Breakdowns in accurately and consistently communicating essential information were commonly reported sources of severe problems in implementation. Programs often do not have the most basic information regarding the program activities of contract agencies, which could be used as a basis for enforcement (Pressman & Wildavsky, 1979; Van Meter & Van Horn, 1975). The mental health system has not been immune from this phenomenon in the implementation of CSPs and integrated systems of care.

The ability to enforce compliance with implementation plans through positive incentives or negative sanctions is critical. Without it, agencies either will refuse to cooperate or will "take the money and run" (Pressman & Wildavsky, 1979; Van Meter & Van Horn, 1975; Williams & Elmore, 1976). Strong political leadership supporting the program is frequently an essential ingredient for successful implementation. This political clout is the only resource that many social programs have to enforce cooperation and compliance, due to the lack of more tangible resources (Nakamura & Smallwood, 1980; Pressman & Wildavsky, 1979).

Of all the elements in the model, the *characteristics of the implementing agency*—especially its technical capacity to implement a program/policy—are usually under the control of the agency administrators. While it is one of the most obvious variables in implementation success, it is also a primary source of implementation problems, perhaps because the capacity to implement is frequently taken for granted (Pressman & Wildavsky, 1979; Williams & Elmore, 1976). The key components of an agency's capacity are (1) competence, size, and range of expertise of the staff; (2) organizational structure and management capacity, particularly the ability to manage subunit activities; (3) openness and effectiveness of the internal communication system and communication links with the external environment; (4) political resources and skills of the organization (e.g., trust and support among legislative and government officials and key interest groups); (5) resource base; (6) linkages (formal and informal) with policymakers and program monitors/evaluators/funders; and (7) extent and effectiveness of information gathering and processing networks.

In sharp contrast to an organization's technical capacity, the economic, social, and political conditions in the immediate environment at the time of implementation are least easily influenced by managers. Yet, these conditions can have significant effects. The total economic resources are significant because under scarce resource conditions, other organizations will resist implementation efforts that might result in diminishing or reallocating the scarce resources (Paulson, 1974; Pressman & Wildavsky, 1979). Public opinion, especially that of elites, can be of significant help or hindrance to program implementation (Kimberly, 1975). All of these areas have historically been problems for the implementation of integrated systems of care for persons with major mental illness. The degree of mobilization of interest groups to support or oppose the program is another critical variable (Pressman & Wildavsky, 1979; Van Meter & Van Horn, 1975; Williams & Elmore, 1976). In this case, the growth and influence of the family movement and consumer organizations, especially the National Alliance for the Mentally Ill (NAMI) and its local affiliates, has been a significant asset.

The final element to be considered in any implementation system is the disposition of the implementers. There are a number of factors, however, that influence the disposition of an implementer. The extent to which individuals understand the program, the degree of their approval, and the intensity of their beliefs are critical determinants of their actions. If the program goals contradict their own goals, beliefs, or perceived self-interest, they will not support it. Programs that threaten the current prestige, status, rewards, and current relationships and alliances will be resisted. The resistance of many professionals to working with seriously mentally ill persons and their families because of the perceived loss of prestige and status, and the belief that office bound psychotherapy requires more skill—and hence is more prestigious and desirable than case management and rehabilitation technologies—are well documented in the literature (Paulson & Paulson, 1991). Because current operating procedures and routines provide a sense of security, disruptions to these are frequently opposed unless it is clearly demonstrated that the new program will bring specific improvements and benefits. Therefore, a person who agrees with a program's goals may still oppose it if self-interest is perceived to be jeopardized.

In establishing a CSS, there are likely to be instances where agencies that have agreed in principle to participate and collaborate still fail to follow through in practice. There are a number of reasons to explain this failure:

1. *Direct incompatibility with other commitments*—A CHMC may determine that implementing a supported employment program will compete with its sheltered workshop, which provides badly needed funds for the agency.
2. *Compatibility, yet preference for other projects*—An agency that depends on local community funding might prefer its outpatient therapy program because it serves a wide spectrum of the community, and this provides greater support by voters for local levies.
3. *Existing commitments that demand time and attention and/or other priorities that are more important*—For example, pressure from state funders, family groups, or the local community to do something for the homeless mentally ill may mean that services to children receive a lower priority and substantially less agency funding.
4. *Differences over leadership and organizational roles* (i.e., who controls the program and who does what)—It is not uncommon in instances where there is a county or local mental health authority for there to be disputes between the authority and the contract agencies over their respective roles.
5. *Legal and procedural differences*—It is not uncommon for there to be conflicts between case managers and income support, housing, or vocational programs over eligibility requirements and program rules.
6. *The lack of resources or power to obtain the commitment of others who are needed to take action*—Few mental health agencies have significant resources that can serve as incentives for other large agencies to cooperate with them.

All of these reasons are likely to be operating in one form or another with many of the agencies involved in a coordinated system of care for seriously mentally ill persons, especially in those agencies such as housing or Social Security, where such clients represent a small percentage of the total caseload and are not a high priority.

In summary, the ideal conditions for establishing a CSS would have the following characteristics: The social and political environment would be supportive of the program. In other words, the program would be considered noncontroversial and consonant with local values and priorities. In addition, the program would not diminish the resources in the local economy available for competing programs. The goals, objectives, guidelines, and procedures of the program would be clear and specific, and adequate new resources would be allocated for the program. The implementing organization would have the necessary characteristics and technical capacity to implement the program. The communication and monitoring mechanisms among the organizations involved would function satisfactorily. When necessary, the responsible organizations would be willing to apply sanctions and incentives to ensure compliance. Program implementers would have participated in all phases of program planning and decision-making, so that their interests were considered in the program design and implementation strategies. Finally, sufficient incentives would be included, so program participants would be favorably disposed to implement the program.

Implementation Structures

In both the implementation and the interorganizational literature, most of the emphasis has been on a focal organization. These approaches inherently assume a certain degree of administrative control, internal communications, and coordination over program implementation. We have tended to look at the implementation of social programs from a lone organization's view, failing to appreciate the involvement of other organizations. In other words, "when a new program is enacted, it is assigned to a single organization, and everyone walks away secure in the belief that somehow (perhaps by magic) it will be implemented" (Hjern & Porter, 1981).

A pioneer study on labor training systems has challenged the accuracy of this organizational focus in explaining both the implementation and the ongoing operations of social programs. This research indicated that the number of actors, the extent of interorganizational relationships, and the patterns of interaction were much more complex than was apparent from formal and official descriptions. Reports from agency executives consistently underestimated these interactions (Hjern & Porter, 1981). Hjern and Porter (1981) concluded that focusing on single organizations and their interaction with other organizations was inadequate to describe, analyze, and manage the degree of interdependence they observed.

They propose that there are implementation structures for programs, which are legitimate units of administrative analysis. *Implementation structures* can be viewed as informal interorganization networks that evolve for the purposes of a specific program. A single agency is a part of many of these informal interorganization networks. This is consistent with the image of a "Service Mosaic" (Cleveland Federation for Community Planning, 1983; Solomon, Gordon, & Davis, 1984).

Most mental health programs depend on the ongoing actions of individuals in a variety of organizations. For example, in many counties CMHC and probate court programs for outpatient commitment are assigned to the CMHC. This type of program cannot function without both the court and the mental health agency personnel engaging in activities that go well beyond coordination and cooperation. The program has an administrative (program) rationale of its own, which is beyond the rationales of each of the organizations. However, the mental health agency, to which the program is technically assigned, has limited control over the court personnel who are so essential to the program; therefore, the mental health agency must rely on persua-

sion to obtain the desired results. As a consequence, the director of the CMHC may direct workers to institute particular program changes that they cannot implement because the workers in the other agencies—in this case, the court—are prohibited by their own organization's policies.

Supported employment and housing programs, as well as services to dually diagnosed clients (mental illness/substance abuse or mental illness/mental retardation), are other examples where such organizational interdependencies are especially important for program success.

To the extent that this model is true, theories for the management of mental health agencies are anachronistic. Policy, planning, program, and resource allocation decisions are based on the assumption that agencies have a degree of control over programs that they implement. However, the necessary degree of control may not exist. The decisions fail to take into account the program implementation structures that have evolved, albeit not legally or through official sanction. This represents the reality in many localities where the CSS is made operational through interorganizational activities, but without any entity having the overall authority or administrative responsibility for the coordination of the system.

The Hjern and Porter model does not attempt to describe the interorganizational dynamics that occur in these implementation structures, which would lead to success or failure. Moving to the next step, the present author has developed a multiple incentive framework, which can serve this purpose. It also integrates the interorganizational theory and implementation frameworks.

The Multiple Incentive System Framework

Buried in the different analytic frameworks of the implementation literature is a common thread. The self-interest of the implementers must be satisfied, neutralized, or reconciled with program goals and implementation tasks if implementation is not to be derailed. In other words, most implementation problems are incentive problems.

The multiple incentive system framework is based on the findings that behavior is determined by its consequences, real or imagined (Bandura, 1969). The framework was developed out of a 10-month field research project on goal displacement and implementation problems in a county welfare department. It has also been applied to social program implementation (Paulson, 1981), mental health administration (Paulson, 1983a), goal displacement in public organizations (Paulson, 1983b), and the interorganizational delivery of mental health services (Paulson, 1984). The conceptual underpinning of the multiple incentive system framework is that there are four major sources of reinforcement and punishment (incentives) in any organization, which are the external, the official, and the unofficial incentive systems, and the intrinsic reinforcement characteristics of the job.

An *incentive system* is defined as the rewards and punishments dispensed, the mechanisms by which they are distributed, and the assessment (e.g., performance evaluation) criteria used for evaluating performance, to determine the appropriate incentive consequences. The structure and interaction of these various incentive systems shape and maintain organizational behavior, and they must be considered when analyzing the efficiency of program implementation efforts. By focusing on the source of incentives, the multiple incentive model identifies the group of actors responsible and identifies the potential alterations in incentives that may change the system and the resultant behaviors in the desired direction.

Incentive Systems and Intraorganizational Implementation

For programs to work, each of the incentive systems must be sufficiently congruent. The external, official, and unofficial reinforcement systems have to support the desired implementation behaviors, and the intrinsic reinforcing characteristics of these tasks must be as pleasant as possible. To do less is to invite workers to seek their own rewards and minimize their costs—that is, to protect their self-interests by engaging in behaviors that may well subvert the program.

The multiple incentive system framework lends itself to a political view of organizations. Groups, such as decision-making coalitions, will attempt to maximize control over the organizational incentives available to them and to use their power to further their own views and aspirations (Cyert & March, 1963). The implementation of a new program inevitably affects the balance of incentives in an organization and represents differential opportunities to the decision-making coalitions. For instance, the introduction of a CSP may possibly strengthen influence and power of those persons who advocated a CMHC's responsibility to serve persons with major mental illness and may enhance the prestige of case managers, to the perceived detriment of therapists who served persons without major mental illness.

Most intraorganizational program implementation occurs in response to task environment stimuli in the form of new program opportunities, changes in funding priorities, or legislative mandates, such as those that occurred with the new federal and state emphasis on services to persons with major mental illness. The interplay between the external constraints resulting from these environmental changes and the internal routines will determine the nature of opportunities and costs available to organizational coalitions (Montjoy & O'Toole, 1979).

Interorganizational Implementation

If more than one organization is part of the implementation effort, such that no one organization has most of the control, the implementation problems multiply. Each organization involved in interorganizational implementation efforts is subject to the aforementioned intraorganizational problems, greatly increasing the chances of failure. The requirement of coordinated and cooperative action among separate organizations adds an entirely new dimension. CSSs are a case in point. Local mental health authorities or CMHCs were not expected to implement all elements of a CSS themselves, but rather to plan, coordinate, and—where applicable—fund the relevant programs.

The greater complexity of interorganizational programs and diversity of actors involved greatly increase the likelihood of conflicts and contradictions in the implementation process. This complexity makes it more important to have a theoretical framework that simplifies the analysis and organization of essential factors. Examples from the implementation of CSPs are used in this chapter to illustrate the applicability of the multiple incentive system framework to interorganizational problems.

Clear and consistent expectations and evaluation criteria are essential for a functioning incentive system and ultimately for effective program implementation. From its inception, there has been confusion around interpretations of many of the 10 elements of the CSS. It is common for there to be disagreements and lack of clear and consistent definitions as to what are effective programs in case management, supported employment, and housing, as well as the nature and extent of consumer and family participation in treatment and decision-making bodies.

Each organization that offers contributions needed for interorganizational implementation has a different task environment and unique set of power dependency relationships that it must manage. Program implementation will probably fail if the activities required are contrary to the task environment demands and the measures used for assessing agency performance. In other words, if the commitments requested from the agencies are not congruent with what their funding sources or regulatory agencies require, and/or they inhibit successful performance on evaluation criteria, participation is not likely. The various agencies that make up a complete CSS (e.g., housing, social security, welfare, police, hospitals, vocational programs), have

different task environments and are thus assessed and rewarded differentially, making the establishment of common goals and coordinated action problematic.

Goal dissensus results when the differing needs of agencies coexist with unclear and contradictory mandates. Mental health agencies face incompatible expectations from entities such as family and consumer groups, local government, state mental health authorities, housing authorities, bureaus of vocational rehabilitation, or neighborhood residents where facilities are located. Each has a different concept of what the mental health agency should be doing and therefore what is expected from it in exchange for cooperation. Satisfying one group's expectations often means disappointing another group. If the implementing organization has substantial resources or sanctioning power, which it can use as leverage in its negotiations, such problems are not insurmountable.

It follows that another important factor is the availability of resources to win the cooperation of other agencies. If sufficient resources are provided, organizations are willing to make adjustments in their procedures or to absorb additional activities that may not directly enhance their ability to perform successfully on evaluative criteria. However, they are less willing to cooperate simply because cooperation will enhance service delivery or because it is said to be the "right thing to do."

Most agencies implementing social programs are poor and thus have few incentives to offer other organizations. Poverty, in this case, refers to all organizational resources and not just money. Resources include information, expertise (e.g., staff with advanced specialized training in working with persons with major mental illness), and political and sociopolitical support, such as the trust of funding agencies, prestige, and legitimacy. Similarly, case managers are expected to elicit cooperation with few, if any, of these resources at their disposal to leverage this cooperation.

The debilitating effect of poverty on securing the cooperation of other agencies is exacerbated by uncertainty. In the turbulent and heterogeneous environment of most social program implementation, uncertainty is a fact of life. The political nature of most social programs heightens this uncertainty because the duration and strength of the governmental commitment is usually unsure. This uncertainty causes other organizations to be unwilling to negotiate with them. The four factors of poverty, uncertainty, goal dissensus and unclear and contradictory expectations are disincentives that make securing the cooperation of other agencies extremely difficult for mental health agencies and—therefore— major sources of overall implementation problems.

The factors affecting the role of other incentive systems in implementation success do not vary significantly in interorganizational implementation, except that the additional complexity makes the alignment of all the systems more difficult. In cases where the actions of other organizations are required, the implementing organization needs to know the reward systems of the organizations from which cooperation is being sought. If the cooperating organization does not reward its workers for the requested actions, and the implementer cannot negotiate for such rewards, the implementing organization needs to discover means of providing incentives itself. Otherwise, as workers manipulate the situation for their own benefit, implementation games will occur (Bardach, 1977).

When implementation involves multiple organizations, there is inevitably a greater number of professions and occupations involved, which have different sets of norms and values. Furthermore, workers in these organizations have been socialized into different world views. This increases the likelihood of conflict. Resource competition and unclear expectations will further augment the probability of these conflicts. Physical separation reduces the opportunity for personal relationships and can enhance misperceptions and negative stereotypes among agencies, which can result in aversive contacts among workers in organizations that are expected to cooperate. Interorganizational

implementation must devote the time, effort, and mechanisms to reverse these unofficial barriers to cooperation. Similarly, differential recruitment, selection, and training practices make it unlikely that workers will find the same task intrinsically rewarding.

Mental health agencies encounter all of these problems in implementing CSPs. In short, CSS failures can be explained, to a great extent, by the lack of incentives promoting interorganizational action. This lack of incentives often results in discouraging the program's implementation.

Because implementation depends on interorganizational cooperation and coordination, the conflicting needs and interests of the different actors make success an increasingly difficult goal. The complexity of this process has outstripped the capacity of current theories to analyze the implementation dynamics. The multiple incentive system approach is an initial step in providing a coherent framework for analyzing implementation problems and designing successful implementation structures.

A CASE EXAMPLE

It should be clear from this discussion that the development and management of well integrated systems of care for persons with major mental illness is fraught with potential difficulties. Because most of the chapter has essentially focused on an abstract level, it is helpful to look at the findings from an indepth case study of the interorganizational relationships in an emerging CSS, which is somewhat typical of many mental health systems. This concrete example provides a basis for discussing practical recommendations regarding strategies to facilitate a well-coordinated interorganizational system of care. A study funded by the Ohio Department of Mental Health of an urban Ohio county is the basis of the case example.

County "X" mental health service delivery system can be described as a loosely coupled system (Weick, 1969) with a low degree of formalization, medium intensity, and a high degree of reciprocity. Interorganizational exchanges occurred principally for the purposes of exchanging clients and information. Once those exchanges took place, each organization tended to go its own way with little integration or ongoing treatment collaboration among organizations serving the same clients. There were three identifiable subsystems, consisting of the community mental health agencies, the psychiatric hospitals, and the non-mental health agencies. The relationships among these subsystems contained a degree of friction, particularly between the mental health and non-mental health subsystems.

The lack of formalization meant that in most instances, the mechanisms for controlling exchanges were absent or occurred informally (Reid, 1964). Coordination was almost exclusively ad hoc case coordination rather than a mix of case, program, and system coordination.

More important, few of the incentive systems supported interorganizational service delivery. The productivity rates and reimbursement system of the external incentives did not lend themselves to reinforcing the kind of service delivery that is most effective for severely mentally disabled persons. The official incentives did not explicitly monitor, reinforce, or sufficiently recognize these interorganizational services in job expectations or in calculating workloads. Nor were official incentives used to positively encourage the development and maintenance of the informal service delivery networks.

The major conclusion of the study was that formal arrangements are necessary but not sufficient to guarantee effective interorganizational cooperation and coordination in service delivery efforts. Furthermore, the quality and intensity of the formal relationships between two organizations were not a good indicator of the quality of the informal networking at the service delivery level. These informal networks were analogous to implementation structures because they were comprised of workers in many different programs and agencies. Furthermore, particular organizations' activities were made possible by various interorganizational networks.

These informal networks were developed by workers, either on a case-by-case basis or as a result of collegial friendships. There was very little formal structuring of worker interaction with other agencies. The identification of systems problems and the handling of conflicts were almost always negotiated on an informal basis, with only the most serious and prolonged issues shifted to more formal channels for resolution.

Despite the complexity of the interorganizational systems, many of the factors that were identified as important in the smooth working of the formal and informal networks were rather obvious, if not mundane. Areas where problems were identified were the ability to establish relationships, information exchanges, referral acceptance and collaborative treatment, and consensus on roles and responsibilities. An agency's ability to establish effective working relationships was one of the most important factors in developing interorganizational structures. Yet, this proved to be surprisingly difficult to accomplish. The size and structure of the interacting agencies seemed to be important to the development of formal or informal networks. In large agencies, such as the department of human services (welfare), where functions and geographical areas served are not differentiated, and where turnover in cases and workers is frequently high, it is very difficult for workers from other agencies to establish informal relationships.

Because the exchange of information was one of the primary reasons for interorganizational interaction, the ease with which information flowed back and forth in a timely manner and in usable form was critical in forming the workers' interorganizational relationships. Misunderstandings about the need for particular information within specified time frames (e.g., acute care facilities, the courts) or the technical way in which particular information should have been presented (e.g., Social Security disability claims) caused ongoing friction. Considerable importance was also placed on receiving periodic feedback regarding client progress or the disposition of a referral. Such feedback was frequently lacking, which discouraged workers from making referrals.

Surprisingly, contacting workers in collaborating agencies was frequently problematic due to differences in scheduling and processing messages. This resulted in telephone tag being a regular occurrence. The absence of standardized policies and procedures around confidentiality and the release of information proved to be another barrier to the ease of communication. In short, when feedback and information exchanges were scarce and difficult among agencies, workers were considerably more reluctant to refer to or collaborate with these agencies, on either an informal or a formal level.

The absence of regular joint training or information exchanges among organizations or the failure to reach all of the people who needed it made it difficult for workers to meet face-to-face, even if they had been communicating by telephone for a number of years. Given the tremendous difference in trust and rapport that can occur, even as the result of a single meeting, creating such opportunities would seem to be important.

Referral acceptance was another factor that dramatically affected the overall cooperative relationships. It did not take many rejections caused by confusion over eligibility requirements or the domain served by the agency, or many severe delays caused by waiting lists, before a worker became reluctant to contact an agency as a collaborative resource. There was no effective means within the service network to update agencies concerning waiting lists or current service capacity, which resulted in workers' understandings about an agency being based on outdated, inaccurate information.

Collaborative treatment and/or case consultation is important when several agencies are concurrently involved in treatment or when it is likely that a client will be returning to the referring agency for follow-up treatment. While all agencies publicly and officially supported this concept, ongoing treatment collaboration among workers in differ-

ent agencies occurred infrequently. Workloads, agency incentives, differences in treatment philosophy, and scheduling conflicts all contributed to this situation. If workers were not included in case conferences or did not feel that their information and advice was valued, they were less likely subsequently to rely on the collaborating agency.

Disagreements or confusion over the respective roles and responsibilities of agencies and the predominant treatment philosophy was another element that was problematic in maintaining working relationships and resulted in shaping interagency referral patterns. The informal structure of the system contributed further to the considerable degree of role confusion. Not surprisingly, one of the most important predictors of interorganizational coordination and perceived effectiveness was the presence of a conflict resolution mechanism.

As a result of the research a series of logical steps were recommended, which could result in improvements in system functioning. These recommendations are likely to have applicability to CSSs in general. These recommendations involve (1) improving the quality of communications, (2) developing more regularized mechanisms that are likely both to increase mutual knowledge and understanding (hence to prevent disputes) and to resolve problems and disagreements when they do arise, and (3) encouraging and shaping the formation of informal networks.

There seems to be a need for meetings among key agencies at least once or twice a year, for the purposes of orienting new workers (a major problem with high turnover) and updating experienced workers on changes in services, policies, and procedures. To be effective, such meetings should have a mix of staff levels present and should go beyond the superficial presentations, to allow for a free exchange of the problems that are being experienced among the systems.

Specialized joint training around technical issues that present continuing problems among organizations or systems—such as joint training of Social Security and mental health workers to teach the mental health workers in the proper completion of the Social Security forms that meet legal and medical criteria necessary for disability determinations, or joint training of police and mental health crisis workers to establish a better understanding of the unique roles and functions of each system and the specific skills that each can bring to a crisis situation involving a mentally ill person—can also greatly facilitate working relationships. Such training can also be used as an initial step in the development of formal protocols among the systems.

An additional option is the use of joint meetings to establish consensus on how mutual case interactions should be handled. This is similar to the reliability training conducted with research assistants or quality assurance committees which perform content analyses (Newman & Sorenson, 1985). In such meetings, cases are presented, which represent typical problems and misunderstandings between the two groups. Representatives of each group discuss how they would have handled their respective part and the rationale for their actions. This helps both sides understand each other's concerns and issues.

Combining these more formal meetings with informal gatherings, such as open houses, provides staff with a real opportunity to mix and exchange ideas and to meet the "face behind the telephone voice". Respondents in County "X" continually emphasized the important payoffs of such events. Once personal contacts had been established, they greatly facilitated the development of working relationships and trust. The result is both parties are more willing to be responsive and flexible regarding each other's needs than they would be with a stranger.

Without firsthand knowledge of another person or organization, assumptions regarding motivations and beliefs are more likely to be misunderstood and distorted. These distortions enter into the evaluation of competence and performance. Moreover, under conditions of trust between two parties, the greater the understanding of another position or philosophy, the greater the likelihood that a disagreement will not interfere with mutual coordination. These three types of events (joint training, formal meetings, and informal meetings) should help enhance the quality of communications, referral acceptance, collaborative treatment, feedback, and evaluations (or actual improvements) of a counterpart unit's performance and competence, and they should diminish the difficulties in communicating ideas and gaps in expectations and philosophy. All of these factors were found to be critical in producing effective interorganizational relationships.

Another obvious recommendation is to make greater use of liaisons which could further encourage improvements in all of the aforementioned areas. The liaison role should be one of a problem solver and troubleshooter whose use is voluntary. The obligatory use of one person as a gatekeeper renders the system much too dependent on an individual personality, and ineffective liaisons are certainly worse than no liaisons.

Some liaisons could also serve in an additional capacity as specialists in program areas such as housing that are particularly critical in community support systems. In most entitlement programs, for example, the rules and regulations are extremely complex and change on a regular basis. It would be both unreasonable and inefficient to expect every case manager to be able to develop sufficient expertise and keep current in these areas. Depending on the total demand, it should be determined whether it would be more effective to establish a specialist in each mental health agency, whether they could be shared by several organizations, or whether one specialist could perform the function for the whole system. In some instances, as with Social Security, both the organizational and program liaison function could be combined providing the demand for services was not too great. In all cases, these specialists would be providing ongoing case management. They would simply have part of their time allocated to keeping abreast with these areas in order to maintain their effectiveness as trouble shooters and resources for other case managers.

Greater use of formalized protocols and interagency or systemwide agreements also greatly facilitates the coordination among the different sectors. While these arrangements are not answers to problems in and of themselves, they do provide a basic framework within which the more informal adaptations can take place. Further, they also make mutual expectations clearer and the terms of the relationship more explicit.

Conclusion

Developing coordinated and effective systems of care among rehabilitation, mental health, and other supportive services is a delicate, complex, yet accomplishable task. The ongoing struggle to find a quick fix for coordination problems in recent decades has consistently met with failure and provides ample evidence that there is no "free lunch." In other words, for every solution which has been tried there are tradeoffs attached. Shifts in approaches usually result in some of the problems of the prior strategy being resolved, while new problems emerge. It is clear that the soundest strategy is to identify the costs and benefits of each alternative and to choose the approach that best fits the particular local circumstances and maximizes the benefits, while developing mechanisms to counteract any negative aspects of the approach.

There are several major lessons to be learned from prior experience and relevant theory. To begin with, approaches that rely on moral exhortation (the "you really oughta wanna " approach) or logic alone will not work. Policies and fiscal payment systems must provide the proper incentives and sanctions to reward and shape both organization and worker behavior. Statements of intent, accompanied by conflicting or insufficient incentives, will not succeed on a systematic basis. In addition, managing coordinated systems of care is, in many ways, a political process such that ongoing negotiation and bargaining among organizations and constituent groups are a fact of life. This means that policies and decisions must not only be logical but also politically feasible in that particular interorganizational context.

Second, most prior efforts at coordination and integration of interagency service systems have focused almost exclusively on the formal system. A successful effort requires that similar attention also focus on identifying, shaping, and maintaining informal networks as well. Finally, interventions must consider both the systems level macro issues and the more pragmatic, mundane, micro issues because both contribute to the success or failure of integrated systems of care.

Success in developing interagency collaboration will depend on planners, policymakers, and practitioners recognizing the political realities of interorganizational relationships. The simple fact that organizations are unlikely to engage in activity simply because it is the right thing to do if the costs outweigh the benefits to the organization and its decision makers require that the system incentives receive substantial attention. The complexities of interorganizational relationships preclude the development of any single approach that will fit all circumstances. Keep in mind that all participants must profit from the collaboration and must also be willing to negotiate compromises that will maximize the fit between the circumstances in the local situation and the advantages and disadvantages of a variety of possible approaches.

References

Aiken, M., Dewar, R., DiTomaso N., Hage, J., & Zeitz, G. (1975). *Coordinating human services.* San Francisco: Jossey-Bass.

Anthony, A., Cohen, M., & Farkas, M. (1990). *Psychiatric rehabilitation.* Boston: Center for Psychiatric Rehabilitation.

Bandura, A. (1969). *Principles of behavior modification.* New York: Holt, Rinehart and Winston.

Bardach, E. (1977). *The Implementation Game: What happens After a Bill Becomes a Law.* Cambridge, MA: MIT Press,

Brekke, J. (1987). The model-guided method for monitoring program implementation. *Evaluation Review, 11,* 281–299.

Chamberlain, R., & Rapp, C. (1991). A decade of case management: A methodological review of outcome research. *Community Mental Health Journal, 27,* 171–188.

Cleveland Federation for Community Planning

(1983). *The aftercare mosaic: A study of patients in transition-discharged psychiatric patients in the community*. Cleveland, OH: Federation for Community Planning.

Cyert, R. M., & March, J. G. (1963). *A behavioral theory of the firm*. Englewood Cliffs, NJ: Prentice-Hall.

Farkas, M., & Anthony, W. A. (1989). *Psychiatric rehabilitation programs*. Baltimore: Johns Hopkins University Press.

Hjern, B., & Porter, D. O. (1981, April). *Implementation structures: A new unit of administrative analysis*. Paper presented at the Annual Conference of the American Society for Public Administration, Detroit, MI.

Kimberly, J. R. (1975). Environmental constraints and organizational structure: A comparative analysis of rehabilitation organizations. *Administrative Science Quarterly, 20*, 1–9.

Litwak, E., & Hylton, L. F. (1974). Interorganizational analysis: Hypothesis on co-ordinating agencies. In Y. Hasenfeld & R. A. English (Eds.), *Human service organizations*. Ann Arbor, MI: University of Michigan Press.

Mager, R., & Pipe, P. (1970). *Analyzing performance problems or you really oughta wanna*. Belmont, CA: Fearon Publishers.

Montjoy, R. S., & O'Toole, L. S. (1979). Toward a theory of policy implementation. *Public Administration Review, 39*, 465–476.

Nakamura, R. T., & Smallwood, F. (1980). *The politics of policy implementation*. New York: St. Martins Press.

Newman, F. L., & Sorenson, J. E. (1985). *Integrated Clinical and Fiscal Management in Mental Health*. Norwood, NJ: Ablex Publishing Corporation.

Paulson, R. I. (1974). "Poverty, Uncertainty, and Goal Dissensus: The Causes of Underspending in Model Cities Programs," Unpublished mimeo.

Paulson, R. I. (1977) "A Behavioral View of Goal Displacement in a Social Service Agency," Unpublished Doctoral Dissertation, University of California, Berkeley.

Paulson, R. I. (1981). Social program implementation: An incentive systems perspective. *Journal of Urban Affairs, 3*, 63–74.

Paulson, R. I. (1983, March). "Incentive Management: A New Management Approach for Community Mental Health Centers," Annual Meeting of the National Council of Community Mental Health Centers, Detroit, Michigan.

Paulson, R. I. (1987). "The Interorganizational Delivery of Mental Health Services in Hamilton County," Final Report, Ohio Department of Mental Health Research Grant.

Paulson, R. I., & Paulson, P. S. (1991). *Clinical training for the long-term seriously mentally ill: A multidisciplinary review and assessment*. Cincinnati, OH: University of Cincinnati, School of Social Work.

Pressman, J., & Wildavsky, A. (1979). *Implementation* (2nd ed.). Berkeley, CA: University of California Press.

Reid, W. (1964). Interagency co-ordination in delinquency prevention and control. *Social Service Review, 38*, 418–428.

Solomon, P., Gordon, B., & Davis, J. (1984). *Community services to discharged psychiatric patients*. Springfield, IL: Charles C. Thomas.

Van Meter, D. S., & Van Horn, C. E. (1975). The policy implementation process: A conceptual framework. *Administration and Society, 6*, 445–488.

Weick, K. (1969). *The Sociology Psychology of Organizing*. Reading, MA: Addison-Wesley.

Williams, W., & Elmore, R. (1976). *Social program implementation*. New York: Academic Press.

Chapter 13

Quality Assurance and Evaluation of Psychiatric Rehabilitation Programs*

ROGER A. BOOTHROYD
MARY E. EVANS
DAVID L. SHERN
SANDRA L. FORQUER

Introduction

The goal of this chapter is to discuss the development and implementation of quality assurance (QA) and program evaluation (PE) in psychiatric rehabilitation programs. A premise of this work is that QA/PE of rehabilitation programs should embody recent developments in both the QA and PE fields as well as be sensitive to the goals and methods of rehabilitation.

Since the late 1980s, important changes have occurred in the QA and PE fields, as well as in the role of psychiatric rehabilitation in public mental health systems. With regard to mental health policy and programming, the changes accompany the increasing inclusion of psychiatric rehabilitation philosophy and (to a lesser extent) technology in public mental health programs. In the QA area, as represented by the Joint Commission for the Accreditation of Healthcare Organizations (JCAHCO),

the changes involve the incorporation of Deming's principles and techniques for continuous quality improvement (Appel, 1991), which differs from the retrospective quality monitoring that typified previous JCAHO accreditation standards in its efforts to study processes to improve outcomes. Finally, in the PE field, the changes relate to the increasing acceptance of many of the principles of fourth generation evaluation (Guba & Lincoln, 1989), a stakeholder focused evaluation approach in which the evaluator incorporates the perceptions of all stakeholders both in the definition of evaluation problems and in analysis and interpretation. The changes in these largely independent fields are strikingly congruent and converge on a common set of themes that involve redefinition of the legitimate roles of professionals and consumers, a fundamental commitment to the importance of context in understanding human performance, and a strong focus on documenting

*This work was supported in part by funding from the National Institute on Disability and Rehabilitation Research (#H133C00109) and the National Institute of Mental Health (#R18MH48215).

and understanding the outcomes of interventions from multiple perspectives. The convergence among these areas provides both a context and a rationale for approaching QA and PE in psychiatric rehabilitation programs.

After briefly describing these changes in each area and highlighting their commonalities, we present a heuristic model of mental health services research (Shern, Evans, & Veysey, 1992). This model includes features that typify the changes in QA, PE, and mental health policy. Additionally, it provides a useful explanatory framework for better understanding the consumer and system outcomes that may accompany psychiatric rehabilitation interventions. The heuristic model serves to integrate the common themes and to offer a conceptual framework for use in QA, PE, or mental health services research applications.

The chapter concludes with an example from an ongoing rehabilitation program, which, while not fully incorporating our idealized approach to QA/PE, includes many of its features. In explicating the example, areas are highlighted in which the study may be expanded to more fully implement the state-of-the-art themes in QA and PE. This chapter is intended to develop a context for PE and QA of psychiatric rehabilitation programs that is informed by recent, parallel developments in each of these fields and that is both integrated and made operational through a heuristic model of the functioning of mental health programs.

Principles of Psychiatric Rehabilitation in the Public Mental Health System

Our perspective regarding the important changes in the public mental health sector reflects our experience as managers in the New York State mental health system. New York, like many other states, is undergoing a series of system reforms that are intended to complete the transition from an institutional system of care to one that emphasizes community treatment and support (Shern, Surles, & Waizer, 1989). The reforms involve regulatory, financing, and programmatic inter-

ventions designed to better integrate inpatient, emergency, community support, and ambulatory services, as well as to provide effective alternatives to inpatient care and to stimulate variability in the services and supports available in communities (Surles, Blanch, Shern, & Donahue, 1992).

It may be argued that earlier reform efforts in the deinstitutionalization era involved the adaptation of institutionally based models and expectations into community settings (Shern et al., 1989). Group community residences, for example, duplicated many of features of institutional care (activities of daily living [ADL] services, isolation from normal community housing, stigmatization through visibility, highly structured daily activities). The current reform involves a transition from institutionally based community treatment models to ones in which individuals are integrated into normative community roles and settings. Rehabilitation values guide many of the specific reform efforts.

Morrissey and Goldman (1984) have identified four reform cycles that characterize American approaches to the treatment of individuals who are severely disabled by mental illness. In their analysis, the National Institute of Mental Health's Community Support Program (CSP) represented the fourth cycle. Unlike earlier reform efforts, which sought to prevent chronicity, the CSP movement offered "direct care and rehabilitation . . . rather than focusing on preventing chronicity by early treatment of acute cases" (p. 790). It featured the integration of community services across the broad range of existing human services, as an alternative to creating a new type of treatment program.

Recent attempts to reform the New York system embody the philosophy of the CSP movement but seek to correct what, from our perspective, are the shortcomings of the model as it has been implemented most frequently. Table 13.1 summarizes the recurrent themes that characterize the reforms in mental health, QA, and PE. With respect to mental health reforms, features of the CSP movement—as implemented—are contrasted to current reform, described as a "rehabilitation and re-

Table 13.1 Themes Emerging from Reforms in Mental Health, Quality Assurance, and Program Evaluation

Field/Theme	General Orientation	Role of the Professional	Role of the Consumer
Mental health treatment	*From* deficit reduction, using normative skills training approaches and the provision of formal supports *To* skill enhancement activities and environmental supports, tailored to clients' goals related to recovery and meaningful community roles	*From* a dominant and prescriptive caretaker *To* a coequal and cooperative service provider	*From* a dependent, incompetent and passive service recipient *To* an actively involved and competent service participant
Quality assurance	*From* a criteria driven process that identifies practitioner errors *To* a continuous, systematic estimation of the relationship between improving processes and enhancing outcomes	*From* a prescriber and monitor of service standards *To* a collaborator in the quality improvement process	*From* a recipient of service *To* a customer of service who helps to determine the appropriateness and effectiveness of service
Evaluation	*From* one-shot studies using evaluator specified outcomes for rank-ordering programs *To* ongoing multiperspective examinations of programs that link program context to multiple outcomes	*From* an expert who determines what to study and how best to study it *To* a facilitator who identifies stakeholders and incorporates their issues and concerns into evaluations	*From* a person who is incapable of providing useful information regarding program success *To* one of the stakeholders included in all stages of the evaluation process
Common themes	*From* a static appraisal of objects, using rigid prespecified criteria *To* a dynamic characterization of persons or programs adapting to changing environments	*From* a professional who is an expert and prescriber *To* a professional who is a facilitator and collaborator	*From* a consumer who is a noninvolved and passive recipient *To* a consumer who is an active and important contributor

covery era." The two reform eras may be distinguished in these important areas: their general orientation, the role of professionals, and the role of consumers.

Role of Consumers and Professionals

In the CSP era, persons diagnosed with serious and persistent mental illness (SPMI) often were considered to be incompetent to conduct their affairs in the community and therefore dependent on others for their basic supports. Consumers were viewed as unable to provide reliable reports of their status and needs and to have limited insights into their psychiatric illness. Given this orientation toward consumers, mental health professionals held a dominant role both in the design and execution of service plans and, subsequently, in data collection efforts.

In contrast, the rehabilitation and recovery era is characterized by a different set of assumptions about consumers and the roles of caregivers. Consumers are considered competent to make important decisions regarding their life and are central to the planning of treatment and supports. Consumers and caregivers are viewed as cooperative in a client-centered and directed process. The caregiver's perspective is not preeminent, and interventions are in support of consumer goal attainment and focus more on consumer skills than on functional deficits.

General Orientation

Another major change that characterizes the transition from the CSP to the rehabilitation and recovery era is an increasing focus on contextual variables in the design of service interventions. Given the view of clients that typified the CSP era, interventions often focused exclusively on ameliorating consumer deficits. CSP programs assumed normative consumer needs (e.g., socialization skills, ADL retraining) rather than tailoring interventions to address specific consumer goals. In the rehabilitation and recovery era, consumer

goals are central to the design of interventions that provide the skills training and environmental supports needed to achieve consumer goals rather than exclusively concentrating on correcting the deficits related to the consumer's illness. Informal sources of support and natural support mechanisms are key to this process. Understanding the specific environmental context within which the consumer will live, work, and recreate, therefore, is central to the entire process of treatment and support.

Because the expectations for long-term support and the dependency of individuals on these supports dominated the CSP era, expectations for consumer change were limited. As with the interventions that were employed, when outcome assessment occurred, it generally involved the exclusive collection of data from caregivers rather than from consumers. Given the deficits orientation that guided the implementation of programs during the CSP era, evaluation data concentrated on the measurement of functional characteristics outside of environmental contexts. Much emphasis was placed on ADL, reflecting in part the institutional character of individuals discharged from long-term state hospital treatment. Similarly, the reduction of psychiatric symptoms was a common outcome indicator. If included, satisfaction measures were often related specifically to treatment rather than to the domains that characterize current quality of life assessments, such as recreation and leisure activities (e.g., Lehman, 1988; Test, 1984, for summaries of outcome measures employed within the CSP framework). Importantly, data from caregivers, either in terms of client ratings or chart notes, were the primary data for PE and QA activities. Spirited debates would often occur among researchers regarding the ability of consumers diagnosed as having SPMI to report accurately on their status or symptoms. Consistent with the belief about consumers, outcome data generally were based on the caregivers' perspective.

In contrast, outcome data in the rehabilitation and recovery era focus on the outcomes experienced by consumers from the consumer perspective. Rather than viewing the consumer in isolation, the data attempt to place him or her within an environmental context and to assess the system of care as it relates to the attainment of consumer goals. Multiple sources of data are employed, where possible, including the consumer, caregiver, and collaterals—most especially family members. The caregiver's perspective in isolation generally is not acceptable as a sole measure of process or outcome. While the normative measures of functioning and symptom reduction continue to be employed, functioning measures assess the acquisition of skills, targeted toward particular client goals and the degree to which these goals are attained. In the CSP era, consumers were often considered black boxes, with measurement strategies rarely including social psychological characterizations. In the rehabilitation and recovery era, measures of esteem, mastery, and efficacy are employed as measures of the impacts of programs on the consumers' attitudes and beliefs about their ability to participate actively in their community reintegration. Consistent with the principles of fourth generation PE discussed later herein, consumers of the evaluation data and most importantly direct consumers of the mental health services are involved in designing PE and QA strategies to ensure that their perspectives regarding the intent and outcomes of the program are accurately represented.

The approach to designing PE and QA processes presented in this chapter, therefore, is grounded in a system reform perspective that incorporates the elements of psychiatric rehabilitation. As seen in the following discussion, the major changes that typify this system reform parallel important changes in both the QA and PE fields and have an impact on the measures and measurement strategies used in QA and in evaluation of psychiatric rehabilitation programs.

From Quality Assurance to Quality Improvement: A Brief History

Efforts to define and measure the quality of patient care have been documented in the literature for more than 80 years (Donabedian, 1988; Williams & Brook, 1978). Although QA has included structural, process, and outcome measures[1] since the early 1900s, major shifts have occurred recently in general orientation, and in views of the roles of both consumers and professionals. As this chapter subsequently demonstrates, these shifts parallel those occurring in the mental health treatment and evaluation practice. An overview of these changes is provided in Table 13.1.

Changing Orientations

One of the earliest QA studies was conducted by the surgeon Ernest A. Codman, who in the early 1900s, began to study the outcomes of his patients 1 year postsurgery. Referred to as the "end result system" (Brook, Avery, Greenfield, Harris, & Lelah, 1976), Codman's study led to the funding of a mortality review by the Carnegie Foundation in 1911. A physician, Abraham Flexner, after completing a pilot review (1910) and being alarmed by the number of practitioner errors identified, advised the foundation to redirect the focus of the study from outcomes to structural issues. His recommendation was based on the premise that attention to structural measures (i.e., credentials, licensure and certification requirements), would improve the capacity of practitioners to provide high quality care. Flexer's structural study produced the concept of the "scientific curriculum." Proponents of this curriculum postulated that if all medical students studied exactly the same subjects, patients could be assured that all physicians would be competent.

Structural measures dominated the field until the Joint Commission on Accreditation of Hospitals (JCAH, which later became the Joint Commission for the Accreditation of

---

[1]*Structural measures* have focused on issues of credentialing, licensure, and certification; *process measures* have examined issues of resources utilization and efficiency; *outcome measures* have studied cases of poor or unexpected outcomes, identifying practitioner error in untoward events.

Healthcare Organizations, JCAHO) emerged in the 1950s and published its first standards designed to assess the quality of care. These standards focused on the completion of mortality and morbidity reviews. While no specific measurement techniques or strategies were recommended, individual case review, similar to today's psychological autopsy (i.e., a post mortem review of a patient's psychiatric history and treatment in order to identify factors that may have contributed to the patient's death), was the accepted methodology during this period (JCAHO, 1991).

By the mid-1970s, JCAH released revised standards, which required the development of criteria reflective of optimal quality care. Quality of care criteria, for the first time, specified how delivery of care should occur and thus emphasized process criteria over structural and outcome criteria. Retrospective audits of medical records examined practitioners' documentation against these preestablished criteria. Often referred to as the "four A's," these criteria addressed issues of availability, accessibility, acceptability, and appropriateness.

In its 1979 book of standards, JCAHO revised its use of retrospective audits. The retrospective audit, as previously employed, focused specifically on individual practitioners, units, or wards, and it lacked a systemic approach to ensure resolution of any problems identified. These standards introduced a time limited evaluation cycle focusing on problem identification, retrospective study, and recommended actions and follow up that were referred to as "clinical care evaluation studies." Specifically, these studies focused on problems related to high risk, high volume, high visibility, and high cost. This problem focused cycle became the mainstay of QA through the middle of the next decade.

In the mid-1980s, JCAHO again published new standards, issuing in a third period of change. These standards moved away from the heavy reliance on retrospective audits toward concurrent review methodologies. Systemic monitoring and evaluation were introduced to the field as the preferred methodology. Specific hospital departments were required to develop clinical indicators for the procedures and services they provided and to establish thresholds that would automatically trigger reviews of practice. A second change introduced in the 1985 manual was the delegation of major review functions to the medical staff itself, versus members of a QA department or committee. Medical staff was required to perform drug usage studies, surgical case reviews, medical record reviews, and pharmacy and therapeutic reviews. These reviews were designed to identify practitioners whose practice deviated from the norm. Hospitals were required to maintain individual practitioner files of what it called "incidents" that were utilized in the reprivileging process. This "bad apple" approach to monitoring care addressed problems in practice by limiting practitioners' privileges or, in the most serious cases, not renewing privileges and thus appearing to solve the problem.

A fourth generation for QA was introduced in the 1992 *JCAHO Accreditation Manual for Hospitals*. These changes represent the most dramatic shift in assumptions and values about assessing the quality of patient care. In contrast to earlier approaches, which focused on identifying outliers through departmental monitoring, the current approach espouses a philosophy that most problems are systems problems, not people problems. This new approach, continuous quality improvement (CQI), borrows directly from the work of E. W. Deming (Walton, 1986), whose concepts for improving quality were a major strategy in the Japanese post–World War II industrial growth.

Core to CQI is a focus on *both* process and outcome. CQI postulates that improved processes result in improved outcomes. Functional capacities and performance, consumer satisfaction, level of functioning, and symptom reduction and the processes that foster outcomes are all measured and studied. Also central to Deming's approach is the idea that improvement is a continuous, ongoing endeavor. The focus is always on targeting a new process for improvement or on fine tuning the adjustments already under way. Continuity of effort is a fundamental principle of CQI.

Key qualitative distinctions exist between QA and CQI. In QA the attainment of a predetermined threshold can result in its elimination as a problem to be monitored, whereas in the CQI model, the goal is to redefine the threshold in the direction of better care; thus, measurement remains continuous. CQI is cyclical, involving what Deming describes as a "PDCA" cycle (Walton, 1986) of "planning, doing, checking, and acting." This approach incorporates the principle that in order to improve outcomes one needs to know what produces them.

Deming also stresses that top leadership must embrace CQI principles and methods. Those methods include the use of specific statistical techniques aimed at identifying where production processes are impeding the delivery of high quality care. CQI focuses on the critical importance of leaders sharing a common vision and sense of mission. It espouses the value of data driven decisions and communication of results. The focus is on systems and their processes and how they interact to produce desired outcomes.

The Deming philosophy espouses that statistical measurements are essential for assessing an organization's performance in meeting its mission. These measurements are designed to provide information on how well functions are being performed, to establish ranges of acceptable and nonacceptable performance, and to target areas for improvement. The statistical methods utilized by Deming support the principles of CQI. In describing the *cause and effect diagram*, also referred to as the "Ishikawa diagram," Ishikawa noted that "the creation process itself is educational . . . helps the group focus on the issue at hand, reducing complaints and irrelevant discussion . . . results in active search for cause" (Walton, 1986, p.100). *Flowcharts* are viewed as useful in identifying ways to improve a process. *Pareto charts* are used to determine priorities, such as sorting out major reasons for delay. Walton describes the Pareto technique as a means of sorting the "vital few" from the "trivial many" (p. 105). *Run charts*, which record data over time to identify trends, *histograms* measuring frequency of an event,

and *scattergrams*, which chart the relationship between two variables, are also viewed as essential CQI tools. *Control charts* facilitate the analysis of processes and assist in detecting when something goes wrong; adapted from industry, they are run charts with statistically determined upper and lower limits drawn on either side of a process average (p.114). These methods eliminate numerical quotas as a measure of outcome, (i.e., the number of persons served) and emphasize instead continuous goal achievement and not just the delivery of service at the cheapest cost. Thus, cost effectiveness replaces cost efficiency as the higher value.

Role of Consumers and Professionals

In contrast to the QA era, the CQI places the consumer at the core of evaluative measures. The external customer or recipient of care is the focus of all process and outcome measurements, and consumer input and feedback about both the services provided and their outcomes are highly valued in the new framework (Lohr, 1990). Deming stresses that evaluative measures must include feedback from both the external customer (client, recipient of care) and internal customers and suppliers (practitioners, payors). Methods include surveys, grievance procedures and continuous monitoring of procedures, resource uses, and patient care.

The contrasts described earlier between the CSP and the rehabilitation and recovery era also are applicable to the QA–CQI transition. In CQI, the professionals' roles shift from dominant/directive to cooperative/collaborative with consumers of service. CQI also advocates for partnerships between and among stakeholders in using data to improve outcomes. Berwick (1989) recommends that the role of regulators include "aggregating data centrally to help caregivers learn from each other, providing technical support and studies of efficacy of technologies and procedures thus expanding the scientific basis for specifying rational processes of care" (p. 55).

Reforms in Evaluation Practice: A Brief Historical Review

Concurrent with reforms in mental health and QA were reforms in PE. Major shifts occurred in the orientation of PE and in the roles of consumers and evaluators, which closely paralleled the changes taking place in mental health and QA. An overview of the shifts in these areas is presented in Table 13.1. Detailed accounts of PE reforms can be found in Worthen and Sanders (1987) and Madaus, Scriven, and Stufflebeam (1987) but are briefly summarized here to illustrate the striking similarity with the changes that occurred in mental health and in QA.

General Orientation of Evaluation

The primary approach in early evaluation efforts was to rank order and compare programs based on the administration of evaluator selected outcome measures. This attempt to determine which programs produced the greatest benefits resulted in programs being grouped on the basis of broadly established criteria and compared on the outcomes of interest. In general, summative studies prevailed which directed little attention toward understanding the effects of programmatic differences. As the limitations of norm referenced comparisons became more apparent, evaluators began to examine programs in terms of the extent to which stated objectives were achieved. While standardized measures continued to have a major role in evaluation practice, criterion referenced interpretations gained greater acceptance. With criterion referencing emerged a recognition that the uniquenesses of individuals and programs were probably associated with the outcomes of interest, and evaluation shifted into a period of increased description. Evaluation results were increasingly used as a means of improving programs (i.e., formative evaluation designed to assist in program development), in contrast to merely providing program to program comparisons (i.e., summative

evaluation designed to determine overall program effectiveness).

Concerns arose regarding the limiting of evaluations solely to the attainment of program goals because little information, if any, was obtained about the interventions themselves. In response to this concern, evaluators began designing social experiments that would open so called black box programs. These approaches were rich in process information and increased the ability to identify specific program components associated with success or failure.

Program context became an important consideration in evaluation designs, as evaluators began to focus on processes and on linking these processes to outcomes. From social experimentation emerged the realization that evaluators could no longer perceive competing political, social, and cultural positions as external barriers that obstruct objective assessment of programs but must recognize that these diverse views constitute the reality within which programs exist and evaluation is conducted and therefore must be incorporated into the evaluation. Recognition that the best answer to an evaluation question was dependent on the perspective from which the problem was viewed increased the status and involvement of all stakeholders in evaluation activities. This period was, and continues to be, heavily influenced by work of Guba and Lincoln (1989) and their conceptualization of fourth generation evaluation.

Role of Consumers and Professionals

Over the years, the roles of consumers and evaluators have evolved from the evaluator as expert and determiner of the evaluation issues to be addressed into a cooperative and collaborative partnership, in which consumers have the same level of input in the evaluation process as do other stakeholders. In the early days of evaluation, input from consumers was nonexistent, and the evaluator determined what to evaluate. This era can be characterized as a period when evaluations were "done to" consumers, as opposed to being "done with" them.

As success began to be assessed in terms of the attainment of prespecified goals, the role of the evaluator was expanded and included the identification of programmatic strengths and weaknesses, with respect to these objectives. The role of consumers, however, remained one of a passive nonparticipant. The movement to understand processes and interventions again broadened the evaluators' role because they were asked to draw conclusions regarding the value of programs. Policymakers and administrators increasingly looked to evaluators for go/no go decisions. For the consumer, however, little changed.

It was not until the reforms associated with fourth generation evaluation principles that consumers were recognized as an important stakeholder in the PE process. It was further realized that consumers probably would have different perspectives from other stakeholders regarding the issues that should be evaluated and that their views were important to incorporate into evaluation efforts. While early evaluation orientations assumed one reality (i.e., that one evaluation issue or question should result in a single answer or recommendation), the assumption underlying fourth generation evaluation recognizes the presence of competing values and multiple realities that are dependent on the perspective from which the problem is viewed. Given this assumption, it became imperative that evaluators involve all stakeholders in the evaluation process, so that the multiple perspectives could be incorporated. The role of the evaluator becomes one of consensus facilitator, responsible for identifying the stakeholders, eliciting and reporting their constructions about the issues to be evaluated, and generating a consensus among the groups. Consumers become empowered as a result of their involvement and are less likely to become disenfranchised or maneuvered into accepting their culpability. Furthermore, consumer involvement increases the likelihood that unanticipated outcomes will be identified.

Commonalities Among Psychiatric Rehabilitation, Quality Assurance, and Program Evaluation

There are several areas of congruence between current events in the fields of QA and PE as they apply to the study of psychiatric rehabilitation. Most important, perhaps, is the recognition that psychiatric rehabilitation is a consumer driven process and that QA and PE efforts must focus on the involvement of consumers as stakeholders in identifying areas for monitoring and evaluation, as providers of data about the process in which they are engaged, and as interpreters of the data. Similarly, QA staff, program staff, and evaluators need to recognize that psychiatric rehabilitation is context specific, and monitoring and evaluation must focus on the process and outcomes of rehabilitation within a given context. This mitigates against the use of global measures of functioning or quality of life and argues for measures of context specific functioning, quality of life, and satisfaction.

It is also essential to recognize that the primary focus of PE and QA efforts is on outcome and that the assessment of quality of care or of client outcome must be conducted over time to capture continuous change. Despite the focus on outcomes, both PE and QA recognize that it is important to examine process in order to understand what produces the outcomes that are observed. Neither QA nor PE supports a black box approach to the study of psychiatric rehabilitation, recognizing that the development of methods to improve outcomes is based on an understanding of what produces the observed outcomes.

Current thinking in the fields of QA and PE favors the use of multiple sources of data to assess the phenomenon under study and to inform policy. Stakeholders are involved in all aspects of the endeavor, from surfacing issues related to quality of care, or effectiveness of interventions, to data collection, analysis, and interpretation. Persons affected by programs are viewed as partners with the evaluator in assessing program structure, process, and outcomes. Obtaining measures of consumer satisfaction and consumers' perceptions about service programs and interventions is an important aspect of all evaluations of psychiatric rehabilitation programs.

A final integrating theme is the emphasis on continuity of effort. Both QA and PE are seen as continuous efforts, sensitive to changes that occur in individuals involved in the rehabilitation process. Activities related to quality improvement and evaluation, therefore, require continual assessment and refinement. All stakeholders must be engaged in this process of assessment, interpretation of findings, and refinement of measures and approaches, if monitoring and evaluation activities are to be maximally useful in decision-making.

Overview of the Heuristic Model

While the commonalities in the QA, PE, and mental health fields suggest a general orientation to studying psychiatric rehabilitation programs, they do not suggest a specific set of domains that may be included in this study or the hypothesized interrelationships among these domains. This specification is essential for making operational a QA/PE effort, in terms of both specifying the areas that should be measured and the relationships among these areas that may contribute to the outcomes of the program. In an effort to provide this integrating structure, a heuristic model for mental health services research was developed at the New York State Office of Mental Health (Evans, 1991; Shern et al., 1992). The model, which is presented in Figure 13.1, is a conceptual framework that organizes the various influences within a mental health services environment that are hypothesized to affect either consumer or service outcomes.

Primary conditions within the model are organizational variables and consumer characteristics, status and environments, and caregiver characteristics that interact to produce or influence other components of the model. These basic elements are essential in descriptive research and in evaluations focused on structure, and they are important aspects in the development of more analytical investigations. Many of the data required to examine these components are often available from existing databases, although special surveys, key informant interviews, and other techniques may be necessary to obtain data of particular interest in any given research study.

Organizational variables comprise auspice (e.g., profit or nonprofit), funding sources, performance incentives governing organizational behavior, stated mission, and structure of the organization. The general structure of the interorganizational environment, particularly as specified in contracts among agencies, is also an important aspect of this class of variables.

Caregiver characteristics include relatively enduring factors, such as demographic characteristics and professional discipline, as well as skills and attitudes, values and beliefs regarding clients with psychiatric disabilities. These latter characteristics may be amenable to change and are often assessed as measures of success in training programs.

Consumer characteristics include variables such as demographic characteristics, clinical status variables, and personal variables. Personal variables might include level of self-esteem and client goals. Notable clinical variables include diagnosis, functional abilities, and symptomatology, while demographic variables include age and/or developmental level, gender, socioeconomic status, education, and social support variables. Consumer characteristics may be broadly interpreted to describe families and other naturally occurring or therapeutically created support groups of which a person is a member; that is, the consumer may be a family with whom a case manager is working or a small group of clients in a self-help group. The *consumer's status and environment* refer to the present living, learning, and working environments and the roles of the individual within those environments.

The second set of variables, service environment and caregiver behavior, is inclusive

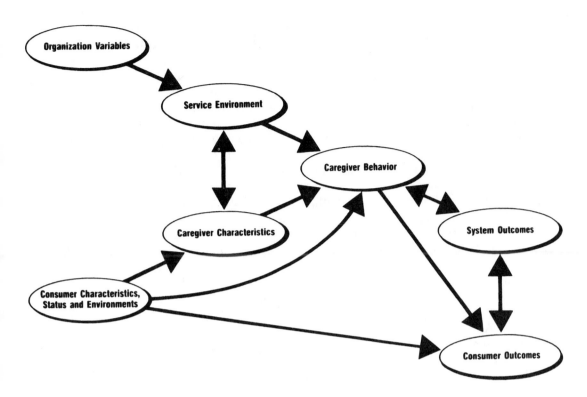

Figure 13.1. Heuristic model for mental health services research.

of those variables most often the focus of process or formative evaluations. Together with the primary conditions, they allow evaluators and researchers to describe who is receiving what kind of care from whom under what conditions. The *service environment* is the cultural setting in which caregivers interact with consumers. It comprises program model (e.g., self-help group, psychosocial club, supported employment program), management policies such as work schedule and staffing, physical environment, atmosphere, and staff training interventions.

Caregiver behavior includes the frequency and duration of caregiver–client contacts, as well as the content of these contacts. Contacts may involve services provided directly to the client or collaterals or advocacy on the part of a client or group of consumers. In psychiatric rehabilitation approaches, much of the caregiver's behavior is focused on working with consumers to develop goals and a plan to meet these goals, which then guides the caregiver's future behaviors.

The final set of variables, system outcomes and consumer outcomes, are the focus of treatment outcome studies. System and consumer outcomes affect each other but represent discrete domains comprising variables that can be measured independently of those existing in the other domain. *System outcomes* focus on the efficiency resulting from a particular intervention or program (e.g., the increase in the number of consumers served in a special employment program as a result of job development activities of program administrators or the increase in number of referrals for a supported housing program, as a result of an educational program offered for local providers of mental health services). System outcomes also include changes in costs or cost effectiveness of services. *Consumer outcomes*, include enhanced functioning; improved quality of life; accomplishment of consumer goals related to living arrangements, employment, or learning; increased self-esteem; and other intended and unintended consequences of the interaction of consumer characteristics, caregiver behavior, and system outcomes.

The model as displayed here indicates some of the hypothesized relationships among the domains. In any particular evaluation or research project, not all domains may be studied and not all possible relationships are investigated; rather, the model is tailored to the project and is based on theory, prior research in the field, and expert judgment.

In general, specifying a model and one or more approaches to an evaluation is useful, in that it helps to bring structure to the evaluation or research project. Models identify the components of the phenomenon under study and indicate the hypothesized relationships among these components, while approaches help to frame the questions and identify sources of data and the means of collecting these data. Any given evaluation may make use of more than one approach; for example, both objective oriented and naturalistic approaches could be used (see Worthen & Sanders, 1987, for a description of approaches to evaluation).

USING THE HEURISTIC MODEL: A REHABILITATIVE CASE STUDY WITH PERSONS WHO ARE HOMELESS AND MENTALLY ILL

A research demonstration program underway in New York City (NYC) is presented to illustrate the use of the heuristic model (Shern, Anthony, & Tsemberis, 1990). The program is an innovative approach to housing, designed specifically for street dwelling persons with serious disability related to mental illness. It reflects the values and technology of psychiatric rehabilitation, emphasizing continuity in the relationships between clients and caregivers, and includes on-site rehabilitation in stable, long-term housing that, to the degree possible, reflects client choice.

A true experimental design is being employed, in which individuals are randomly assigned either to the experimental program or to the control condition that will receive the standard treatment afforded to mentally ill street people. Standard treatment reflects a

program model that is inherently transitional in its approach, including a continuum of care from outreach through drop-in centers to shelters and ultimately long-term housing. Each of these differing points on the continuum may be organizationally independent and informally coordinated. Extensive development of housing for the homeless mentally ill in NYC will increase the access to long-term, permanent housing for both experimental and control clients. Individuals from both groups are being extensively monitored for 12 to 18 months, during which time data are being collected regarding participants' quality of life, housing status, and service utilization. It is hypothesized that this psychiatric rehabilitation intervention with a strong outreach component and enhanced housing availability will be more effective in decreasing homelessness, decreasing inpatient and emergency service utilization, and improving clients' quality of life than will standard treatment.

The logic model that guides this project strongly conforms to the general structure of the heuristic model, although it excludes organizational variables and system outcome variables (See Figure 13.2). As in the heuristic model, the arrows in this logic model represent hypothesized relationships among domains. These potential causal paths are investigated in an integrated evaluative research and QA effort.

In this research demonstration project, the program model is informed by a rehabilitation philosophy that emphasizes the importance of client choice in developing rehabilitation goals. Progress through the program is conceptualized as including four phases: engagement, assessment of survival status with the provision of basic supports, rehabilitation readiness assessment, and rehabilitation. Each of these phases has identified subcomponents that may be used to map progress in the program.

A data system was developed to map this process and to provide the information needed to implement the logic model and to continuously monitor the program. While the data system and major study hypotheses were

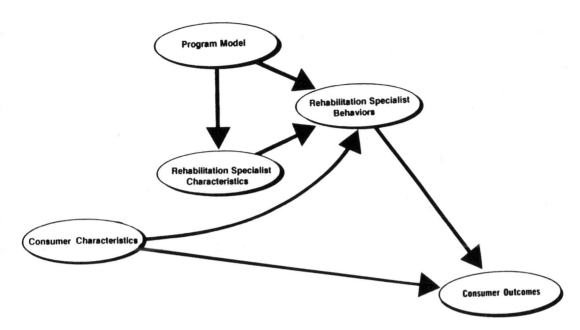

Figure 13.2. Homeless mentally ill program logic model.

developed without the direct input of the ultimate beneficiaries of the program (i.e., homeless, disabled individuals), they were reviewed and approved by an advisory committee that included policymakers, service providers, researchers, and primary consumers of mental health services. Multiple perspectives therefore were represented in selecting the important research questions and in reviewing their implementation.

The data system has four major subcomponents that serve both the evaluative research and the QA functions. Each of these subcomponents are illustrated in Table 13.2. As may be seen from Table 13.2, the data system may be divided into two major areas: data reported directly to interviewers by program clients and data that are routinely collected from the rehabilitation specialists. The interviewer collected data generally involve client outcomes and service utilization that are measured at either 1 month or 6 month intervals, depending on the measures. All data include both provider and client identifiers, thereby enabling client or provider specific description, as well as analyses of the relationships between client and caregiver variables.

Measures focusing on the volume of human services that clients use from both the formal and informal systems of care (e.g., organized clinics through soup kitchens) are collected monthly, to help ensure that accurate service utilization data are obtained. The number of days in differing types of housing (including homelessness) is also assessed, as is involvement with the criminal justice system.

The 6-month client interviews address general areas of client status and living environment, including the identification of client goals and ratings of the degree to which the goals are attained. Objective and subjective quality of life (see Lehman, 1988) in seven major life domains are prominently featured outcomes. Objective quality of life measures assess aspects of the clients' environment and their participation in it. Subjective measures address the clients' satisfaction with their status and participation. Other status measures—such as physical health, alcohol and other drug use, social psychological well being, and mental health symptoms—are also included. A full historical and demographic description is collected at baseline.

Table 13.2 Rehabilitation Program for the Mentally Ill Among the Street Population

Data Source	Client Reported to Research Interviewers		Provider Recorded Data	
Major Content Area	Service Utilization/Housing	Client Goals and Status	Rehabilitation Activities	Client Progress
Frequency of data	Every month	Every 6 months	Continuous	Every Week
Specific examples of content areas involved	Services utilized •Mental health •Health •Dental •Social services •Drug (alcohol) Housing status Legal involvement •Arrests •Victimization •Social/Psychological status	Quality of life (objective and subjective) •Leisure activities •Finances •Family relationships •General social relationships •Safety •Recreation Goal attainment Alcohol and other drug involvement Social/Psychological status •Self-esteem •Mastery Psychiatric symptoms	Activity type •Engagement/outreach •Connecting •Assessing readiness •Goal setting •Functional assessment •Resource assessment (among others) Service location •Program site •Other homeless organizations •Clinical settings (among others) Contact type •Phone •Face to face interview •Group (among others) Contact duration Client fund use	Place client on progress map •Connecting •Survival status •Providing basic support •Rehabilitation readiness •Services use plan •Development of overall rehabilitation goals •Functional assessment •Formulation of rehabilitation plan (among other program stages)

The activities of the rehabilitation specialists are documented through an activity log system. This system captures each contact with clients or collaterals. Activities are classified according to the type of activity (e.g., engagement, assessing readiness, goal setting), the location (e.g., program, street), the type of contact (e.g., face-to-face, telephone), and the duration. Data regarding the expenditure of funds for clients are also included with the activity data. The operation of the program and the implementation of the rehabilitation model are quantitatively summarized with the activity logs that are used for continually monitoring the program activities.

The rehabilitation specialists also complete a weekly rating of client program status which involves placing the client on a map of program progress. This weekly rating provides an easily assessable barometer of the rate at which clients are moving through the program phases.

The measures included in the project data system are used for implementing three domains in the research logic model: client outcomes, client characteristics, and rehabilitation specialist behaviors.[2] The logic model is used for designing the QA and PE activities. Consistent with our overall orientation, the ultimate focus of these activities involves understanding the relationship between client outcomes and the performance of the program.

As a first step in this process, weekly reports are produced, which summarize the program activities both for the overall program and for each of the individual rehabilitation specialists. These reports are useful in describing the variability among the staff in implementing the program and serve to frame discussions regarding the correspondence between caregiver activities and expectations derived from the program model. These quantitative summaries of caregiver activities and the structure provided by the coding

system greatly facilitate discussion of program management and implementation.

A second step in this process involves relating the description of specialist activities to the progress of clients in moving through the program. By summarizing the activity for each client and his or her progress through the program, we not only discover areas in which the data are inadequate to describe specialist activities or client progress but also begin to identify the relationship between the type and intensity of program effort and client outcome. These discussions, therefore, assist us in continuously monitoring the adequacy of the data system and of the program in achieving its objectives.

The interviewer collected data are used in a similar fashion. Due to the frequency with which these data are collected, they are not as immediately available for program monitoring as are the activity and summary progress ratings. Analyses of the interviewer data proceed in much the same manner as the weekly progress ratings, except that the multiple outcome measures provide a more detailed description of client status and satisfaction than the summary rating. While the summary ratings may be used both to monitor activity on a specific case and to evaluate the study's overall strategy, the interviewer collected data are primarily useful for evaluating and modifying the overall strategy. Although not discussed in this example, data from control subjects are also available and will be extremely helpful in assessing the success of the program in meeting its primary objectives. When coupled with the information regarding the relationship between caregiver behavior and client outcome, these data are very useful in identifying the components of the model that most directly affect outcome. In these analyses, multivariate controls are used both to assess the direct effect of client characteristics/environments on client outcomes and to investigate their indirect impact on outcomes moderated through the specialist behavior.

This example illustrates how the heuristic model can guide the study of psychiatric rehabilitation programs. The approach taken

---

[2]Data are also collected that measure rehabilitation specialist characteristics, but they are omitted from this discussion.

in this study is consistent with the earlier discussion of the major features of contemporary QA, PE, and public mental health policy.

Summary

The common themes that characterize recent reforms in mental health treatment, QA, and PE have been identified and discussed in this chapter. The strong parallels among the developments in these fields included their general orientation, as well as their conceptualization and treatment of consumer and professional roles. These developments represent important reforms that should be incorporated into QA and evaluation of rehabilitation programs.

While these common themes suggest a general orientation to studying psychiatric rehabilitation programs, they fail to identify the specific domains that might be examined or the hypothesized interrelationships among the domains. Because the specification of these domains and their interrelationships is necessary to make operational QA and PE activities, a heuristic model for mental health services research was presented. This model organizes the domains within a psychiatric rehabilitation services environment and suggests their hypothesized relationships.

The chapter concluded with an example of a research and demonstration project examining the effects of providing psychiatric rehabilitation to homeless persons with psychiatric disabilities. This project represents contemporary themes in QA, PE, and public mental health policy. It includes multiple stakeholders in the development of the program model and evaluative research design and a relatively comprehensive explanatory model inclusive of client, program, and contextual variables. These variables are conceptually consistent with the heuristic model and were operationalized through a data system that provides timely information on both the implementation of the program, and its outcomes. In addition to weekly data, more detailed client interview information on both experimental and control subjects is used to understand the interrelationships of client and program data in producing client outcomes. Stakeholders will be involved throughout the analysis to inform the evaluator's interpretation of the data. An integrated approach to QA and PE, therefore, results in a data system that is useful both for the continuous improvement of program outcomes and for enhancing our general understanding of the effectiveness of rehabilitation for this subject population.

References

Appel, F. (1991). From QA to QI: The joint commission and the new quality paradigm. *Journal of Quality Assurance, 13*, 26–29.

Berwick, D. (1989). Continuous improvement as an ideal in health care. *New England Journal of Medicine, 820*, 53–56.

Brook, R. H., Avery, A. D., Greenfield, S., Harris, J. L., & Lelah, T. (1976). *Quality of medical care assessment using outcome measures: An overview of the method* (R-2021/1-HEW). Santa Monica, CA: The Rand Corporation.

Donabedian, A. (1988). The quality of care. How can it be assessed? *Journal of the American Medical Association, 260*, 1743–1748.

Evans, M. E. (1991). Working smarter: The use of priorities and a model in designing nursing research. *The Journal of the New York State Nurses Association, 22*(3), 4–7.

Flexner, A. (1910). *Medical education in the United States and Canada* (Bulletin 4). New York: Carnegie Foundation for the Advancement of Teaching.

Guba, E. G., & Lincoln, Y. S. (1989). *Fourth generation evaluation.* Newberry Park, CA: Sage Publications.

Joint Commission on Accreditation for Healthcare Organizations (1991). *Transition from QA to QI: An introduction to quality improvement in health care.* Oakbrook Terrace, IL: Author.

Joint Commission on Accreditation for Healthcare Organizations (1992). *Accreditation manual for hospitals.* Oakbrook Terrace, IL: Author.

Lehman, A. F. (1988). A quality of life interview for the chronically mentally ill. *Evaluation and Program Planning, 11*, 1–12.

Lohr, K. N. (Ed.). (1990). *Medicare: A strategy for quality assurance* (Vol. 1). Washington, DC: Institute of Medicine, National Academy Press.

Madaus, G. F., Scriven, M., & Stufflebeam, D. L. (1987). *Evaluation models: Viewpoints from educational and human services evaluation.* Boston, MA: Kluwer-Nijhoff Publishing.

Morrissey, J. P., & Goldman, H. H. (1984). Cycles of reform in the care of the chronically mentally ill. *Hospital and Community Psychiatry, 35,* 785–793.

Shern, D. L., Anthony, W. A., & Tsemberis, S. (1990). *Housing homeless mentally ill street people: A rehabilitation approach* (NIMH Research Demonstration). Unpublished manuscript, Bureau of Evaluation and Services Research, New York State Office of Mental Health, Albany, New York.

Shern, D. L., Evans, M. E., & Veysey, B. M. (1992). Human resource, program and client correlates of mental health outcomes. In W. Jacobson, S. N. Burchard, & P. J. Carling (Eds.), *Community living for people with developmental and psychiatric disabilities,* (pp. 263–283). Baltimore: Johns Hopkins Press.

Shern, D. L., Surles, R. C., & Waizer, J. (1989). Designing community treatment systems for the most seriously mentally ill: A state administrative perspective. *Journal of Social Issues, 45,* 105–117.

Surles, R. C., Blanch, A. K., Shern, D. L., & Donahue, S. A. (1992). Case management as a strategy for systems change. *Health Affairs, 11*(1), 151–163.

Test, M. A. (1984). Community support programs. In A. S. Bellack (Ed.), *Schizophrenia: Treatment management and rehabilitation.* Orange, FL: Grune & Stratton.

Walton, M. (1986). *The Deming management method.* New York: Perigee Books.

Williams, K. N., & Brook, R. H. (1978). Quality measurement and assurance: A literature review. *Health and Medical Core Services Review, 3,* 3–15.

Worthen, B. R., & Sanders, J. R. (1987). *Educational evaluation: Alternative approaches and practical guidelines.* New York: Longman.

Chapter 14

Forensic Issues in Rehabilitation and Mental Health

A. ANTHONY ARCE
MILES C. LADENHEIM

Since the 1960s, the delivery of mental health services and the limits of professional practice have been increasingly shaped and defined by legislative statutes, legal decisions, and administrative regulations. In the wake of the civil liberties movement, attention was focused on the problems and abuses of persons with severe mental disabilities who were housed in institutions, and efforts were directed toward redressing past injustices. Civil libertarians argued that these persons were being deprived of their civil liberties by being confined to what was essentially a jail, without due process. Furthermore, in many instances, these unjustified incarcerations lasted a lifetime when, in fact, no crime had been committed. Coincident with these developments, the evolution of the community mental health ideology led to a shift in the locus of care from institutional to non-hospital-based treatment alternatives. Spurred on by court decisions, state legislatures revised mental health laws and enacted statutes requiring that the mentally disabled be served in the "least restrictive alternative," thus provoking additional legal challenges to clinical decision making.

While clinical practice, be it mental health or psychiatric rehabilitation, must rest on the possession of a reasonably thorough knowledge base and a requisite set of skills and techniques, the actual delivery of care to the individual patient requires the exercise of professional judgment to achieve a proper fit to patient needs. As third-party payors and other regulatory agencies invade the therapeutic process, the clinician's control (i.e., the exercise of professional judgment) becomes severely limited or compromised. Legal and bureaucratic rigidities do not often allow for the most efficient or effective ways of dealing with the various crises and emergencies that arise in the course of the care of these persons with mental disabilities. Flexibility in approach is constrained by the need to abide by rigid rules and regulations imposed by federal, state, and local governments in order to comply with legislative mandates and court decisions. In order to function effectively in the patient's best interests, today's clinician must learn and understand the rules by which the mental health care system operates at its interface with the law.

The adjective *forensic*, derived from the Latin *forum*, meaning "public debate," is defined as "pertaining to, connected with, or used in courts of law." *Forensic or legal psychiatry* refers to the clinical–legal interface where clinical concepts and practice overlap with legal concepts and procedures. The field encompasses issues that arise in both civil and criminal proceedings.

From the civil perspective, the regulation

of involuntary hospital commitments served as the springboard for courts and legislatures to intervene in many areas of clinical practice. The right to treatment, the right to refuse treatment, the duty to warn, the securing of informed consent, standards of care, and professional liability are but a few of the issues of civil forensic interest to the practicing clinician. Many of these issues are far from being satisfactorily or universally resolved, in a legal sense, because their application is subject to interpretation by state and federal jurisdictions. For instance, the right to refuse medication, one of the most litigated civil rights issues in the care of mentally disabled persons, has been the subject of numerous federal and state decisions, and there is still no overall legal consensus.

This chapter summarizes the salient civil forensic issues with which mental health service providers should be familiar, to facilitate their interactions with patients, families, employers, and other service providers. These issues include involuntary commitment, both inpatient and outpatient; the right to treatment and the right to refuse treatment; competency, consent, and confidentiality; the duty to warn; and professional liability. The discussion focuses on the management of adult patients who are not subjects of the criminal justice system. Issues involved in criminal proceedings, such as pretrial examinations, criminal responsibility, probation, and parole are not addressed. Similarly, specific forensic issues concerning minors, such as—among others—custody, parental rights, treatment, and emancipation, are beyond the scope of this chapter.

Readers must bear in mind that the aim of this chapter is to present a conceptual framework to facilitate an understanding of the issues involved. As already stated, because the laws governing the application of these principles vary from state to state, it is not possible to discuss the specific provisions of each individual state's applicable statutes. Readers are advised to seek information specific to their respective states from their agency's legal counsel or the state's office of mental health. The authors have appended a series of selected references that provide additional relevant information.

Competency and Consent: Overview

The law of informed consent derives from the law of battery. "Every human being of adult years *and sound mind* has a right to determine what should be done with his own body; and a surgeon who performs an operation without his patient's consent commits an assault and battery for which he is liable in damages" (emphasis added; *Schloendorff v. Society of New York Hospital*, 1914).

This doctrine has a specific requirement that in order to give consent (and, implicitly, to withhold consent), an individual must be "of sound mind." It was this requirement that allowed the historical exemption from the informed consent requirement as applied to psychiatric inpatients, on the reasoning that a psychiatric inpatient was presumed incompetent. In other words, once admitted to a psychiatric facility, a person was given whatever treatment was ordered by the facility staff without informing the person in advance of the nature of the treatment and without regard for the person's wishes.

This presumption has been turned on its head since the 1960s. The evolution began with a challenge to the status of voluntary inpatients who were henceforth to be presumed *competent* until and unless a formal adjudication of incompetency was made. This is now generally accepted law in all states.

The more controversial development occurred in the wrangling over the status of *involuntarily committed patients*. In cases brought by civil libertarian lawyers beginning in the late 1970s, courts began to hold that even *involuntarily* committed patients retained all their presumption of competency, including the right to withhold consent to psychotropic medication. This area is still in legal flux and is addressed in more detail in a later section of this chapter.

Competency

Competency refers to the present mental ability to enter into a decision or transaction. Competency (or incompetency) is never defined globally. Someone is not said to be either competent or incompetent; rather, it is defined only in relation to a specific action (e.g., competent to stand trial, competent to make a will, competent to consent to experimental surgery, competent to handle personal funds and property). The presumption is in favor of competency; that is, every adult is presumed to be competent until proven otherwise. Furthermore, incompetency is a *legal* determination, *not* a medical one. Although mental health professionals are frequently called on to render opinions about present competency or incompetency, only a judge can officially find someone to be incompetent.

The necessary elements for competency vary with the circumstances. In general, in order to be competent to make a given decision or transact a certain action, a patient must understand and appreciate the nature and consequences of what they are deciding or doing. The *understanding* component is cognitive; the *appreciation* component involves both an emotional aspect and a requirement for rational thought manipulation. An analogy to this dichotomy can be found in the everyday experience of buying a car: "Understanding" would require that the buyer know what he or she is buying, and how much is being paid; "appreciation" would require that the buyer also be able to articulate a rational or reasonable reason for buying the car, be familiar with the various "pros and cons" of the purchase (risk/benefit analysis), and also have some sense of any possible alternatives to this particular purchase.

Understanding may be impaired by intellectual or organic deficits, innate or acquired, such as developmental disabilities or severe brain damage, while appreciation may be impaired by depression, mania, or a thought disorder. For example, a depressed person may not care about the consequences of his or her decisions. A grandiose individual may likewise be unable rationally to consider any consequences of his or her decisions or may overstate the possible benefits, while a paranoid individual may overstate possible risks. In all of the foregoing examples, a finding of competency is not warranted.

Clinicians are most often asked to render an opinion on the person's *civil competency*—that is, their capacity to manage their own affairs. This requires an assessment of the person's *understanding* of the source and extent of their property or income and an *appreciation* of how such property or income must be managed to meet the person's basic needs (shelter, food, clothing, health care, etc.).

Competency to stand trial requires that the defendant demonstrate an understanding of (1) the nature of the charge, (2) the relative seriousness of the charge, (3) the titles and roles of the principals in the courtroom (i.e., judge, jury, prosecutor, etc.), (4) the possible outcomes and consequences of the trial or hearing (e.g., relationship of the sentence to a guilty or not guilty finding), (5) the behavior expected of the defendant in the courtroom; and (6) the ability to cooperate with counsel in preparing the defense. The first four test the cognitive component, and the last two test impulse control and thought processes (e.g., paranoia), respectively.

Testamentary capacity or competency to make a will requires that the person *know* (1) the general extent and nature of his or her bounty (wealth) and (2) who his or her natural heirs are (the testator does not have to give anything to the heirs, but just has to know who they are).

Consent to Treatment

Except in an emergency, all voluntary patients (and some involuntary patients) *must* give their *informed consent* before treatment can be given. Courts have debated the exact meaning and scope of "informed consent." It is clear, however, that a patient must be informed of the nature of the illness or problem giving rise to the need for treatment, the proposed course of treatment, alternatives to treatment, risks and benefits of the proposed treatment(s), and the risks of not receiving treatment at all. Generally, a patient is given some version of a consent to treatment form to sign when he or she begins treatment in either an inpatient or outpatient setting. Some facilities also require a similar form before routine psychotropic medications are prescribed.

In order for informed consent to be valid, it must also be a *competent* (understanding and appreciation) consent. There is nothing magically legal in obtaining a patient's signature on the bottom line. The patient's signature is only meaningful if he or she *understood and appreciated* the printed form that is being signed—that is, understood and appreciated all the necessary elements to give a competent consent. In this sense, a written signature is really nothing more than a written memorial that informed consent has already been orally given by the patient, after a consideration by the patient of the indications, risks, benefits, and alternatives to the proposed action or decision. Therefore, whenever a patient signs a form, a progress note should also be entered, giving details that the patient did indeed give consent to the proposed decision or action. The printed form is now memorializing this consent in writing.

In *Zinermon v. Burch* (1990), it was held that a patient must be competent *even to voluntarily sign into a psychiatric hospital.* This opinion was based on a theory that entrance into a psychiatric hospital, even voluntarily, involves some kind of deprivation of liberty, and that someone who is not able to understand and appreciate the elements of informed consent is *not competent* to waive his liberty (even if they clinically need treatment!). Rather, the Supreme Court stated, it would be preferable in that instance to institute involuntary proceedings (as this would afford the patient the procedural protections of a hearing, access to a lawyer, etc.) or petition a court for a guardianship appointment (an expensive and time-consuming process).

This leaves the question, What should be done in those instances when a seemingly incompetent patient wishes to sign into a hospital, there are no grounds for involuntary commitment, and guardianship proceedings are not feasible? The authors suggest the following approach: Have the patient and his or her closest available support person *both* sign the voluntary admission form. This satisfies the only two possible conditions of competency—if the patient is competent, he or she has validly signed him- or herself in; if the patient were to have been legally adjudicated as incompetent in a hypothetical court proceeding, however, and a guardian appointed, it would probably be the closest available support person who would be appointed as guardian. This person has already signed the form, thereby protecting the patient's rights even if incompetent (remember that formal incompetency can only be declared by a judge, not by a doctor). This is a mechanism that is recommended *whenever* a patient whose competency is in doubt wishes to assent to or decline a proposed treatment (e.g., continuing neuroleptic medications in the face of possible tardive dyskinesia).

Voluntary Treatment

Any person can apply for treatment of mental illness or alleviation of psychiatric symptoms, of their own free will, in an outpatient or inpatient facility. The applicant must sign the applicable consent to treatment form for outpatient care, or application for voluntary hospitalization for inpatient care. Voluntary treatment on an outpatient basis is not regulated by mental health laws, but service providers must be licensed under the applicable state statutes, either as private practitioners or as mental health agencies.

In order to practice their respective professions, whether independently or in an agency, mental health clinicians must have met the educational requirements of their respective disciplines and have passed the required state licensing examination. The treatment of patients in private practice is regulated by the scope of practice, as defined by the licensing statute and the professional code of ethics. It is generally assumed that consent to treatment has been tacitly granted when a person voluntarily seeks treatment from a private practitioner. Nevertheless, independent practitioners are held accountable for being familiar with the laws protecting the patient's civil rights (e.g., obtaining informed consent for the administration of medication, the confidentiality of treatment records). In most states, licenses must be renewed periodically.

Agencies providing mental health services must also be licensed annually by the appropriate state agency, most often the state's department of either health or mental health. Agencies are required to submit evidence of written policies and procedures that implement the rules and regulations promulgated by the licensing agency, including provisions for the protection of individual civil rights. Agency operations are more heavily regulated and monitored than is private practice. Generally, there are specific requirements for admission and discharge, evaluations or assessments, treatment planning, staffing patterns, record keeping, supervision, and so on. Most agencies require that a printed consent-to-treatment form be signed by the patient prior to initiating services.

A person seeking admission to a psychiatric facility must sign an application for voluntary hospitalization, which must describe the proposed treatment and must state that the applicant will be discharged on written request. This is required by legislative statute in every state. If permitted by law, the application may state that the facility may detain the individual for up to a certain maximum number of hours, after written request is made, before granting discharge. This latter provision allows the medical staff to initiate involuntary commitment if the patient meets applicable standards (usually dangerousness to self or others).

Involuntary Commitment of Inpatients

Origins of Involuntary Commitment

The regulation of hospital care for the mentally disabled population originated in the middle of the nineteenth century, with the development of state-run hospitals. Prior to that time, mentally disabled individuals were, for the most part, confined in jails or almshouses. Because there were no laws governing hospitalization, admission to the few quasi-public institutions that existed (Williamsburg Asylum, Pennsylvania Hospital) was arranged by families on behalf of the patient. As states assumed the responsibility for the care of mentally disabled individuals, enabling legislation was required, to justify the need for commitment and the expenditure of public funds. There was little concern for the rights of these patients because the prevailing wisdom held that "moral treatment"—that is, humane care in an asylum—would restore the patient to sanity.

Up to the middle of the twentieth century, laws governing the involuntary hospitalization (civil commitment) of individuals who were mentally ill attempted to meet the needs of either the state's *parens patriae* function (literally, "parent of his country," which refers to the historical duty of the king, or state, to care for those with disability) or the state's *police powers* function (to ensure public safety and civil order). The ostensible substantive criterion for involuntary confinement was the presence of mental illness for which treatment was indicated. Usually, only the opinion of one, or at most two, psychiatrists was necessary for a commitment. However, as the civil liberties movement gathered momentum in the 1960s, involuntary confinement, even on the grounds of "need for treatment," began to be perceived as an unwarranted deprivation of civil rights and unjustified under the *parens patriae* concept.

Concept of Dangerousness

By the end of the 1960s, the concept of dangerousness as the sole grounds for involuntary commitment had gained ascendancy, with California being the first state to pass enabling legislation. Since then, every state has revised its commitment law to conform to the dangerousness standard, which holds that involuntary commitment is justified only for persons who are dangerous to themselves or others.

The specific behaviors that constitute the legal standard of dangerousness to self or others generally include suicidality, self-mutilation, homicidality, and assaultiveness with the infliction of physical harm. In most states, the expression of suicidal or homicidal ideas or threats and the observation of behaviors in furtherance of such ideas or threats within stipulated time limits (usually the previous 30 days) constitute sufficient justification for the initiation of commitment procedures.

The majority of states also provide for involuntary commitment of individuals who are so "gravely disabled" as to be unable to meet minimal survival needs (i.e., inability to perform activities of daily living). However, the interpretation of "gravely disabled" varies from state to state and even among jurisdictions within a given state.

Procedures for Involuntary Commitment

The procedures for carrying out involuntary commitments are stipulated in state laws. Usually, certain persons—such as family members, friends, law enforcement personnel, mental health professionals, or others as stipulated—must file a petition describing the behaviors that they have personally witnessed and that justify involuntary hospitalization. In most circumstances, a formal court hearing must be carried out, in which it is established that the person is mentally ill and dangerous to self and/or others.

At the hearing, the interests of the state are represented by appropriately designated personnel, and expert testimony from medical personnel is presented. A panoply of due process protections is granted to the patient at the mental health court hearing. These include the patient's legal right to contest the petition and to be represented by legal counsel who cross-examines both the petitioners and the expert witnesses.

If the court finds that the evidence supports the petition, the patient is committed to a hospital for a specified period of time stipulated in the law. Continued retention of the patient in the hospital beyond the initial period requires periodic court review at intervals specified in the respective state statute. Each new court hearing is held on the hospital's petition for continued retention. When the patient has recovered from the illness, discharge from the hospital follows on medical recommendation without further judicial intervention. If at any step in the foregoing process, the court finds that the petition has no merit, the patient is discharged forthwith or committed to outpatient treatment if that is an option.

Finally, a person who has been committed and believes that such commitment is unjustified also has the right to file a petition for a writ of habeas corpus, which must be heard by the court at once. This last procedure is rarely used because the relatively short-term commitment lengths that are currently ordered under mental health laws afford frequent recommitment hearings and, hence, frequent chances for a patient to challenge his or her commitment.

Despite the apparent acceptance of the dangerousness standard by most courts, many questions concerning substantive and procedural issues remain unanswered and constitute fertile ground for future litigation. The dangerousness standard has been criticized on both counts: From the substantive perspective, concerns have been expressed about the unreliability of clinicians in predicting future dangerous behavior and about the criminalization of the mental health care system by assigning to it police functions; in addition, the restriction of involuntary commitment only to those who are considered dangerous leaves unattended a large number of seriously mentally ill individuals who are in need of care. From the procedural point of view, the standard has been criticized for the often adversarial nature of the proceedings, more akin to a criminal than a civil trial, which may undermine the therapist–patient relationship.

Clinical Assessment of Dangerousness

The most significant challenge posed by current civil commitment statutes to the clinician actively engaged in direct patient care is the assessment of patients for committability on the basis of dangerousness, in spite of amply supported observations that a clinicians' accuracy in predicting future violence to self or others is no better than the average person's. Numerous empirical studies (e.g., Roy, 1982) have verified that the most valid predictor of future dangerousness (to self or others) is a history of previous suicidal or violent behavior (which often is disallowed as "irrelevant testimony" in mental health court). Beyond that, a number of other demographic factors have been correlated with a higher than average prevalence of violent behavior. Age in late teens and early twenties, male gender, black race, lower socioeconomic class, history of alcohol or other drug abuse, low scores on standardized intelligence tests, and residential or occupational instability are among the factors mentioned by Monahan (1981).

Gutheil and Applebaum (1982) suggest that an analysis of environmental factors is advisable because violence is often situationally determined. They conceptualize environmental issues as "risk factors" and "resource factors," which are in turn subdivided into "external" and "internal." *External risk factors* include the loss of significant objects (e.g., spouse, therapist) or of supports (e.g., job, housing); the more acute the losses, the greater the risk they represent. *Internal risk factors* include any conditions that would reduce impulse control such as alcohol or other drug use, cognitive disability, or organic illnesses. *External resource factors* include the availability of personal supports (e.g., family, friends) and of specialized resources (e.g., social agencies, residential alternatives). *Internal resource factors* include such personal strengths or assets as interpersonal skills, social competence, flexible psychological defenses, educational achievement, or occupational stability. The presence or absence of these factors must then be balanced to achieve an overall assessment of the likelihood of violence. The authors conclude that this process is more art than science and will result in many incorrect predictions, but it is the best we currently have. The same process is applicable to the prediction of suicidality, utilizing in addition, the risk/rescue rating system suggested by Weissman and Worden (1972).

One rehabilitation-oriented model for the assessment of committability on the basis of "grave disability" in most ambulatory patients is based on a detailed review of the patient's current level of functioning in managing the tasks of daily living in spite of continuing evidence of active psychopathology, combined with an assessment of existing or potential environmental supports (Wilbert et al., 1976).

Preservation of the Therapeutic Alliance

A second challenge posed by commitment laws is the preservation of the therapeutic alliance in the face of the coercive nature of the commitment process. The basic element of a therapeutic relationship is trust. Assigning to the professional a role that is likely to be perceived by the patient as punitive rather than helpful has the potential for undermining trust and—thus—the relationship. However, studies of patients following voluntary and involuntary treatment found no difference in satisfaction with the outcome of hospitalization (Spensley, Edwards, & White, 1980). In retrospect, most patients were appreciative of the care received.

The experience of the vast majority of clinicians has shown that patients are appreciative of interventions that provide external controls. The authors' experience is that the potential for disruption in the therapist–patient relationship is minimized by the participation of the patient in the process. A forthright approach in explaining the rationale for the recommendation for hospitalization and honest responses to the patient's questions will foster the patient's continuing trust and strengthen the foundation of the therapeutic alliance. It has also been the authors' experience, however, that in some cases, this apparently coercive nature serves to allow the severely regressed patient to maintain the outward denial of illness (which may be needed as an intrapsychic protective mechanism) while still enabling the patient to get the treatment that, on some level, the patient knows is needed.

Involuntary Commitment of Outpatients

Since the advent of deinstitutionalization and the shift in the locus of care for mentally ill individuals from the hospital to the community, it has become clear that a sizable number of patients fail to participate in voluntary outpatient treatment. Many patients never follow up on their first outpatient appointment following discharge from the hospital and, of those who do, a large number drop out of treatment after a few visits. In addition, as pointed out before, the restriction of involuntary hospitalization to those persons who are considered to be dangerous has left a large number of chronically mentally ill patients bereft of needed hospital care. As a result, mental health professionals are confronted with a population of chronic patients who consistently refuse treatment—chiefly medication—and whose lives alternate between decompensation in the community and rehospitalization. Even while in the community, the level of functioning of these patients is so compromised that they cannot maintain a stable residential address, obtain financial benefits, and develop appropriate supports. The problem of providing a positive service approach to these challenging patients has fostered consideration of involuntary outpatient commitment as a possible strategy. The term *involuntary outpatient commitment* is often used generically to denote three different approaches to the concept: *as conditional release, as substitute for confinement*, and *as preventive commitment*.

Conditional Release Model

The conditional release model, also referred to as "trial visit," "parole," or "furlough," has been statutorily available in most states for many years and is analogous to parole in the criminal justice system. When involuntarily committed patients were considered to be fit for release, they were often placed on trial visit status, rather than discharged outright, on condition that the patient comply with certain requirements, usually follow up visits at a local aftercare clinic and continuation of medication. Because the patient continued to be carried on the hospital rolls, the hospital superintendent had the authority to order the patient's rehospitalization without a formal hearing. Such trial visits lasted for varying periods of time, after which the patient could be unconditionally discharged.

Although available in most states, a survey of state mental health program directors and attorneys revealed that most were ignorant of the existence of these statutes, and most indicated that the model was used in less than 5% of cases (Miller, 1985). In recent years, conditional release has fallen into disuse because of the lack of procedural options to deal with noncompliant patients. In addition, a number of courts have held that revocation of outpatient status deprives the patient of liberty, thus requiring judicial review and evidence of dangerousness before rehospitalization can be allowed.

Substitute for Confinement Model

The substitute for confinement model is a disposition based on the "least restrictive alternative" and is ordered by the court at a civil commitment hearing that permits the patient to remain in the community *undergoing treatment* in lieu of hospitalization. It is analogous to probation in the criminal justice system. The decision often follows a compromise between the parties involved (the state solicitor and the defense attorney) when the evidence for dangerousness is unconvincing, but there is a clear need for treatment. Although ordered by a court, enforcement has been problematic because of the lack of procedural options in cases of noncompliance. One option is to cite the patient with contempt, but in one case, a Florida appellate court reversed a trial court decision ruling that noncompliance with court-ordered outpatient treatment did not demonstrate "contemptuous intent" (*C.N. v. State*, 1983).

Preventive Commitment Model

The preventive commitment model is akin to the substitute for confinement model, in that it is also a court disposition, is based on the least restrictive alternative, and is intended for individuals who do not meet the statutory standard for involuntary hospitalization but need treatment. Its purpose is to prevent predictable deterioration of a person's mental condition that will eventually lead to inpatient commitment. It is administered under a lower commitment standard and fewer procedural protections.

To date, only a few states have enacted statutes that allow preventive commitment. All such existing statutes share the following criteria: the presence of mental illness; in the absence of treatment, the individual will soon meet the standards for institutionalization; and the mental illness prevents voluntary treatment. Each state may also have additional requirements. For instance, North Carolina requires a finding that the person is capable of surviving safely in the community with the help of friends, family, or others; and Hawaii requires a reasonable prospect that the treatment will be beneficial. Both North Carolina and Georgia require that a determination be made that treatment is, in fact, available before a commitment is made (Stefan, 1987).

Due Process Protections

Procedures for implementing the laws also vary from state to state, but, in general, there are fewer safeguards for outpatient than for inpatient commitment. After a clinical determination, a court hearing within a stipulated time period, which may vary from 10 days to as long as 6 weeks, is required. In many states, due process protections are generally less stringent with the rights to counsel and to confront and cross-examine. Statutes also define outpatient treatment broadly to include medication, therapy, partial hospitalization, supervision of living arrangements, and case management services.

Research Findings

A number of empirical studies indicate that preventive commitment is a problematic option in treating severely mentally disabled persons (Bursten, 1986; Miller & Fiddleman, 1984). Miller and Fiddleman studied the North Carolina program and found that involuntary outpatient commitment was most successful with patients who needed medication. However, the program in general lacked success for the following reasons: the disinclination of clinicians to treat unwilling patients; the inappropriate use by the judges of outpatient commitment, ordering it even against the recommendation of clinicians; the variability of social supports; and the high cost of monitoring and treating such patients. On the other hand, favorable reports have also been published (Geller, 1986; Hiday & Goodman, 1982; Hiday & Scheid-Cook, 1987), which indicate that the major factor in the success of these programs is the active participation of clinicians in the system.

From the legal perspective, preventive commitment raises questions about the erosion of the civil rights of mental patients at the risk of failing to provide needed treatment. However problematic its complexities, it may be worth pursuing in the continuing struggle to design a system that is sensitive to both the needs and the rights of mentally disabled persons.

Right to Treatment

The concept of a federal constitutionally guaranteed right to treatment is of theoretical interest only, as clinicians working in psychosocial agencies are mandated to follow state and county regulations in providing treatment. The idea that there was a quid pro quo implicit in an involuntary commitment—that the only reason the state could confine someone to a mental hospital against his will was to provide that treatment necessary to allow them to eventually be released—first arose in a 1960 article by Birnbaum. Courts thereafter began to endorse this concept, in particular the U.S. Court of Appeals for the District of Columbia circuit (Ro*use v. Cameron*) in 1966, and the U.S. Court of Appeals for the Fifth Circuit in the early 1970s in *Wyatt v. Stickney* (which set out minimum standards of care required in the Alabama state hospital system). This emerging right to treatment, however, was more narrowly defined by the U.S. Supreme Court in 1975, in *O'Connor v. Donaldson*. That case concerned a nondangerous but mentally ill patient who had been involuntarily hospitalized for years in the Florida State Hospital, and who had only received *custodial* care. The Supreme Court declined to find an unconditional right to active treatment for any involuntary patient but instead held that any *nondangerous*, involuntary patient, who could otherwise survive safely in the community with the help of family or friends, must be given active treatment (not just custodial care) if hospitalized. On the other hand, a *dangerous* involuntary patient only had a constitutional right to custodial care, although a state could, of course, require more.

There has never been a Supreme Court decision guaranteeing a right to treatment for *voluntary* patients. In a 1982 case concerning a developmentally disabled patient (*Youngberg v. Romeo*), the U.S. Supreme Court tackled the issue of seclusion and restraints. It held that in general, a patient had a qualified right to be free of seclusion and restraints, and that this qualified right afforded that they could only be placed in seclusion or restraints upon the exercise of *appropriate professional judgment* (hence, the need for a physician's order when someone is placed in seclusion or restraints). Furthermore, the Court held that a

developmentally disabled patient *was* entitled to whatever "treatment and habilitation" was needed so that he or she could learn how to stay out of seclusion and restraints. However, defining the extent of this necessary treatment and habilitation was similarly left to the discretion of appropriate professional judgment. The concept of a right to treatment is one cornerstone of all other substantive patient rights that have evolved in the past three decades.

Right to Refuse Treatment

The concept of professional judgment has also figured in the right-to-*refuse*-treatment cases of the past decade. Whereas previously we were concerned with whether a patient could be forced into a hospital (in discussing commitment laws), here we are concerned with whether a patient can still refuse treatment even after being committed to a mental hospital. Unlike the right-to-treatment issue, the right to refuse treatment *does* have practical consequences for both patients and health care providers.

The old rule of law stated that once a patient was committed to a mental hospital, he or she was presumed incompetent to make decisions about psychiatric treatment and, hence, could not refuse the recommended treatment modalities, including medications. In this respect, psychiatric treatment was exempted from the informed consent requirements that had applied to medical/surgical treatment since the turn of the century.

Litigation concerning psychiatric treatment has historically focused on three broad categories: psychosurgery, electroconvulsive therapy (ECT), and psychotropic medications. Psychosurgery is no longer generally practiced, and a consensus has been reached by courts concerning ECT, in that the informed consent model has generally been applied. ECT can be given to a competent patient who has given informed consent but can be given to a nonconsenting patient only after he or she has been legally adjudicated (i.e. by a judge) as incompetent, a guardian or surrogate decision-maker has been appointed, and the guardian has then given consent.

Cases began to appear in the late 1970s concerning whether an involuntary patient could refuse medications, and this issue has now been decided by many state and federal courts. Opinions on this question have generally split into one of two categories: (1) those that mandate a formal, two-step judicial process similar to that described for ECT, and (2) those that say that medication refusal is a clinical event, not a legal event, and therefore only requires an informal, administrative/consultative process, as sufficient in satisfying due process requirements. These latter decisions rely on the professional judgment standard: As long as the decision to medicate is made by the appropriate professional, the patient's rights have been protected. Applebaum (1988) has referred to these two models as "rights-driven" and "treatment-driven," in describing the selected emphasis that is placed.

Examples of the two-step judicial process (the rights-driven model) can be found in Massachusetts and New York. In order to override an involuntary patient's medication refusal, the patient must first be declared incompetent *by a court* (the first step), and then a "substituted judgment" must be made by the court (the second step) in which the judge decides whether the patient him- or herself would have chosen to receive the medication, if he or she were competent. This is the current trend in those *state courts* that have been deciding cases of this nature based on state law, rather than federal law.

An example of the administrative/consultative process (the "treatment-driven" model) can be found in Pennsylvania. In order to override an involuntary patient's medication refusal, the treating psychiatrist must obtain a second opinion from a colleague, who makes an independent review of the medical record and interviews the patient. If the second psychiatrist concurs with the decision to medicate, the patient can then be medicated against his or her will. If the second psychiatrist disagrees, then a third psychiatrist's opinion is obtained, who gives the tie-breaking vote. If the third

psychiatrist agrees with the decision to medicate, then the patient can be medicated against the patient's will. If the third psychiatrist should also disagree with the decision to medicate, however, the patient cannot be medicated against the patient's will without invoking yet another procedure. The central concept in the administrative/consultative process is that a judicial hearing is *not necessary*. No formal or judicial adjudication of incompetency is required, and the decision as to whether to override a medication refusal is treated as a clinical issue, rather than a legal issue. This is the current trend in decisions of *federal courts*, including the Supreme Court, that have been hearing and deciding cases of this nature based on federal law, rather than state law.

Because of these two divergent models that courts have used in deciding *when* and *by whom* medication refusal can be overridden, laws vary by jurisdiction. The U.S. Supreme Court has never directly addressed this issue for civilly committed inpatients. However, in a related case decided in 1990 (*Washington v. Harper*), it upheld the use of an informal, administrative/consultative process in allowing an overriding of a prisoner's medication refusal. The Court relied on the professional judgment doctrine it enunciated in the *Romeo* case and explicitly rejected the argument for a judicial hearing. A careful reading of this decision, together with another case decided on the same day (*Zinermon v. Burch*, discussed subsequently), indicates that the Supreme Court is more concerned with maintaining clear standards and distinctions for involuntary vs. voluntary hospitalization but is otherwise leaning back to the old rule of law, which states that once involuntarily hospitalized, a patient loses the right to refuse recommended psychiatric treatment. The Court has said that these are *medical* decisions, not legal decisions and, hence, are better made by doctors, rather than judges.

Confidentiality and Privilege

Mental health patients have a qualified right to *confidentiality* in their treatment and have a statutory *privilege* against having their confidences revealed in court testimony. Note the distinction: *Confidentiality* is an ethical guideline (as in the Hippocratic oath) referring to any unauthorized or unlawful disclosure of information obtained in the course of treatment, while *privilege* refers to a specific law enacted by a legislature that prohibits a treatment provider from testifying about information obtained in the course of treatment "that would tend to blacken the character of the patient." Each state has privilege built into the statutory code (as it does for attorneys and clergy), although the degree of protection offered differs from state to state. Courts have recognized that patients can implicitly waive their right to privilege if they place their mental state or treatment into issue in a court. In a malpractice suit, for example, a treatment provider *could* testify about those matters needed for his or her defense, even if they would otherwise fall under the privilege psychotherapist–patient.

Confidentiality and privilege belong to the patient, not to the clinician, and they can be waived *only* by the patient if he or she competently chooses to do so. Generally, the patient is asked to sign a release of information form to signify that confidentiality has been waived for the *specific* purpose written on the form.

Neither confidentiality nor privilege is absolute. Three specific exceptions have been recognized for the duty of confidentiality: child abuse, particular subpoenas, and danger to self or others. In addition, statutes can also provide for the nonconsensual release of information in particular circumstances, such as to the various state and local mental health authorities in the course of official business; to reviewers and inspectors, including the Joint Commission on the Accreditation of Healthcare Organizations (JCAHO); to attorneys assigned to represent the person at a commitment hearing; and to third party payors, in order to verify that services were actually provided. In the case of third party payors, only the diagnosis, staff names, dates, and types and costs of therapies or services may be released nonconsensually.

In accordance with child abuse reporting statutes, information about suspected or proved child abuse *must* be communicated to the designated authority without delay. Duly authorized subpoenas may require the breaking of confidentiality, but only to the *minimum extent necessary* to achieve compliance with the law in order to protect the patient or others from harm. It must be emphasized that routine subpoenas do not per se waive confidentiality. However, a subpoena requires a response. The patient should be contacted to request permission for releasing the information. If denied, the therapist's attorney should be contacted for further advice or action. A subpoena can be invalidated by a judge when the requesting attorney has exceeded the limits permissible by law.

If the patient expresses *suicidal* ideas or intent, notification of next of kin or significant other (e.g., guardian) is a prudent course of action to protect the patient from harm, as well as the therapist from potential liability. Finally, in recent years, the concept of a *duty to warn* has arisen as a result of a court decision (*Tarasoff v. Regents of the University of California*, 1974). While not statutorily required in all states and subject to varying interpretations, it is generally recognized that a therapist has a duty to warn and/or protect an intended victim whom the patient has threatened to harm. In order to fulfill this duty, courts usually require that an identifiable victim be warned and that the police be notified, or the patient be hospitalized.

In each of the preceding instances, it is advisable to try to obtain a patient's consent before revealing the information. Where this is not possible (or the patient outright refuses) and the information nevertheless needs to be revealed for the aforementioned reasons, a progress note should be entered describing the situation necessitating the (limited) breaking of confidentiality. Note that there is never a complete license to reveal confidential information, unencumbered by ethical rules. The patient should furthermore be notified of the breaking of confidentiality at the earliest possible time, provided it is safe to do so. At all times, it should be remembered that confidentiality can always be broken in an emergency, but only to the extent necessary for immediate management of the problem.

Alcohol and other drug rehabilitation facilities fall under separate federal guidelines for confidentiality and privilege, which offer added protections to patients than is otherwise obtained in mental health treatment. The underlying policy rationale is to encourage voluntary treatment of addictions. It was recognized that without these extra protections, patients would be reluctant to discuss their addictive life style, which invariably involves past and/or present criminal activities.

Professional Liability

Legal Basis for Standard Care

A medical malpractice action (or malpractice of any type of health care provider) falls under the law of negligent torts. It requires what are known as the four D's: duty, dereliction, damages and directly.

1. There must be a clinician–patient relationship established, creating a *duty* on the part of the clinician.
2. There must be a *dereliction* (the negligent act) of that duty.
3. There must be *damages* sustained by the patient.
4. These damages must have resulted *directly* (i.e., proximate cause) from the dereliction of the duty (falling below the standard of care required by the duty).

As implied, a dereliction is generally considered to be an act of commission or omission that causes the treatment rendered by the clinician to fall below the applicable standard of care. Some acts are so egregious that they are considered cases of *res ipsa loquitur*: "the thing speaks for itself." Examples include a surgeon leaving a sponge in a patient's anatomic area of operation, or therapist–patient sexual activity.

Concept of Standard of Care

There is no universal standard of care because the practice of medicine and other professions is constantly in a state of flux, as the knowledge base and technology advance and expand. In addition, the locality of the practice may influence the standard to which a practitioner may be held. Practice parameters, or guidelines published by reputable professional organizations, are gradually gaining acceptance as defining a particular standard of care. Practitioners are expected to conform their work to such accepted professional norms. Generally, however, the standard of care is established at each trial, by the use of opposing expert witnesses, on a case-by-case basis, after the fact.

Clinical Implications

Some additional explanation is needed. American law is "case law," which means that legal rules are laid down when individual cases are decided. Together, these *precedents* (the rules derived from decisions made in previous cases) make up the body of the law. Often, however, precedents are contradictory, which makes it hard to predict the outcome of a potential legal dispute.

Therein lies the root of the malpractice problem. Some clear rules have been laid down, which practitioners are expected to follow (generally falling along the lines of "accepted professional norms"). However, the clinician often is faced with a legal dilemma *without clearly enunciated legal rules to follow*. Even if the clinician researched the law before making a wrenching clinical decision (for example, in deciding whether to break confidentiality to warn a third party of a vague but potentially serious threat, or a threat of unclear intent), he or she may *still not know* what the law requires! Precedents may be contradictory, and the law does not give advance rulings but only gives opinions *after the fact*. Often, it develops the law *after* the clinical event has occurred and applies it retroactively. Hypothetically, even if a clinician had a malpractice lawyer present when a sensitive clinical decision was being made, and the clinician asked the lawyer what the proper legal decision would be, the lawyer may not know the answer. Rather, the reply would be, "You make the best clinical decision you can. We will review it afterward and *then* we will see whether it was wrong."

Therefore, because most litigation is based on a retrospective review of the care delivered, the clinical record is the key to the evaluation of the standard of care. It has been stated that if it does not appear in the record, it did not happen. What should be added, however, is that *the clinical record can be a clinician's best friend in defending against a malpractice action*. Whatever has been documented in a contemporaneous manner (i.e., at the time it happens) is assumed to be accurate and valid unless proven otherwise. The basic defense against malpractice is to *document, document, document*. Some people might deride this by pejoratively labeling it "defensive psychiatry," but the authors prefer to think of it as practicing "safe psychiatry."

This cannot be overemphasized. The best way to win a malpractice suit is to *avoid* being named in one to begin with. If, because of clear, careful, contemporaneous documentation (the key piece of evidence at trial), a plaintiff's malpractice lawyer believes that it does not represent a good case, he or she will not pursue an action. Poor chartwork, on the other hand, may force the clinician (or the clinician's insurance company) into an early settlement because of the difficulty in mounting a defense in the face of poor documentation.

This illustrates the legal tightrope on which the clinician is often poised. Knowledge of forensic principles can be indispensable in helping a clinician avoid legal enmeshment. There may come a time, though, when a clinician is faced with a problem outside the scope of previous education, training, or experience. When traditional consultative tools (e.g., consultation with a peer, consultation with a supervisor in the same field, consultation with a practitioner in a field having a

higher degree of training and skill), are unavailable, it is important to remember that, above all, *what the law requires are reasonableness* and *common sense* ("what a reasonable person in similar circumstances would do").

A patient's or family's decision to bring a malpractice action usually arrives only after much deliberation. Patients and families generally do *not* want to sue their caregivers. Studies have shown that rage, stemming from a sense of powerlessness, is often the deciding factor in bringing suit. As clinicians, we use our skills to help patients diffuse their uncontrollable anger and learn a sense of empowerment. These are also keys to reducing malpractice risk.

Conclusion

This chapter provides some of the parameters in which mental health treatment and psychiatric rehabilitation operate. These then are some of the legal ramifications of clinical practice today, in mental health treatment and rehabilitation. Some of the forensic issues in this chapter may be of academic interest to some clinicians, planners, and researchers; and others may not be of direct concern in some areas of practice. However, the authors trust that the discussion of these issues can be useful in helping service providers, be they mental health or rehabilitation providers, fulfill their goal of helping their clients while maintaining the legal safety of both their clients and themselves.

References

Applebaum, P. S. (1988). The right to refuse treatment with antipsychotic medications: Retrospect and prospect. *American Journal of Psychiatry, 145,* 413–419.

Birnbaum, M. (1960). The right to treatment. *American Bar Association Journal, 46,* 499–505.

Bursten, B. (1986). Posthospital mandatory outpatient treatment. *American Journal of Psychiatry, 143,* 147–151.

C.N. v. State, 433 So.2d 661 (Fla. App. 3 Dist 1983).

Geller, J. L. (1986). Rights, wrongs and the dilemma of coerced community treatment. *American Journal of Psychiatry, 143*, 1255–1258.

Gutheil, T. G., & Applebaum, P. S. (1982). *Clinical handbook of psychiatry and the law.* New York: McGraw-Hill.

Hiday, V. A., & Goodman, R. R. (1982). The least restrictive alternative to involuntary hospitalization, outpatient commitment: Its use and effectiveness. *Journal of Psychiatry and Law, 10*, 81–96.

Hiday, V. A., & Scheid-Cook, T. L. (1987). The North Carolina experience with outpatient commitment: A critical appraisal. *International Journal of Law and Psychiatry, 110*, 215–232.

Miller, R. D. (1985). Commitment to outpatient treatment: A national survey. *Hospital and Community Psychiatry, 36*, 265–267.

Miller, R. D., & Fiddleman, P. B. (1984). Outpatient commitment: Treatment in the least restrictive environment? *Hospital and Community Psychiatry, 35*, 147–151.

Monahan, J. (1981). *Clinical prediction of violent behavior.* Rockville, MD: NIMH.

O'Connor v. Donaldson, 95 S. Ct. 2486 (1975).

Rouse v. Cameron, 373 F.2d 451 (D.C. Cir. 1966).

Roy, A. (1982). Risk factors for suicide in psychiatric patients. *Archives of General Psychiatry, 39*, 1089–1095.

Schloendorff v. Society of New York Hospital, 211 N.Y. 125, 105 N.E. 92 (1914), [Cardozo, J.].

Spensley, J., Edwards, D. W., & White, E. (1980). Patient satisfaction and involuntary treatment. *American Journal of Orthopsychiatry, 50*, 725–727.

Stefan, S. (1987). Preventive commitment: The concept and its pitfalls. *Mental and Physical Disability Law Reporter, 11*, 288–297.

Tarasoff v. Regents of the University of California, 529 P.2d 553 (1974).

Washington v. Harper, 110 S. Ct. 1028 (1990) .

Weissman, A. D., & Worden, J. W. (1972). Risk rescue rating in suicide assessment. *Archives of General Psychiatry, 26*, 553–560.

Wilbert, D. E., Jorstad, V., Loren, J. D., Wirrer, B. (1976). Determination of grave disability. *Journal of Nervous and Mental Disorders, 162*, 35–39.

Wyatt v. Stickney, 503 F.2d 1305 (5th Cir. 1974).

Youngberg v. Romeo, 102 S. Ct. 2452 (1982).

Zinermon v. Burch, 110 S. Ct. 975 (1990).

Chapter 15

The Future of Mental Health and Rehabilitation Services*

CILLE KENNEDY[†]
PHYLLIS L. SOLOMON
ROBERT W. FLEXER

How are disabilities related to mental health and rehabilitation services? For the most part, community-based services for people with mental disorders are implicitly designed to address their disabilities. The domains of disability most characteristically resulting from mental disorders are self-care, work, social relations, and troublesome behavior (e.g., aggressiveness, withdrawal) (Gruenberg, 1982). To recapitulate the definition from Chapter 3, *disability* is the limitation in functioning when a person is engaged in an activity such as work, social intercourse, and the like. Disability occurs when the whole person is in action (versus *impairments,* which occur at the organ level, or *handicaps,* which are societally determined).

Disabilities are situation-specific and resource-dependent. For example, a person who has a mental disorder and is unkempt and disheveled while cleaning the house on a Saturday morning will not be considered disabled in the domain of self-care, whereas the same person in the same state of dishabille

would be considered disabled for self-care in a work situation. A homeless person with the same mental condition might exhibit the same unkempt and disheveled appearance *solely* from the lack of bathing and laundering facilities; this person is not disabled for self-care. Knowing a person's mental disorder or diagnosis does not reveal what that person's consequent disabilities are. Conversely, knowing a person's disability will not disclose the impairment causing the disability. The chapters in this book reveal an awareness of and sensitivity to the complexity of these issues and take into account the individual, the social situation, and environmental resources.

People unable to work because of their mental disorders constituted over one quarter of all those receiving Supplemental Security Income (SSI) disability benefits in 1989. In that same year, disability for work due to mental disorders accounted for the largest percentage of adults receiving Social Security Disability Insurance (SSDI), nearly a quarter

---

*The opinions expressed in this chapter are those of the authors and do not represent the opinions of any agency of the U.S. government.
†This article is U.S. government work. It was written as a part of my official duties as a government employee. Therefore, it cannot be copyrighted. The article is freely available to you for publication without a copyright notice, and there are no restrictions on its use, now or subsequently. I retain no rights to the article.

of those on the rolls. These percentages—and the absolute number of people with severe mental disorders—are increasing annually. What do these figures imply for the future of mental health and rehabilitation? First, because people with severe mental disorders constitute the largest single group of individuals receiving Social Security disability benefits (an indicator both of severe disability and of high Federal expenditure), the provision, quality, and effectiveness of mental health and rehabilitation services ought to receive equivalent attention. Second, the inability to work—the reason for which SSI and SSDI benefits are awarded—is but one type of disability experienced by persons with mental disorders. Mental health and rehabilitation professionals must understand and address a broad spectrum of disabilities along with environmental, societal, and attitudinal barriers.

Current federal initiatives related to mental health and rehabilitation services include legislation, strategic planning for research on mental health services, stimulation of and support for demonstration projects and research on disabilities, mental health and rehabilitation services, and coordination of federal agencies on issues related to rehabilitation of people with severe mental disorders.

Federal Legislation

Two federal laws are having a major impact on the field of mental health and rehabilitation services for people with severe mental disorders. *The State Comprehensive Mental Health Services Plan Act of 1986* (P.L. 99-660, Title V) requires states to develop and implement state comprehensive mental health plans for community-based services for people with severe mental disorders. The legislation requires states to submit 3-year plans to the National Institute of Mental Health (NIMH) and, upon approval of those plans, to demonstrate their implementation with a target date of fiscal year 1993 for complete implementation. The incentive for compliance is the state's receipt of its full block grant for

alcohol and other drug abuse and mental health. Requirements under P.L. 99-660 are that each state do the following:

Develop an organized community-based system of care for people with severe mental disorders

Identify quantitative targets to be achieved in implementing such a system

Provide services that would enable individuals with severe mental disorders to gain access to mental health services

Provide rehabilitation services, employment services, housing services, medical and dental care, and other support services to allow people who have severe mental disorders to function outside of inpatient institutions

Undertake activities to reduce their rate of rehospitalization

Outline case management services

Describe programs of outreach and services being provided to homeless individuals with severe mental disorders

Describe consultation activities with employees of state institutions and nursing homes.

Other requirements include the formation of state planning councils, which must include family members and consumers as representatives; coordination of services for children and adults; the utilization of state and local public and private resources for the enhancement and delivery of designated services; and the development of quantitative measures to document the improvement of services under the law. In addition to the actual provision and coordination of services under this law, one of its major accomplishments is to make people with severe mental disorders a priority in state mental health systems, as they have been in the federal government since the Community Support Program (CSP) was developed in 1977.

The Americans with Disabilities Act of 1990 (P.L. 101-336), commonly known as the ADA, is civil rights legislation ensuring equality for people with disabilities, resulting from both physical and mental disorders. It provides a national mandate for the elimination of discrimination against people with physical and mental disabilities in the critical areas of employment, housing, public accommodations, education, transportation, communication, recreation, institutionalization, health services, voting, and access to public services (P.L. 101-336, § 2(3)). It is the first such legislation in the world (Dart, 1990). The immediate ramifications of the ADA—as civil rights legislation—for people disabled by mental disorders are not clear. While discrimination on the basis of their disabilities is illegal, it is not readily apparent what "reasonable accommodation" in the work place (P.L. 101-336, Title 1, § 101 (9) (B)) would apply to a person disabled by a mental disorder. The *Community Support Network News* (1991) focused a recent issue on the ADA, to educate the mental health and rehabilitation fields about the ADA and to use it as a catalyst for positive change in the lives of people disabled by mental disorders.

The ADA is being used as a rallying flag around which much new interest and activity are occurring nationwide. The ADA also acts as a spotlight bringing fresh attention to many ongoing activities aimed at increasing participation in society by people with disabilities.

National Institute of Mental Health and Related Activities

Among the ongoing activities at the NIMH, which coincide with the interest generated by ADA, is the publication of the strategic plan, *Caring for People with Severe Mental Disorders: A National Plan of Research to Improve Services* (NIMH, 1991a). The purpose of the plan is to focus attention and "propose a national strategy for bringing the full power of scientific research into the ongoing effort to find ways to improve services and ultimately the quality of life of people" (p. iii) who have severe mental disorders. The plan, developed by three panels of experts and many special consultants, is divided into three sections: clinical services research, service system research, and research resources. The expertise involved in the development of this plan included consumers, family members, researchers, clinicians, and administrators. The central question asked by the plan, in order to guide future research to improve mental health services, is, What works, under what circumstances, and for what kinds of individuals? The plan summarizes the current state of scientific knowledge and identifies the areas in which future research is urgently needed to improve care for people with severe mental disorders. In the section devoted to clinical services research, the plan gives equal weight to the need for research on rehabilitation services as it does to research on treatment. It is the first time such a high profile for research on rehabilitation has been given in a plan developed for the NIMH.

Activities being conducted as part of implementation of the Plan include a program announcement, "Research on Disabilities and Rehabilitation Services for Persons with Severe Mental Disorders" (NIMH, 1991b). The announcement seeks to increase NIMH's existing portfolio of research support on disabilities and rehabilitation services for people with severe mental disorders. Research, currently being funded, which falls under this category includes investigations of supported and transitional employment, a long-term follow-up of the effects of rehabilitation on the life course of former state mental hospital patients, the positive and negative effects of receiving Social Security disability benefits, and the effectiveness of intensive community-based social skills training. An important feature of this body of research, reflecting a premise of the plan, is that people with severe mental disorders are not seen as homogeneous. The studies all aim at understanding what works for whom.

The CSP (described in Chapter 4) supports research demonstration projects to test the comparative effectiveness of various approaches to providing three key community service components: case management services; crisis response services, and psychosocial rehabilitation. Among other ongoing projects supported by the CSP are consumer-operated services and two rehabilitation research and training centers. The two centers are cofunded by the National Institute on Disability and Rehabilitation Research. Other research in NIMH investigates the efficacy of *psychoeducation*, a treatment intervention that restructures family communication styles with a goal to attain positive outcomes for people with schizophrenia.

A major investigation, supported by the federal government (with NIMH as the lead agency) and by the Robert Wood Johnson Foundation (RWJF), is the National Evaluation of the RWJF—Housing and Urban Development Program on Chronic Mental Illness (Shore & Cohen, 1990). The design of the national evaluation (Goldman, Lehman, Morrissey, Newman, Frank, & Steinwachs, 1990) is consistent with the thinking represented throughout the chapters in this volume. The national evaluation has four major components. It contains a housing study to investigate the development, use, and impact of housing on a cohort of adults receiving services under the program on chronic mental illness. A second study examines the changes to the organization, financing, and delivery of care resulting from the program's intervention. A third study focuses on the costs and patterns of care to people enrolled in medical assistance programs, and on the impact that the restructuring of finances, under the program, has on the providers of those services. The fourth major component is the client study, which seeks to understand the effect that the new resources and reconfigured services have on the recipients of those services. Among the research questions asked in this study component is: What is the impact of the intervention on the client's own sense of wellbeing?

Federal Interagency Activities

One situation most poignantly demonstrates the failure of society in general and, more specifically, of the ability of mental health and rehabilitation services to develop and provide resources in ways that individuals allow themselves to accept available services: the situation of people who are simultaneously homeless and have mental disorders. The

Report of the Federal Task Force on Homelessness and Severe Mental Illness, *Outcasts on Main Street* (1992), states that "the fate of all homeless Americans *can and must* change for the better" (p. ix) and offers more than 50 action steps that federal departments participating in the task force will take to end homelessness among adults who are severely mentally disordered. Additional recommendations are made to state and local governments and to the private sector, to encourage their necessary leadership in ending homelessness. The report emphasizes the role of vocational and psychosocial rehabilitation as essential in helping people with severe mental disorders become contributing members of society.

Among the action steps are two major federal initiatives. The first is a systems integration initiative, the Access to Community Care and Effective Services and Supports (ACCESS) Initiative, which makes grants available to states to test promising approaches to services integration in 20 to 30 communities. This innovative interdepartmental effort involves the Department of Health and Human Services, in collaboration with the Department of Housing and Urban Development (HUD), the Department of Labor, the Department of Education, the Department of Veterans Affairs, and the Department of Agriculture. The combined and coordinated resources from these federal agencies permit integration of basic life supports (e.g., food, clothing, and shelter) with treatment services, linkage of services at the client and system levels, and clear delineation of clinical, fiscal, and administrative responsibility. The second initiative, Safe Havens, expands housing options and alternative services. A new, competitive demonstration program under the auspices of HUD, Safe Havens is designed to provide low cost, stable housing for adults who are both severely mentally disordered and homeless, and who are initially unable to participate in structured residential programs. Safe Havens offers a low-demand environment fashioned to provide safety, security, supervision, and support to 12 to 15 residents in each safe haven. Residents have the opportunity to establish ties to treatment, benefits, and other support services.

A second federal task force in which NIMH has played an active role is the *Public Health Service Task Force on Improving Medical Criteria for Disability Determination*. The task force was formed in response to a request from the commissioner of the Social Security Administration for assistance in (1) improving physician knowledge about disability programs, (2) improving rehabilitation and the return to the work force, (3) increasing research to better discriminate those who are disabled from those who are not, and (4) developing a definition of *disability* that will gain widespread acceptance and can be presented to the U.S. Congress. The task force has been addressing these issues as they bear on people disabled by physical and mental disorders. The forthcoming report from the task force will identify both a strategy for a research agenda on disabilities, and the resources needed to implement the strategy. Because of the increasing numbers of people receiving federal disability benefits, coupled with the impetus provided by the ADA, it is anticipated that disabilities and rehabilitation services for all disabled populations will receive increased federal attention and resources.

The Interagency Committee on Disability Research (ICDR) is mandated by the Congress to coordinate and report on federal activities related to disability and rehabilitation research. The NIMH has assumed an active role on this committee, bringing an awareness of disabilities based on mental disorders to the fore. This process has sought to sensitize participants to the issues of disability that are similar between physical and mental disorders, and to highlight the disability issues more characteristic to mental disorders. For the most part, disabilities characteristic—but not unique—to mental disorders are the specific domains (self-care, work, social relations, and troublesome behavior) mentioned previously herein.

A subcommittee of the ICDR is the Interagency Committee on Disability Statistics (ICDS). The ICDS provides a federal forum for the exchange of information about disability statistics and statistical information, provides recommendations on the need for federal disability surveys, reviews and critiques federal disability instruments, and provides recommendations about disability classifications. The ICDS has taken an active role in promoting the inclusion of questions inquiring about disabilities due to mental as well as physical disorders in all federal surveys. The ongoing capacity to enumerate and collect more specific information on the domains of people's lives affected by disabilities is of utmost concern. The desire for information is propelled by its utility for policy, resource, and service planning. NIMH participation has ensured the inclusion of data on disabilities due to mental disorders and has served to identify measurement issues in the collection of routine data that systematically exclude information about disabilities resulting from mental disorders.

The Private Sector

Both federal agencies and the private sector have made initial inroads in appreciating the importance of the connection between disability insurance programs of private insurance companies and the public sector disability benefits and rehabilitation and health benefits. In the private sector, the cost of mental health benefits rose 27% between 1987 and 1988 (Mental Health Policy Resource Center, 1990). The long range effect of this increase is that when private insurance disability benefits run out, these individuals will be eligible for, and likely to receive, SSDI. Once they become recipients of SSDI, these individuals will probably be served by the public sector for their mental health, health, and related care. In an attempt to respond to the ADA, and to minimize the amount of disability benefits expended, the private sector is looking to rehabilitation for people disabled by mental disorders. They are also looking to research to understand what is working for whom and at what cost. This mutual quest is one direction of activity for the future.

The Future of Rehabilitation Services

This overview of ongoing federal activities offers a baseline for the trajectory of future activities. The chapters throughout this book describe activities that are open to empirical investigation. Data on program effectiveness and potential weaknesses when programs are adapted to other localities will provide direction for activities at the federal level, in turn affecting activities in the states and localities and vice versa.

To use these activities as a trajectory of the future of rehabilitation and mental health services, an examination of the influence of past federal activities directed at serving severely mentally disabled individuals on current service delivery will provide some evidence for assessing future direction. Koyanagi and Goldman (1991) assessed the degree to which the recommendations of *Toward a National Plan for the Chronically Mentally ill* issued by the U.S. Department of Health and Human Services (DHHS) in 1980 were accomplished. This plan was the result of the 1978 President's Commission on Mental Health, which commissioned DHHS to develop a national plan for the care of persons with severe mental illness, with a focus on Medicaid, Medicare, SSI, and SSDI.

Despite the fiscal conservatism of the 1980s, these authors found that many of the recommendations were accomplished. For SSI, prerelease programs for persons being released from state institutions were adopted. There were also substantial improvements in the work incentive program, as individuals could return to work and retain part of the cash benefits. Furthermore, individuals remained eligible for Medicaid benefits even when their cash assistance was reduced to zero. With regard to SSDI, criteria for eligibility of severely mentally disabled individuals was improved. However, similar work incentives for SSDI, as for SSI, were not accomplished. The most significant changes under Medicaid were the initiation of the case management option and the expansion of rehabilitation to include psychiatric rehabilitation services. The case management option enables states to target these services to persons with mental illness. Many states have expanded the rehabilitation option to PSR. With regard to Medicare, there has been an expansion of mental health services that are reimbursed (Koyanagi & Goldman, 1991).

In the past decade, the CSP of the NIMH has made substantial progress (Parrish, 1989). Parrish (1989) also notes that "many states have endorsed community support concepts and have designated the long-term mentally ill as a priority population for services" (p. 107). Furthermore, CSP has "significantly advanced the state-of-the-art for delivering biomedical and psychosocial rehabilitation services to individuals with the most challenging clinical disorders" (Goodrick, 1989, pp. 457–458). CSP has been evaluated favorably for its impact on state and local mental health programs and for mobilizing staff and client support for the development of community support systems (Vischi & Stockdill, 1989). In addition, CSP has played a major role in the growth of the consumer and family movements through promotion of the philosophy of involvement of families and consumers in developing policies and programs. The most significant contributions of CSP in this area have been in the direct funding of these groups for advocacy, support, and direct provision of service (Chamberlin, Rogers, & Sneed, 1989). Moreover, the philosophy of CSP and rehabilitation is reflected in the model plan for a comprehensive community-based system (NIMH, 1987), which is a technical assistance document to help states implement P.L. 99-660. In reading these initial plans and updated progress reports, it is quite evident that states have incorporated a rehabilitation orientation for persons with severe mental disabilities.

There is little question that we have a long way to go to achieve a comprehensive array of mental health and rehabilitation services for persons with severe mental disabilities. However, as is evidenced from this discussion, federal activities have influenced progress in this arena. Therefore, it can be expected that these new activities at the federal level will have a similar impact and that they will increase our knowledge base in the field through the increased research efforts of NIMH. However, optimism is tempered by a number of countervailing realities, such as (a) a lack of resources, as well as lack of incentives and penalties to shifting existing resources from traditional mental health services to rehabilitation oriented ones; (b) continued negative attitudes about the capabilities of severely mentally ill individuals; and (c) a lack of personnel trained in rehabilitation technologies and techniques (Parrish, 1989).

Turning Inroads to Highways

In this book, the editors set out to map the employment, education, and community living possibilities for people with severe mental disabilities, both individually and collectively. *Rehabilitation* is the process whereby these possibilities become realities. Individual values, aspirations, dreams and life style expectations must be the starting point in rehabilitation, while quality of life, satisfaction, and fulfillment derived from housing, jobs, and education must be the outcome by which we evaluate our efforts. The contributions in this book describe in a consistent philosophy and a variety of approaches in facilitating the individual's rehabilitation. The philosophy of the dignity, worth, and potential for growth of all individuals, even those with the most severe disabilities, provides for unity, while perspectives reflected in diverse disciplines offers tools to meet multiple needs. Progress in rehabilitation and mental health services will be realized by growth in philosophy, theory, and practice.

We hope that this book helps to change the beliefs of those working or planning to work in the field to a more positive view of those individuals with severe mental disabilities. Also, we hope that this book serves to fill some of the gaps in knowledge of the technologies and techniques in the psychiatric rehabilitation field for those employed in or entering the field, such as providers, planners, researchers, policymakers, and administra-

tors, as well as those collaborating with the system, such as families, service recipients, and advocates. Furthermore, Koyanagi and Goldman (1991) commented that "To move forward, the mental health field must work even better with others—with the disability community, with businesses, and with those involved in the mainstream programs. Most important of all, we must work better among ourselves. Divisiveness could so easily bring to an end the momentum built up in the 1980s" (p. 905). This means a working together of all vested groups—service participants, families, and interdisciplinary groups of mental health and rehabilitation professionals. Our further desire is to achieve rehabilitation for all individuals with severe mental disabilities through mutual respect for what each party has to offer, resulting in an active coalition for implementation and advocacy.

References

Chamberlin, J., Rogers, J., & Sneed, C. (1989). Consumers, families, and community support systems. *Psychosocial Rehabilitation Journal, 12*, 93–106.

Community Support Network News. (1991, December). (Available from the Center for Psychiatric Rehabilitation, 730 Commonwealth Ave., Boston, MA 02215.)

Dart, J. (1990). ADA: Landmark declaration of equality. *Worklife: A publication on employment and people with disabilities, 3*(3), 1. Washington, DC: President's Committee on Employment of People with Disabilities.

Goldman, H. H., Lehman, A. F., Morrissey, J. P., Newman, S. J., Frank, R. G., & Steinwachs, D. M. (1990). Design for the national evaluation of the Robert Wood Johnson Foundation Program on Chronic Mental Illness. *Hospital and Community Psychiatry, 41*(11), 1217–1221.

Goodrick, D. (1989). Mental health system strategic planning. In D. Rochefort (Ed.), *Handbook on mental health policy in the United States.* New York: Greenwood Press.

Gruenberg, E. M. (1982). Social breakdown in young adults: Keeping crises from becoming chronic. In B. Pepper & H. Ryglewicz (Eds.), *New directions for mental health services: The young adult chronic patient* (Vol. 14, pp. 43–50). San Francisco: Jossey-Bass.

Koyanagi, C., & Goldman, H. H. (1991). The quiet success of the National Plan for the Chronically

Mentally Ill. *Hospital and Community Psychiatry, 42,* 899–905.

Mental Health Policy Resource Center. (1990, July). *Policy in Perspective* (p. 4). (Available from Mental Health Policy Resource Center, 1730 Rhode Island Ave., N.W., Suite 308, Washington, DC 20036.).

National Institute of Mental Health. (1987). *Toward a model plan for a comprehensive, community-based mental health system.* Rockville, MD: author.

National Institute of Mental Health. (1991a). *Caring for people with severe mental disorders: A national plan of research to improve services* (DHHS Publ. No. [ADM] 91-1762). Washington DC: Superintendent of Documents, U.S. Government Printing Office.

National Institute of Mental Health. (1991b). Research on disabilities and rehabilitation services for persons with severe mental disorders. Program Announcement PA-91-74. Rockville, MD: National Institute of Mental Health, 5600 Fishers Lane, Room 18C-14.

Parrish, J. (1989). The long journey home: Accomplishing the mission of the community support movement. *Psychosocial Rehabilitation Journal, 12,* 107–124.

Public Law 99-660. The State Comprehensive Mental Health Services Plan Act of 1986.

Public Law 101-336. Americans with Disabilities Act of 1990.

Report of the Federal Task Force on Homelessness and Severe Mental Illness. (1992). *Outcasts on Main Street.* (Available from the Interagency Council on the Homeless, 451 Seventh Street, S.W., Room 7274, Washington, DC 20410.)

Shore, M.F., & Cohen, M.D. (1990). The Robert Wood Johnson Foundation Program on Chronic Mental Illness: An Overview. *Hospital and Community Psychiatry, 41*(11), 1212–1216.

U.S. Department of Health and Human Services Steering Committee on the Chronically Mentally Ill. (1981). *Toward a national plan for the chronically mentally ill.* (DHHS Publication No. ADM 81-1077). Washington, DC: U.S. Department of Health and Human Services.

Vischi, T. R., & Stockdill, J. (1989). The financing of comprehensive community support systems: A review of major strategies. *Psychosocial Rehabilitation Journal, 12,* 83–92.

Index